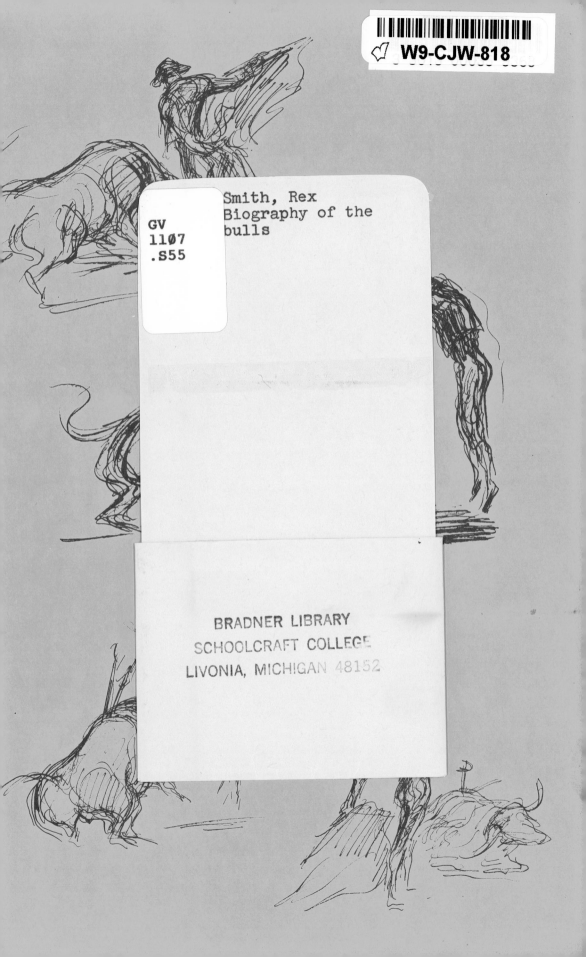

BIOGRAPHY OF THE BULLS

Biography of the Bulls

AN ANTHOLOGY OF SPANISH BULLFIGHTING

Edited by REX SMITH

RINEHART & COMPANY, INC.   NEW YORK   TORONTO

Grateful acknowledgment is made to the following publishers and copyright owners for permission to reprint material from their publications:

DOUBLEDAY & COMPANY, INC., New York, N. Y., for permission to reprint the Epilogue from JUAN BELMONTE, by Manuel Chaves Nogales, translated from the Spanish and with a note on bullfighting, by Leslie Charteris. Copyright 1937 by Doubleday & Company, Inc.

DUELL, SLOAN & PEARCE, INC., New York, N. Y., for permission to reprint an excerpt from VIRGIN SPAIN, by Waldo Frank. Copyright 1926, 1942 by Waldo Frank.

E. P. DUTTON & CO., INC., New York, N. Y., for permission to reprint Chapter I from BLOOD AND SAND, by Vicente Blasco-Ibáñez. Copyright 1951 by E. P. Dutton & Co., Inc. Based on the translation of Mrs. W. A. Gillespie. Copyright 1919, 1947 by E. P. Dutton & Co., Inc.

HOUGHTON MIFFLIN COMPANY, Boston, Mass., for permission to reprint a selection from LA FIESTA BRAVA, by Barnaby Conrad. Copyright 1950, 1953 by Barnaby Conrad.

MRS. REX INGRAM, North Hollywood, California, for permission to reprint two chapters from MARS IN THE HOUSE OF DEATH, by Rex Ingram. Copyright 1939 by Rex Ingram.

ALFRED A. KNOPF, INC., New York, N. Y., for permission to reprint a cut version of a selection from TO THE BULLFIGHT, by John Marks. Copyright 1952, 1953 by John Marks; and to ANDRE DEUTSCH LIMITED, London, England, who granted permission for the Canadian territory.

ALFRED A. KNOPF, INC., New York, N. Y., CHATTO AND WINDUS, LTD., London, England, and A. D. PETERS, London, England, for permission to reprint a cut version of a selection from THE SPANISH TEMPER, by V. S. Pritchett. Copyright 1954 by V. S. Pritchett.

LITTLE, BROWN & COMPANY, Boston, Massachusetts, for permission to reprint two chapters from THE BRAVE BULLS, by Tom Lea. Copyright 1949 by Tom Lea.

PRENTICE-HALL, INC., Englewood Cliffs, New Jersey, for permission to reprint selections from THE BULLFIGHTER FROM BROOKLYN, by Sidney Franklin. Copyright 1952 by Sidney Franklin.

ROUTLEDGE & KEGAN PAUL LTD., London, England, for permission to reprint a selection from TRAVELS IN SPAIN, by Madame d'Aulnoy. Published in London in 1930.

ROBERT RUARK and UNITED FEATURE SYNDICATE, New York, N. Y., for permission to use the selection "Papa" Goes to the Fights, by Robert Ruark.

CHARLES SCRIBNER'S SONS, New York, N. Y., for permission to reprint THE CAPITAL OF THE WORLD, by Ernest Hemingway. Copyright 1936 by Ernest Hemingway. This story first appeared under the title The Horns of the Bull. Also for permission to reprint a selection from SHADOWS OF THE SUN by Pérez Lugín, translated by Sidney Franklin. Copyright 1934 by Sidney Franklin.

TRUE, THE MAN'S MAGAZINE, New York, N. Y., for permission to reprint The Day I Fought With Belmonte, by Barnaby Conrad. Copyright 1949 by Fawcett Publications, Inc. This article first appeared in True under the title Yale Man Versus Toro.

ENDPAPER DRAWINGS BY JOHN GROTH

GV
1107
.S55

PUBLISHED SIMULTANEOUSLY IN CANADA BY
CLARKE, IRWIN & COMPANY, LTD., TORONTO

For the family—
June, Izetta, Rex, Jr.
and Sally Lou

Preface

This is an anthology of tauromachian art and writing. This is no history, such as Bedoya, or Navas, and no encyclopedia, such as the incomparable Cossio. These selections have been made, keeping in mind the confines of one volume, to present representative expressions on the different phases of the Spanish national spectacle.

I have written on the *corrida* from Mexico, Peru and Spain where I reviewed bullfights as a part of my duties as a foreign correspondent. I have attended bullfights from the days of Joselito and Belmonte. I have known many of the tauromachian authorities of my time. I have assembled a collection of books and pictures over the years. I do not pose as an apologist for the fiesta. I do consider myself an informed observer. My interest has, for several years, been purely personal and unrelated to my professional life. I have been able to spend time on the subject for relaxation and pleasure. During that time, I have made this book, hoping that it will clarify some of the misconceptions and cloudy information about a unique ceremony developed in that strange and exciting land, Spain. I think the words written by famous writers and pictures composed by famous artists may be an interesting tapestry of interpretation.

From many lands, books, pamphlets, paintings, drawings, poems, essays, dithyrambs and purple prose have flooded the public with interpretations of the fiesta. Some intone hooded and effete insinuations of sex and psychology. Others use the *corrida* as a trapeze for acrobatics in syntax and color. But there are those who know the drama of sun and shadow, artistry and death, and write about it with ceremony and respect. These are represented here. I have assembled poetry, criticism, essays, fiction and history, with what I consider appropriate and related illustrations. I have used neither paintings nor photographs, because paintings do not reproduce well in black and white, and photographs do not fit the general scheme of this book. The only painting is the cover by Tom Lea, America's greatest artistic authority on the bulls.

The selection of material is entirely my own. If any aficionado fails to find a favorite story, comment, poem, or illustration, I am sorry, but I have only one book to present at this time. Any statements and opinions not attributed to somebody else, in this book, are mine, and I have made the translations from Spanish, except where otherwise credited.

The reader will find here little information on bullfighting from horseback, as now practiced in Portugal, and occasionally in Spain. The long and fine development of the fiesta in Mexico, as well as Peru, Venezuela, Colombia, and other Spanish American countries belongs in another anthology. There are no comments on women bullfighters, for reasons of censorship.

This is purely and simply a selection of writings and art on the Spanish fiesta, as it developed in Spain.

REX SMITH

Contents

BIOGRAPHY OF THE BULLS

The Beginning

The bull came into recorded history as a god. The ancient Persians believed this creature contained the life forces of plants, animals and men. The first man, according to their legend, came out of the right shoulder of the bull, and the animals came out of the left shoulder. It was the symbol of procreation and power.

Samuel Noah Kramer, in his book on early mankind, *From the Tablets of Sumer,* describes the fragments translated of "Gilgamesh and the Bull of Heaven," a poem that apparently came down to the Babylonians from the Sumerians two or three thousand years B.C. The "Bull of Heaven" is a divine though destructive character.

Gilgamesh, a restless, unrivaled king of his city, Erech, was most famous for his sex appetite. The people cried out in anguish because he was insatiable. They appealed to the mother-goddess Aruru, and she made a rival out of clay. That was Enkidu, a brutish wild man. He was tamed and taught the facts of life by a courtesan of the city. The educated cave man challenged the king. The men began a deadly conflict but, somehow, they became reconciled in the middle of the fight. Thus began the intimate friendship of two heroes that was to become a central theme of many legends in literature and history.

After the friends had a series of adventures, Inanna, the goddess of love, became enamored of Gilgamesh. He refused to satisfy her desires. Deeply offended, Inanna persuaded An, the heaven-god, to send the Bull of Heaven against Erech, to destroy Gilgamesh and his city.

The Bull of Heaven came down on his deadly mission, and "began to destroy the city of Erech, slaughtering its warriors by the hundred." Gilgamesh and Enkidu together took up the struggle against the beast, and in a mighty concerted effort succeeded in killing him! But their victory was their doom, the penalty for conflict with the gods. They came to bad ends. The Sumerian poem "Gilgamesh and the Bull of Heaven" is still in fragments and unpublished.

Later, the central myth of the Mithraic religion had Mithra slaying a sacred bull in a grotto. This is depicted in many ancient reliefs. There is also evidence that the Chaldeans worshiped the bull thousands of years, even before the Hittites and the Israelites.

The bull was worshiped in early Israel: ". . . even the humblest reader of the Scriptures is challenged by the rather striking phenomenon which makes the founders of the exclusive, hereditary high-priesthood of the eternal and transscendent Jehovah at the same time the traditional originators of bull worship in Israel. It is certain that Israel came in contact with bull worship in Canaan. Both the Baalim and the heavenly deities were symbolized by the might of the bull.

"In Babylonia the most striking and tangible use of the bull to represent the divine is undoubtedly found in the human-headed winged bulls at the entrances of Assyrian palaces. While in Phoenicia, the protocol of Baal was so strict that the people abhorred the eating of bull or cow flesh.

"The bull cult's bearing upon Israel's religious evolution is shown by the fact it was the recognized worship of the national god Yahweh under the form of a bull. Israel identified Yahweh with Baal." These excerpts are from a study of the subject made by Leroy Waterman for the *American Journal of Semitic Languages and Literature*.

This means that, theologically, the Christian religion had the bull as a symbol of its original god.

When the bull was not being worshiped, it was being used as a high symbol of virility, or being sacrificed. Poseidon (Neptune) considered a black bull garlanded and with gilded horns, his favorite sacrifice.

It was also a famous disguise in The Rape of Europa. Zeus (Jupiter) became infatuated with the daughter of the Phoenician king, Agenor. He appeared to her in the form of a white bull and persuaded her to climb on his back. Whereupon, he swam away to Crete, and had three sons by her, one of which was named Minos. She married the king of Crete, who adopted her sons.

Sometime later, Poseidon sent Minos, then king, a divine bull as a token of his sovereignty over Crete, and as a suggested sacrifice. Minos liked the bull so much he did not want to sacrifice it. That was a mistake because his wife, Pasiphae, who was venerated in Crete, conceived a passion for the bull. Sometime thereafter, she became the mother of Minotaur, a monster with the head of a bull and the body of a man. In the meantime, legend says, the bull had gone mad and been killed by Hercules as one of his Twelve Labors. Minos built the Labyrinth and imprisoned the Minotaur there until the hero, Theseus, killed him. This Athenian had also killed at Marathon, previously, a great bull that had been devastating his father's kingdom, and this gave him his first title of hero.

This same Marathon was the scene of an Athenian victory over the Persians, 490 B.C., and a runner carried the news about twenty miles to Athens, and that was the inspiration for the Marathon race in present-day Olympic Games.

Several peoples of the Near East found the bull the most natural symbol of generative force. In Cappadocia the Hittites worship the bull and sacrificed to it. Similarly. the Greeks conceived the wine-god Dionysus in the form of a bull. The *Boal* of Tarsus was identified by the Greeks with Zeus. Bulls were bred in the times of the Pharaohs for ceremonial fighting purposes. Rameses II participated in these events.

The Rape of Europa

Archaelogical discoveries in Crete record the hunting of bulls and the killing in tournaments. The savage animals were caught, placed in strong cages, and transported to the cities. It was a rite rather than a circus display.

II

There have been four developments in the preliminary history of the bulls. First of all, their divine status lasted some time. Later, they became the highest of sacrifices to gods, who had assumed, by now, human forms. Then, they were the object of chase and destruction by races and tribes who wanted to demonstrate superiority over the religious and civic symbols of their enemies.

Finally came evidence from historians and other writers that the combat between man and bull had reached the evolutionary stage of human courage against animal force. The religious significance waned as the spectacle increased in public interest and value as a test of masculine qualities.

Even before the Punic Wars the native Spaniards used fighting bulls for trials of bravery and hardihood. They were also used as auxiliaries in war. There is a famous episode in Spanish history where bulls helped turn a battle into victory. Barcelona was founded by Hamilcar Barca (Hannibal's father) in 228 B.C. Shortly afterward he marched on Ilici and blockaded the city.

The Celtiberians were desperate against the formidable forces. They finally gathered large numbers of fighting bulls, aided by the mountaineers with their tame oxen, much as bulls are moved from place to place today. Working close with the oxen they managed to fix resin torches on the horns of the wild animals. Then they drove the herd, lighting the torches as they ran, onto the war chariots of the enemy. Hamilcar Barca was killed in the battle and his army destroyed. This was appalling news to the Romans and the Carthaginians, and it inspired great respect for Spanish arms. The fame of the Spanish bulls spread throughout the known world. And it was on popular demand that Julius Caesar presented bullfights to the Romans between 95 and 45 B.C. Augustus, 27 B.C.–14 A.D., built the Statilus Taurus for spectacles known as taurilia.

Asconio Pechano (Quinto) of Padua in the first century B.C., commenting on an oration by Cicero, said they aroused the fighting bulls by throwing out dummies made of straw in the shapes of men. The expression "straw man" came from this practice. Artemidorus wrote of youths fighting bulls near Athens more than two hundred years B.C. Suetonius said Claudius attended bullfights.

The first time, in available reference, the subject appears in fiction was about the third century A.D. in a novel, *Teagenes and Cariclea,* by Heliodoro. It is not clear whether the name was a nom de plume or whether it was that of a famous writing bishop of the time, Heliodoro de Hemeris.

The history and legends of the ages blended mythology into Christianity. Great upheavals of wars and cultures shook the world. Religions and civilizations tumbled in kaleidoscopic confusion. Customs and spectacles became state ceremonies: The pastoral world was obliterated under the heavy feet of the Roman legions, marching toward an awkward alliance with Power and Christianity, and destruction. Out of the ruins came the tortuous creative processes that carried on the line of evolution. During that transition, Spain was in the middle of a melting pot.

So, a brief digression into the history of Spain will be made here, for a thorough understanding of its most national festival. There were few records because the peoples of those regions were so busy fighting that other matters of public interest slipped down to secondary importance. Washington Irving looked at the era with mixed feelings. "Iberia was harassed from ancient times by invaders, Celts, Greeks, Phoenicians, Carthaginians, Romans, then the Suevi, Alain, and Vandals, those barbarians of the North."

It should be noted that the Roman rule in Spain lasted from, generally, 206 B.C. to 409 A.D.

"In the Fifth Century, Goths, then allies of Rome, reconquered the country after three years' war. They inter-married and created a new race, which was a war-like unquiet, yet high-minded and heroic people. Their simple and abstemious habits, their contempt for toil and suffering, and their love of daring enterprise, fitted them for a soldier's life. When they had no external foe they fought one another. The Goths were Arians but embraced the Catholicism maintained by native Spaniards, free from many of the gross superstitions of Rome. . . ."

After almost three hundred years of Gothic domination, the Moors came in 712 and stayed until 1492.

During the early centuries of the Moorish era there was not much mention of bulls, except that warriors tested their mettle by hunting them. The undercurrent of resentment against the Moors became publicly more manifest from the eleventh century, as the resistance approached organization. Coincidentally, the Spaniards began to temper their leaders in bullfights. The Moors were not outdone. They participated in these dangerous festivals and proved themselves to be both skillful and bold with lance and steed. The fighting of bulls reappeared in song, story and history, where it has continued ever since.

III

Before going further into tauromachian history, it would be well to discuss the family tree of the fighting bull as an animal. There are almost as many theories about its ancestry as there are about the origin of the fiesta itself. But the consensus seems to settle on the urus.

In the Neolithic Age, the urus or aurochs existed in Spain and roamed generally over European and Near Eastern countries. This was a large wild animal, with power, ferocity, and a wide and fearsome reputation. They reached a height of six feet at the shoulders and a weight of two thousand pounds, according to naturalists. It was such a hardy beast that the last one, a female, is reported to have died during the seventeenth century in Poland. From prehistoric times to the seventeenth century is a long span. Since the urus had wide dispersal, there is little doubt that the fighting bull of Spain and the prototypes for gods in the Eastern countries came from the same ancestors. These Oriental relatives may have come back with the Moors through North Africa from the Near East and

The urus or aurochs, ancestor of fighting bulls

Egypt, thence into Spain again. The great and deadly water buffalo of Africa was undoubtedly a relative. The semi-savage bulls of Scotland were also reported relatives, as well as similar animals in Switzerland. The bull known as the *toro bravo* today, Spanish historians insist, is a native of the Iberian peninsula, despite his polymorphous past.

Now for the fiesta. Several historians will be quoted on its origin, beginning with José Sánchez de Neira (1826–98) in his famed *Gran Diccionario Taurómaco:*

"Some historians claim the Romans brought bullfighting to Spain during their domination of the country. Others claim the Moors brought the spectacle over from Africa when they conquered the Visigoths in the Peninsula. After searching through many documents, it appears that neither is correct. Apparently the fiesta originated in Spain, for it was here the fiercest fighting bulls were first known to history, long before the Romans. The celebrated archaeological remains, the stone bulls of Guisando, were Roman monuments, erected by Julius Caesar to celebrate his victory over Pompey's forces. One hundred bulls were killed in sacrificial ceremony. There is no record that the Romans practiced bullfighting before the Spanish Era."

The Spaniards had a tremendous influence on Rome. The emperors from Trajan to Marcus Aurelius were Spanish. The great writers, Lucan, the Senecas, Martial, Florus, Quintilian and Pomponius Mila were of the same race.

In ancient times the Spaniards hunted wild bulls

Undoubtedly, Spain sent wild bulls to Rome for ceremonial fetes. There are parts of the stone arenas in several Spanish towns, such as Mérida, Tarragona, Sagunto, Toledo, built specially for fights between bulls and men.

"Fighting, actually, may have begun with the hunting of wild bulls for food or the exercise of soldierly dexterity, but it was in Spain. It is true that the Moors showed interest and aptitude in the bullfight, on foot and on horseback. But it must be remembered they were Spanish Moors, naturalized or native. The Moorish occupation lasted in Spain about 700 years and most of the Spanish had Moorish blood at that time."

Historians, Juan Mariana, Nicolás Fernández de Moratín, Adolfo de Castro, Serafín Estébanez Calderón, and Juan López-Valdemoro (el Conde de las Navas), quoted in *El espectáculo más nacional,* 1900, defend the origin of the fiesta in Spain: "No history of Africa or the Orient in the Mahometan world describes such a spectacle. There is no word for the bullfight in the Moorish dictionaries."

Cristóbal Logano, 1676, stated: "The circus maximus in Rome had tourneys of wild bulls. The outlying governors or commanders brought in the fiercest specimens, caged, for use in the arena when they were fought with swords and lances. The best were from Spain."

Pascual Millán: "Bullfights originated in Spain. Romans practiced the art occasionally. The Moors in Spain fought from time to time."

Juan Bautista Erro y Azpiroz declared the ancient coins of Spain show bull-fighters on horseback lancing bulls, before the Roman era.

Spanish historians deny Pliny's implication that bullfighting came from Thessaly. Pliny (27 B.C.–14 A.D.) wrote that Julius Caesar (100–44 B.C.) was the first to present bullfights in Rome, and thought Caesar had picked up the idea in Thessaly. Erro disputes that, with reports of coins, sculptures and language terms in Spain long before the time of Caesar. Spanish opinion agrees largely that, if the Thessalians fought bulls in Rome, they learned in Spain.

IV

There is a lack of documented history during the time of the Goths and the early Moorish era. Legends exist that have popular faith. The most colorful of these is the epic of El Cid Campeador, Don Rodrigo Díaz de Vivar, who lived in the eleventh century. He lanced bulls in both Madrid and Valencia, between times as Spain's legendary champion knight and leader against the Moors. Forms of bull tourneys appeared from time to time in story and balladry from the ninth century onward, with kings and nobles participating.

The first recorded fights were in the twelfth century. In the annals of the Catholic Kings it was noted that a *corrida* was held in Varea, Logroño, 1133, at the time of the coronation of Alfonso VII. A *corrida* celebrated in León, 1140, honored the marriage of Doña Urraca, daughter of Alfonso VII, to García VI of Navarre.

The fiesta spread over the country more rapidly during and after the expulsion of the Moors, because it was a patriotic assembly and it demonstrated the fitness and boldness of the warriors.

After Caesar and El Cid, the most famous of the toreadors (the ancient name for bullfighters that fell into disuse and later became a theatrical term) was Emperor Charles V who fought a bull in Valladolid, 1527, in honor of the birth of his son, who became Philip II. That son, as it happened, ran into a Papal objection to the fiesta after he became king of Spain.

Pope Pius V had suppressed the fights on penalty of excommunication for participation. Pope Gregory XIII lifted the ban. Then Pope Sixtus V, in 1586, prohibited the clergy from attending fights. The famous Fray Luis de León of Salamanca University led in writing a protest. Philip II supported him, and explained to the Pope: "The fiesta is in the Spanish blood, and we cannot take it away without serious repercussions." Philip's statement brought a Papal decree which repealed the prohibition. The king took this action as a ruler; he was not an aficionado.

The popularity of the fiesta spread in the reign of Philip III when the canonization of three saints, St. Ignatius, St. Francis Xavier and Santa Teresa, were celebrated by *corridas*. Another major event of this Philip's reign was the activities of a man named Miguel de Cervantes Saavedra, who introduced to the world The Ingenious Gentleman, Don Quijote de la Mancha. His life was revealed in two stages, the first part in 1605 and the second came in 1615. His exploits have fascinated more readers than any other character in fiction. The

Spain's legendary hero, the Cid

"father of the novel" recorded his acceptance of the bullfight. He did not make an issue of it but took it as part of Spanish life.

Don Quixote, speaking to Don Diego de Miranda, after the affair of the lions, when he had changed his name from the Knight of the Mournful Countenance to the Knight of the Lions, said:

"A gaily caparisoned knight giving a fortunate lance thrust to a fierce bull in the middle of a great square makes a pleasing appearance in the eyes of the king. The same is true of a knight clad in shining armor as he paces the lists in front of the ladies in some joyous tournament. It is true of all those knights who, by means of military exercise or what appear to be such, divert and entertain and, if one may say so, honor the courts of the princes."

Don Quixote had an experience with the bulls later which will be told separately in this book.

During the time of Philip IV, occasionally he fought bulls himself, and the number of *corridas* multiplied. Nothing much happened in the reign of Charles II, the last of that line of Hapsburgs. But some changes were about to be made.

The advent of Philip V and the Bourbon kings changed the conventions of high society, which first appeared in the adoption of many French customs. This was the first Gallic War, because the Spanish people did not go along. Although the Court substituted a light and airy gaiety for the Austrian austerity, the nation as a whole looked askance at such frivolity. The common people are always last in history to bastardize themselves into another identity upon changes of political regimes. They hang on to their racial traditions, folklore and habits with a stubborn faithfulness.

Philip V did not like bullfights. He objected to their "bold and bloodthirsty ceremony." He was concerned about the number of nobles and potential knightly warriors it disabled. He listened to the ruffle-wristed French and Frenchified courtiers. Voltaire deplored the fact that Madrid was taking on the appearance of Versailles imitation.

So it came about that the nobles disappeared officially from the fiesta. But the fiesta continued. For some time, the knights had maintained assistants on foot, armed with capes, lances and assorted shorter blades. These strong countrymen, familiar with the habits of bulls, maneuvered the animals for the horsemen, and finished off wounded animals difficult to dispatch from horseback. Although at times, the knights dismounted and finished off the bull with a sword.

The transition was simpler than it seems. These foot assistants had developed great popularity with the crowds, because they were performing in greater apparent peril than the horsemen and were exhibiting a courage that caused the people to feel great pride in the Spanish peon as a man.

Then it was that the ceremony of the *muleta* and the sword became the finale of the fight. The preliminary by the *picadors* remained, but only for its purpose of providing power contact for the bull and weakening its heavy neck muscles. The phase of the *banderillas* became more colorful and provided variety to the ritual, as well as serving a useful purpose in determining the fighting characteristics of the bull.

Scene of a bullfight by noble horsemen, in Madrid, toward the end of its time as a knightly tournament

A major appeal of the spectacle for the public was its demonstration of courage in the face of death, while maintaining a theme of grace and dignity. This temerity took on a new exposure as a reaction against the royal decree. A few of the gentlemen disobeyed the order, and all of the foot *toreros* added an extra dash to their boldness in demonstrating the bravery and individuality of the people. Time passed, after the knights were barred from fighting on horseback, and the fiesta grew in popularity to such an extent that the government undertook to build plazas in several cities. This public interest attracted bold men. The basic passes developed from experience in maneuvering the fierce animals for the knights.

One of these bold men was Manuel Bellón. He was a muscular and locally famous bullfighter in the South, surrounded by tall stories and gossip that became legend. He had very dark complexion. His nickname was "The African," because he had spent several years in Morocco as an exile, reportedly, because he had killed a man in Spain during his youth. A story of the incident is in this book.

Bellón talked little but inspired a lot of conversation. He is supposed to have been the first who killed on foot, with the cape draped over his arm like a shield to control the bull, and the sword wielded by the right hand. That was before Francisco Romero introduced the short wooden shaft in the *capote* for better manipulation, and it became known as the *muleta.*

Also, there were the Palomino brothers in Andalusia, who had regional fame for bravery with the bulls before the Romero dynasty. The brawny countrymen of the South were demonstrating their courage and their aptitude for the dangerous fiesta.

But everything was experiment until a legendary man, Francisco Romero appeared. He was born a poor boy in Ronda, lovely city of Southern Spain. Although a carpenter's apprentice, he showed an extraordinary aptitude for bullfighting. The story goes that aristocrats of the city adopted him and became his sponsors. He made a profession of what had been largely a noble diversion. His storied contribution was the basis of all bullfighting that followed—the use of the *muleta,* and the killing by sword thrust, facing the bull.

Practically nothing is known of the first actual fight, but Romero became a celebrity about 1726. There were no critics then, and his fame is based on the recollection of those who saw him. At any rate, he continued in the new profession, developing his technique. He is supposed to have fought over Southern Spain for some years before he retired happily, having lived to sire the Romero dynasty of bullfighters which was to make history. The time of the noble, amateur display of daring was over and the professional spectacle was created.

Francisco Romero

From the Romeros to the Revolution

Juan Romero, born about 1722, Francisco's son, became one of the first bullfighters on foot of historical fame. He was the first to organize the *cuadrillas* of *banderilleros* and *picadors,* which brought about the beginning of the fight ritual that is performed today. This developing spectacle attracted nation-wide attention. Juan was called to Madrid to demonstrate his ability at the Court. The favorable reception there had a lot to do with the general interest in the *corrida.* He was also the father of Pedro Romero, the greatest of the Romero dynasty.

But another bullfighter, who appeared before Pedro, deserves his name in the original scroll of men who actually created the basic forms of the fiesta. That was Joaquín Rodríguez, "Costillares," probably born about 1729 in Seville, who perfected the *volapié* method of swordsmanship, and the *verónica* cape pass. He is also responsible for the beginnings of the *muleta* as an implement of defense and ceremony. Actually, "Costillares" revolutionized the entire ritual and could be considered the "father of the present spectacle."

Despite his creative greatness, he had the misfortune to overlap the lives of Pedro Romero (born 1745), José Delgado ("Pepe-Hillo," born about 1755), the first epochal competition of history, who gave names to the two schools of bullfighting, Rondeña and Sevillana. Romero represented the Rondeña school, named after the city of his birth. This style is characterized by quiet simplicity of movement and formal approach to the different phases of the fight. The cape and muleta are manipulated by the arms in aloof dignity while the feet remain still. The Sevillana school, named after Seville, the city of "Pepe-Hillo's" nativity, has a more decorative technique, with greater freedom of movement and inventive range. It is based on grace and gaiety in the face of death, rather than a solemn and calm pride above tragedy.

The difference is that between art and emotion. Prudencio Iglesias said, in *La España trágica,* "The fiesta is like life where there are two ways of fighting off death. One may fight with artistic display or with austere tranquillity. We may apply these characteristics to other forms of like struggles: Napoleon, who was a destroyer of men, and Moltke, who planned battles so as to save as many lives as possible; Leonardo da Vinci, who was a genius of equilibrium, and Lord Byron, who was a genius and somewhat mad in a bizarre way. . . . In bullfighting may be seen the greatest example of man's seal of character."

With "Costillares," and the great rivalry between the epochal Pedro Ro-

Pedro Romero

"Costillares"

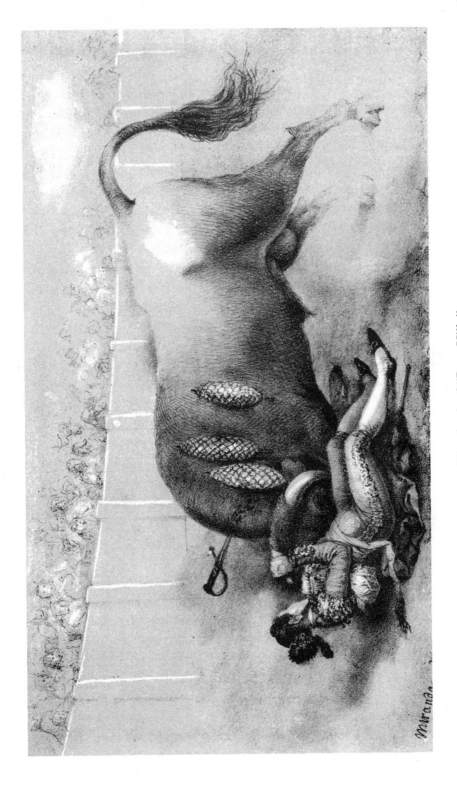

The death of "Pepe-Hillo"

mero and "Pepe-Hillo," the two schools of bullfighting became defined and the lines have remained, more or less, to the present time. All spectacles thrive on rivalries, and the fiesta ebbs and flows with the fanaticism of the public for competing stars of different attitudes and artistic designs.

The three phases of the bullfight were being blended into a ritualistic unity. The *picadors,* with blunted lances, were remindful of the noble predecessors but their purpose was not the same. These horsemen did not try to kill, but tested the bull for bravery and fighting characteristics. They also weakened the heavy shoulder muscles of the bull so that he would charge lower and slower. If a bull attacked favoring one horn, a wound on the opposite side might straighten him. Also, the *picadors* gave the bull an object to hit, so that he would not become aware too soon of the cape's deceit.

The second phase of the *banderillas* was also a transition from the past. Originally only one short, harpoonlike dart was used to arouse the animal for the fighters on horseback. This was a modification of the *rejón,* or lance of death, but had a continuation of the same purpose as the goad.

When Francisco Romero began using the *muleta* and sword, he had *banderilleros* with single darts. Since 1750 the *banderillas* have been considered a most colorful part of the *corrida.*

Don Eugenio García Barañaga in his rules for bullfighting on foot, *Reglas para torear a pie,* 1750, said:

"The most colorful action, and also dangerous, is the placing of the *banderilla* face to face: the bull and man approach each other; the man has the *banderilla* ready and he notes the length of the bull's stride and estimates where its front feet will strike the ground; he places the *banderilla* when the bull's front feet are on the ground and breaks the direction of the charge as he spins out of danger."

Historians are not sure when the present practice of placing the *banderillas* in pairs began, but agree it was toward the end of the eighteenth century. The formalities and graceful ways of handling the *banderillas* developed along with other ritualistic changes in the *corrida.* There are several spectacular *banderilla* maneuvers. Many *matadors* acquired this additional skill, especially in the days when they rose through the ranks to the ultimate stardom. But it is not now a fundamental part of the *matador's* repertoire.

In the eighteenth century, also, there were changes made in the bullfighters' costumes. Francisco Romero fought in a jacket and breeches of leather, held by a broad belt. His padded sleeves were black velvet. The *muleta* he used was about one and one half by three feet, and the sword about three feet long.

The splendid *traje de luces,* glittering suit, of today had its beginnings some years later. There has been much discussion about the actual inventor, but several bullfighters had a hand in its ultimate development. Historian Estébanez Calderón said that Jerónimo José Cándido first adapted to the arena the dress of the flashy young men-about-town. The suit was silk with ornaments of embroidery in gold and silver. The civilian dress in social circles was adorned with gold and silver as well as colored ornaments, in contrast to the sober jet trim-

The first *banderillas* were single barbs

Banderillas in the late eighteenth century

ming on popular dress. The common people wore their hair long and caught in a net at the back of the neck, initiating the powdered wigs of the nobles. A relic of that time remained as the *coleta* of the bullfighters, a tuft of hair on the back of the head, which was cut off upon retirement. This *coleta* later became a small symbol pinned to the hair. The custom has virtually disappeared.

As the spectacle became formalized, the breeding of the bulls assumed vital importance. The entire purpose and performance of the *corrida* depend on this ancient and deadly animal. Courage is based on its ferocity, and grace in danger is subject to the nobility of the savage beast. Beyond the records, the bulls were captured from wild herds in the mountains. By the sixteenth century great nobles and rich landowners had begun to isolate herds on vast estates. A century later there were historical references to these *ganaderías*. King Philip IV had a ranch in Aranjuez. Other *ganaderos* of the seventeenth century were Rodrigo Cárdenas of Salamanca, Villarubia de los Ofos de Guadiana, the Duke of Béjar in Castile, Miguel de Sesma of Navarre, Antonio Ivar Navarro of Old Castile. These are a selection of the historical names.

Several writers consider Don Pablo Valdés, the oldest of the recorded *ganaderos*. His bulls, known as Paso del Portillo, were fought in royal ceremonies along with the wild ones from the plains of Jarama. Therefore, the village of Portillo, Valladolid, gave its name to one of the earliest if not the first-known brand.

The ranches multiplied and names appeared that became famous bloodlines of fighting bulls. The eighteenth century was a time of expansion, and four major regions of Spain became the favored homes of fighting bulls, Salamanca, Sevilla, Madrid and Navarre. These included the surrounding areas, as follows: Salamanca—Cáceres, Zamora and Valladolid; Sevilla—Cádiz, Badajoz, Córdoba and Jaén; Madrid—Segovia, Guadalajara, Cuenca and Toledo.

Some of the bloodlines, Gijón, Cabrera, Vázquez, Peñarauda, Aleas, Marin, Adalid, Bañuelos y Salcedo, Salvatiena, Freire, Guendulain, and others, blended into the hundreds that came down the years in Spain and Portugal, and spread to Mexico, Peru, Venezuela and Colombia.

The fiesta had become a definite part of the national life by the time of the America revolution. It now belonged to the people rather than to the upper classes alone.

By the late years of the eighteenth century, the Sevillian Joaquín Rodríquez, "Costillares," emerged and had added the *volapié* and *verónica* to the *muleta* and sword of Francisco Romero. José Delgado, "Pepe-Hillo," gave the ring terrific competitive spirit and boldness. The Rondeño Pedro Romero brought his majestic variety of skills to the *corrida*. He has always been considered an all-time, all-round star of the first magnitude. He was a master of the cape, *muleta* and sword.

The next epochal fighter was Francisco Montes, "Paquiro," born in 1805. Critics received him with an enthusiasm given masters of all arts, and he was a creative artist. He had no serious rival. Historians disagree whether nineteenth century bullfighting revolved about his magic name. Bedoya indicated that he may have been overpraised by sycophants. Whatever the facts were, he made a steady march to greatness. He had friends in the highest social circles. There was talk that the Queen would give him a title. His popularity was international, as more and more foreign visitors and tourists attended the *corridas*.

Théophile Gautier, famous French author, whose books were popular also in English translations, was one of his strongest partisans. This excerpt from Gautier shows the enthusiasm Montes inspired.

"At the very first step a bull takes in the arena Montes can tell whether he is short or long sighted, whether he attacks bravely or has recourse to stratagem, whether he is light or heavy on his feet, and whether he will shut his eyes to hook with his horn or keep them open. Thanks to these observations, made with the rapidity of thought, Montes is always enabled to vary his mode of defense as circumstances require. However, as he carries his cool temerity to the greatest possible lengths, he has during his career received a considerable number of thrusts, as the scar down his cheek proves, and, on several occasions he has been borne out of the circus grievously wounded.

"One of Montes's feats of dexterity and courage in the ring was followed by shouts, bellowings, vociferations, stamping of feet and thunders of bravos, of which it is impossible to form any idea; a feeling of delirium seizes everyone present, a general giddiness causes the fifteen thousand spectators, intoxicated with aguardiente, sunshine, and blood, to reel upon their seats; handkerchiefs are waved, and hats are thrown up into the air, while Montes alone, calm in the midst of this multitude enjoys in silence the profound feeling of joy which he restrains within his own breast, merely bowing slightly like a man who is capable of performing many other feats of the same description. I can easily understand a man risking his life every minute for applause like this; it is not dear at the price. O ye singers with golden throats, ye fairy footed danseuses, ye actors of all descriptions, ye emperors and ye poets, ye who fancy that you have excited a people's enthusiasm, you have never heard Montes applauded."

With all of his fanatical aficionados in unison, there still were some reviewers who tempered their praise with objective analysis of his flamboyance. They were agreed that he had all the talents, but felt that he should have been supreme where he was only great. One of the fascinating appeals of tauromachian criticism, when it is true and honorable, is the adroit nuances of its adjectivity. Briefly and simply, there was some feeling that his cape work was superlative, but he emphasized the passes he favored. His muleta was excellent but needed his agility to give it complete authority. Montes's knowledge of bulls was not quite profound, but he overcame this by virtuosity. He was a good but not a supreme swordsman, although he should have been, according to his own biographer, Pilatos. He was more a dominating genius than a pure artist.

During the time of Montes there was a secondary rivalry between "Cúchares" and "el Chiclanero." These were excellent *matadors* and attracted many partisans, but they did not reach first magnitude.

Several good fighters followed Montes, but it was not until "Lagartijo" and "Frascuelo" appeared that the most sensational, competitive era of bullfighting

Francisco Montes

began. The public had what it wanted, a rivalry, and this one lasted an incredible twenty-three years.

Rafael Molina, "Lagartijo," 1841–1900, was born in Córdoba. He became a most elegant artist of the Sevillian school. "Lagartijo" could have served as a model for a Roman emperor, according to Prudencio Iglesias in *La españa trágica.* "His bust would have been at home in a museum with the inscription: 'Bust of the virile victor in the gladiatorial arena.' He was also one of the most elegant men in Spain. His figure called for a statue in the robes of a Caesar." His personal touch characterized all his versatility with the cape, *banderillas, muleta* and sword. Several historians insist that he was the most accomplished and complete bullfighter who ever lived.

Salvador Sánchez, "Frascuelo," 1842–1898, was born in Granada. He was the opposite of "Lagartijo," being small, dark and ugly. Heavy eyebrows hooked over the eyes of a wolf. He represented the solemnity and classic simplicity of the Rondeña school. "Frascuelo" had great professional pride and disregard of danger. He was not a versatile artist compared with "Lagartijo," but he inspired deep emotion in his adherents and represented the highest qualities of courageous dignity. His *estocadas* were described by a critic of that time: ". . . the incomparable *matador,* 'Frascuelo,' of the ugly face but beautiful head, poised for the kill with such majestic resolution that it was obvious he would drive the sword truly or die honorably." His loyalty in the arena for fellow fighters was unequalled in history.

The entire nation was divided into two ranks of partisans. This excitement stimulated interest in the fiesta. New plazas were built over Spain. Bullfighting had reached its greatest competitive heights.

There was an inevitable lull after "Lagartijo" and "Frascuelo," but another giant was coming along. That was Rafael Guerra, "Guerrita," born 1862, in Córdoba. He was one of the most versatile of bullfighters. (There is a separate description of him in this book by an American reporter for *Harper's New Monthly Magazine,* July, 1898.)

After "Guerrita" came the era of Ricardo Torres, "Bombita," and Rafael Gonzalez, "Machaquito." These years brought a slight decadence in the fiesta because these two excellent fighters did not reach the eminence of their predecessors. But a golden age was just beyond the horizon, the age of Joselito, the incomparable, and Belmonte, the revolutionist of the entire art.

José Gómez Ortega, "Joselito" or "Gallito," was born May 8, 1895, in Gelves, Sevilla. He was the youngest son of the noted bullfighter, Fernando Gómez (Gallo I), and the brother of the famous Rafael Gómez (Gallo II).

Juan Belmonte García was born in Sevilla, April 14, 1892. His father had a small hardware store.

There have been a number of books, thousands of articles, and certainly words into the millions printed about this era of Joselito and Belmonte.

The golden age of bullfighting came out of the Belmonte revolution. The farther it fades into the past, the more it is wreathed in splendor. However, it was not built on sentimentality, but based sturdily on creative accomplishment. Belmonte was a gnarled, tortured man whose ambition and imagination drove a warped body beyond its limitations to greatness in an art that demands purity of line.

Joselito was his prophet. No man has ever fought bulls more artistically or with greater knowledge than this handsome member of a bullfighting dynasty. He made bright poems of the highest star quality in the arena. There is ample testimony that he performed Belmonte's tragic masterpieces better than the creator. And yet, he left no signature. He remained an interpretive rather than a creative artist. Critics have said Sir Cedric Hardwicke played a better Caesar than George Bernard Shaw wrote. That may be. But he played Shaw's Caesar, and Shaw will be remembered longer because Hardwicke's art cannot be transferred to posterity by any graven symbols.

Belmonte lives in the art of the bullfighters who have followed him. Joselito lives as a memory. Both of them blended into legend.

During their rivalry all Spain was divided into two vociferous and intransigent armies of aficionados. This inspired and provoked strong writing on both sides. However, Belmonte and Joselito remained friends in the eye of the hurricane.

I present here excerpts from opinions of that time.

In 1914, on the second of May, the cornerstone was laid for the Golden Age of bullfighting. So wrote Don Indalecio, the Marquis de la Cadena, in that extraordinary and beautiful book of historical and literary excellence, *La Fiesta Nacional,* published in Barcelona, 1951.

"The bulls were from Contreras and the two that dedicated the era were Azucueco, the fifth, and Tallealto, the sixth. The senior bullfighter who witnessed this miracle was Rafael ('el Gallo'), Joselito's older brother.

"The *faena* of the fifth bull, for the record, should be reproduced as written in *El Toreo,* an objective weekly which published detailed reviews:

" 'Gallito' took the *banderillas* in his special manner.

"Dismissing his assistants, he cited the bull *al quiebro,* but the bull showed signs of jumping. 'Gallito,' wisely and without arrogance, saw that this was not the proper maneuver. He immediately entered *al carteo* and fastened a good pair from the right side. Then, the same type of pair from the left side, showing his excellence from both sides. Afterward, another pair, but one of the *banderillas* fell free. He asked permission to place a fourth pair; he started from the *Carrera* of Section 10, and from there, with little space, he approached the bull with great style and placed the wands.

"Great ovation.

"He took the *muleta* and sword. The *matador* ordered that his assistants leave him completely alone with the bull. He began the *faena* with magnificent passes, combing the sides of the enemy, not moving his feet. A *molinete* followed which terminated with his hip in the face of the bull. He prepared for the kill, to receive the animal on his sword. But the bull would not charge. He hypnotized the enemy, with his face right in the bull's muzzle. He finished it off by entering erectly and placing a perfect half *estocada*.

"The entire plaza was white with handkerchiefs, and the president acquiesced by awarding him an ear, which Joselito tossed into Section 10.

"Lengthy ovation for the bullfighting conscience and science. Joselito saluted the crowd from the center of the ring.

"The *faena* of Juan Belmonte with Tallealto, in my opinion, was unforgettable. It was a mighty demonstration of new norms in bullfighting. Juan fought better than the inventor of ceremony, as Joselito had once admiringly but wistfully said.

"He surpassed himself in this fight. Afterward, an importunate admirer wanted to give the credit to the bull, and said to Joselito.

" 'What a bull this fellow was lucky enough to get!'

" 'And did you notice what a bullfighter the bull got!' replied Joselito."

Henry Baerlein, widely known English novelist, poet and travel writer, also wrote a book on Juan Belmonte, *Belmonte the Matador,* from which I quote:

Juan Belmonte's first fight in Madrid was March 26, 1913. What did the critics say about Belmonte whom they had not seen before, a young man from the provinces, a young man to whom others had applied the word "phenomenon"? Everybody knows that the great critics of Madrid are much annoyed if these distinctions are conferred by other people. But the critics all capitulated: "The freshness and the art of Belmonte," said *El Barquero*, "are indescribable."

In *El Mundo*, Claridades said: "There is only one Belmonte. Here indeed is a phenomenon."

In *Espana Nueva,* the critic Corinto y Oro: "And what I have said, I have said. Belmonte is an fantastic bullfighter."

"What I saw of Belmonte," said Eduardo Muñoz, "sent my heart into my mouth. How long will he last?"

The next day Belmonte was taken to the house of the ex-minister Natalio Rivas, who was afterwards to become a great friend. Several people were present, including the ex-matador Don Luis Mazzantini. Opinions differ somewhat with regard to Don Luis as a matador—some will have it that the bulls were awestruck by his domineering ways and his impressive stature—but there are no two opinions as to what Don Luis thought about himself. And a number of his colleagues and other people had an almost equally exalted view of him. This view was likewise entertained at any rate by one Home Secretary, for Don Luis, after his retirement from the ring, became, as we have mentioned, a civil governor. And it must be said that he was a success. No doubt he was a pompous and conceited man, but the conceit was founded on the fact that he was literate, which most of his associates in the ring were not. And he approved of education, so that in the area which he administered more people learned to read and write than in some other provinces. The bullfighters regarded him with pride, and it was not their custom to allude to him as Mazzantini but invariably as Don Luis Mazzantini. They would say that as he had been governor it would be wrong for any matador to misbehave himself.

It chanced that when Belmonte came into their presence they were talking of the bullfighters of other days, of Joaquín Rodríguez, "Costillares," the civilian who there had developed the pass which later on received the name of *verónica,* and invented the method of killing that is called *volapié.* They were discussing another of the old fighters, Francisco Montes, nicknamed "Paquiro," whom Isabella II—a gay woman but a Christian, according to Pío Nono—had the wish, so they say, to create Count de Paquiro. They talked of Rafael Molina, "Lagartijo," born in 1841, who with the cape was master of them all. So nimble was he with the *banderillas* that a critic—Don Francisco Alcántara—tells us that the rhythm of his lines surpassed that of Greek statuary.

"Don Luis," asked someone, "what do you think of that modern *banderillero* who stands with both feet on a handkerchief and stays there while the bull goes past and he puts the *banderillas* in?"

"Cheap trickery!" retorted the great man. "I would not dream of doing such a thing."

His mood was far from affable when Don Natalio produced a document, one which had attracted him an hour or two before, when he had been idly turning over some of his abundant archives dealing with the bulls. This document was written by no less a personage than "Sobaquillo" [*i. e.,* Mariano de Cavia], and was dedicated to Don Luis. Señor Rivas wanted it to be read out loud.

"Why not let this young man do it?" asked Don Luis as he put the document into Belmonte's hands.

Up to then our friend, through modesty more than timidity, had spoken little. As he took the document from Mazzantini, he pretended not to notice any of the mockery which had informed Don Luis's voice. The room, a ground-floor office in Velásquez Street, was getting dark. So he strode over to the window and with admirable intonation and quite calmly he read every word.

The document had given pleasure in its time to Mazzantini, but on this occasion he considered it was very dull.

Later, on the twelfth of April, when he read an article by Don Modesto, the most feared of critics, he was heard to mumble that as for the bulls of today, one could knock them down with a puff of smoke. Don Modesto's attitude with reference to this young man, Belmonte, had been very dignified before, said Mazzantini. He had abstained from going to the arena. Such a man as he must always lead the populace and not be led by them. They could not sweep him off his feet, they could not compel him to endorse their verdict of "phenomenon." But, on this previous day, curiosity had been too much for the critic and as Belmonte was appearing for the second time he had, in spite of the inclement weather, gone to the ring and sat there, swathed in coats and mufflers and a rug. The result, to which we have alluded, had been an article which Mazzantini grimly read. The title of it was "The Phenomenon!"

Baerlein can be excused his enthusiasm because he was the biographer. But now let us translate Don Modesto's analysis. This famous critic capitulated.

The Phenomenon

Yes, yes, it is Belmonte I am talking about. I have lived through the finest era of the ring, the time of "Lagartijo" and "Frascuelo." I have seen them all develop, Guerra, "Espartero," Fuentes, "Bombita," "Lagartijo Chico" and *Machaquito* and the "Gallos." I can say that I have witnessed in this topmost arena of Spain the good and bad of bullfighting for twenty-five years. And I declare, with my hand on my heart, my gaze to the sky, imploring God to make me see the truth if I have been mistaken; I declare that fighting such as Belmonte's classical style is pure gold, free of brass and alloy, full of integrity, giving the antagonist all the advantage and then dominating him by skill and valour; I swear such has not been seen by "Lagartijo Chico," nor by "Lagartijo Grande," nor by Fuentes, "Bombita," "Espartero," nor by anybody.

But what does this extraordinary youth do that "Lagartijo," "Bombita," "Guerrita," and the Gallos have not done? Well, he accomplishes all their outstanding exploits and he does them much better. He works closer to the bull; he passes it a hundred times across his breast; he holds the enemy prisoner in the flowing folds of the *muleta*. His feet nailed to the ground, he performs this miracle with his arms alone, without permitting any escape for the charging bull. He executes the natural pass and turns slowly on his heels, his left hand delicately holding the enemy in the *muleta*, as if he had him on a wire. He does all this with such domination and care that the heart of the spectator almost jumps out of the mouth. Belmonte is a bullfighter that makes you cry.

There is the style of "Lagartijo," of Guerra, of "Bombita" and of "Gallo," played with the cards face up and with no sleight-of-hand, and no deceit. Pass by pass he moves with the bull until he transforms that fury into the tranquillity of an animal cracker. We have always admired the conquest of brute force by intelligence and art. Usually, as the end approaches the interest declines, because the danger decreases. This does not happen with Belmonte. The last pass arouses in his audience the same emotion as the first. As I have said, he takes no advantage for himself in the fight. At the end, the horns go by at the same one inch distance as at the beginning. Why? Because he does not use his legs to protect his territory. All his talent is in his arms, which force the bull to follow his wishes.

The wild animal bumps him often, and sometimes knocks him down,

The natural pass by Belmonte

The chest pass by Belmonte

but with no great damage. He is always protected by his magical arms, with cape or *muleta;* he is always prepared.

If this great torero develops a style for killing, his present weakness, he will be the greatest of bullfighters in less than two years. I think he will do that because of his formidable ability. I am sure he will, if the ranking authorities are correct that bulls are really killed by the *muleta* preparation. For there never has, there is not now, and, perhaps, never will be a *muleta* like that of Belmonte.

Belmonte does not need his legs. This great recourse of Vicente Pastor and "Bombita" permitted them to fight close to the bull, for they depended on steel-like legs to move them out of danger. Not Belmonte. His unbelievable arms are all he needs, and he demonstrated that yesterday. He was limping on one foot, and could hardly walk when he opened the cape for his first bull.

What a series of three *verónicas!* Passing that bull from muzzle to tail across his body one inch from his shirt front! What a monumental kneeling *farol,* swinging the cape in a slow circle over his head as the horns grazed his body. It was incredible. Tears came to my eyes.

And, then, the *muleta* brought the triumph. He held the bull, controlled him delicately, just enough for the display of the passes. And the most amazing impression I received was that the last pass was just as brilliant, artistic, and dangerous as the first one.

Belmonte reminds me of a man in a fight with a worthy opponent. When he knocks the antagonist down, he does not finish him off, but helps him up, and resumes the battle. Belmonte does not take advantage of the terrific damage of his *muleta.* He defies the animal in its own terrain. He knows that as long as he has that red cloth in his hand the danger is more imagined than real.

Yesterday, with his three bulls, his cape and *muleta* were incomprehensible, beyond the heights of the mighty in bullfighting history.

With the sword, routine; not from lack of courage, but simply because he has not found the style for his kill. He will give exhibitions of many great kills when bulls charge frankly into the *muleta.* Others will cause him trouble for a while. But his *muleta* will prepare them, and he will soon be more deadly than yellow fever.

I would be stupid to think that Belmonte is a catapult that will batter down the pedestals of "Bombita," "Machaquito," Pastor, "Gallo," "Joselito," not to mention other ranking stars of the spectacle. Belmonte cannot yet be compared to them in complete knowledge that is necessary to be a master. So far, he performs with faith and honesty, and with a perfection hitherto unseen.

As a matter of fact, right now Belmonte cannot stand the pressure of competition with Joselito, although he may give the best passes of the encounter. Joselito has more variety. He also uses the *banderillas,* which Belmonte does not, and a number of other maneuvers that give him an advantage.

Yet, Joselito is no genius, and Belmonte is a genius. He fights like nobody else has ever fought before, out of pure inspiration.

Belmonte was born for this art. They had broken the mold for good bullfighters in Heaven. The Supreme Creator took some clay in his fingers and made a small figure.

He breathed life into it, and sent it southward, saying, "There is a bullfighter!"

This little figure fell into Seville, and they baptized him Juan Belmonte.

He is ugly, round-shouldered, knock-kneed, and his long chin droops. But, gentlemen, he was made by the Lord himself and when he opens his cape or spreads his *muleta* he reminds you of his divine origin.

Felipe Sassone, a famous Peruvian-born writer, has lived decades in Spain and long has been one of the occasional but most articulate analysts of bullfighting when he is not writing witty and exciting plays, poems, essays and fiction. His curly hair, his monocle, his vibrant voice and picturesque opinions were a colorful feature of bullfights for those who were lucky enough to sit near him. I sat near him for a few years in Madrid. He was tolerant of me, probably because I had attended lectures at the ancient University of San Marcos, in Lima, of his native Peru. This is a selection from his writing on Joselito and Belmonte.

The intellectuals, and the literary personalities who know little about bullfighting, the masters of aesthetics, Valle-Inclán and Pérez de Ayala, hailed with gay syllables, Belmonte, the prodigy of Triana. Precisely, because they were not experts and, therefore, handicapped by techniques and schools of the fiesta, they liked this innovator. And they eulogized him, without discussing bullfighting. They talked about art and literature, even theology. They enthused about transformation, and pulled out of their erudition the aesthetic and spiritual tranquillity of Miguel de Molinos. The bullfight critics, who wanted to act literary, followed the trail of the masters who did not know what they were talking about, and upset their syntax, filling it full of hyperboles.

Joselito, on the other hand, had no disciples except his most fervent fans, and the hospitality of Pérez Lugín, may he rest in peace for himself, and his contribution to Spanish literature. The public, it must be said, went along with Belmonte. Naturally. He was weak. Joselito was strong. When they applauded Juan, they had the feeling of awarding a premium for merit. When they applauded Joselito, they had the humiliation of paying a tribute that was forced out of them. Joselito was the conqueror. Belmonte was a hero, and our Spanish public, iconoclastic by nature, was annoyed by the facility of the certain winner.

And I? What did I think and feel? I understood bullfighting. I had learned to fight in a fashion. I admired Belmonte without understanding him. Did I like him? Yes, I liked to watch him fight, but I did not approve of him. I enjoyed the impossible as it frightened me, and I was fascinated to see him do what I thought could not be done. He did not convince me. I was a student, and Joselito was the one and only professor. If I had had sons who were bullfighters I would have said, "Look at Belmonte; admire Belmonte; but never, never fight like Belmonte."

On one occasion, at the beginning of the terrific competition between Joselito and Belmonte, when Joselito fought a bull according to the purest and most classical ritual, and Belmonte fought according to his own splendid eccentricities, the public had favored Belmonte. After the fight, I visited Joselito who had imprisoned himself in his house. His eyes were close to tears. His honor, his self-respect had been hurt, this young man who was the expert of experts in bullfighting.

"How is it possible?" he exclaimed. "They do not know what they are seeing. This man is crazy, and at the mercy of the bull. 'Guerrita' was right when he said, 'Better hurry up if you want to see him.' The bulls have not killed him yet, but they catch him every day. It is just a matter of luck. But the bulls will get him eventually. This is not bullfighting."

"I am the best, Felipe, the best! But this afternoon that hunchback fought like the man who invented bullfighting."

That hunchback! I turned my attention to Belmonte, and I had a certain reservation that he moved me merely sentimentally. But one afternoon, in a series of startling *verónicas*, hearing the outbursts of the crowd in unanimous chorus, I noted they came at equal intervals of time. Then I realized he performed the ritual with a rhythm and a measure like music. Ah! Yes? Then it is art!

He fought in the same manner with the *muleta*. That was when I knew he was no hunchback. He was tall and straight. His legs may have been those of a rag doll, but nobody saw them because he did not move them. His figure had the lines of a statue. What was in Joselito the display of figures linked in a frieze became in Belmonte a monument. Belmonte was also an artist, but an artist of his own creation. Yes, this was bullfighting, but fighting closer to the bull than anyone, and everything depended on a miraculous art that came from inspiration alone. Belmonte applied rhythm to bullfighting. He knew just how to adjust himself to the speed of the bull's charge, leading the animal with his living cape or *muleta,* and inventing a new position and a new timing for the performance. Perhaps somebody, Montes, may have fought occasionally in this manner but Belmonte made this style his own. That is why he stands alone in the history of bullfighting because he made his tradition. Joselito was, on the other hand, the perfection of the classical tradition. Belmonte was the revolutionist.

These two formed the foundation for the new era in bullfighting, blending tradition and the future.

Studies of Joselito

Don Pío was the name used by the famous newspaperman and novelist, Alejandro Pérez Lugín, author of *Currito de la Cruz,* translated by Sidney Franklin as *Shadows of the Sun.* He was an outstanding bullfight critic, and a loyal supporter of Joselito. This review was written after Joselito's first appearance in Madrid, as a *novillero,* seventeen years old.

June 13, 1912. The plaza of Madrid is filled with aficionades. I wrote of his first bull: Musket by name, black with light flanks, high body in the ribs, long and lean, horns pointed forward.

Joselito dropped on his knees and awaited the slow charge of the bull with an insuperable change pass of the cape which moved in a slow, swaying circle over his head as he changed the course of the attacking animal. (Ovation.) He rose and administered three *recortes,* or short dominating passes with his cape folded on his arm. Then he spread the cape to its natural length and gave a series of unforgettable *verónicas.* Each one an ovation. Hail Caesar!

"Have you run Galliot?" they asked me in the street after the fight.

He answered: the man I saw was "Lagartijo," Rafael Molina himself, the grand, the immense, the Caliph. From this afternoon I believe in the transmigration of souls. Why? Because the soul of Molina could not be happy in any other body but this boy of the blood and predestination.

What do those "Gallos" have? His father was great. His brother Rafael is great. His brother Fernando is great. Joselito is great. There are no more great ones because Fernando, the father, had no more sons.

Gentlemen, what a race of men! And it is not because they learned about bulls from childhood. This might make them enthusiasts; but the grace, the elegance, the art, and the inspiration? This is a quality of the spirit, not acquired in any university of the world. These "Gallitos" are born artists.

Yesterday the public watched this phenomenon with amazement. Here is revelation and revolution.

The first cape pass yesterday by Joselito in the Madrid plaza was the final punctuation mark to an uninteresting era of bullfighting. It was the capital letter beginning a new epoch.

The day of the artificialities is past. Now for the truth! Now for art! The impartial witnesses saw it. Those who were skeptical were shocked into surrender.

Joselito comes with the same science and domination as his brother, Rafael. But he is more. He acts in the ring as if he were lounging in the patio of his home. He controls the bulls with relaxed nonchalance. He is elegant. He seems to be indolent in gesture, and that is his greatest appeal. Like a schoolmaster with his pupils, he is master of his bulls.

If they do not move at his suggestion, he lets them move of their own free will, briefly. When he has them deceived, his magic cape takes them where he wants them to go. He has a natural grace, a supreme distinction, a knowledge and intelligence for bullfighting beyond his years.

What Joselito did yesterday has to be compared with the great figures of tauromachian history.

José Díaz de Quijano, "Don Quijote," from his *Cinco Lustros de Toreo,* a collection of his articles in *La Fiesta Brava* of Barcelona. This was written on the death of Joselito, May 16, 1920. Díaz de Quijano was a popular novelist, poet and critic.

Dark page. The greatest drama of the arena.

Tragic night, the 16th of May. There are no newspapers on Sundays. There is no detailed information from Talavera de la Reina, where the famous potters now may have another deeply moving allegory to paint on their tiles.

In spite of the lack of news, the brutal rumor invaded the city, the incredible rumor that poured like a tidal wave through the streets and rose like a black cloud over the houses.

Joselito killed by a bull!

Hands tremble at an outrageous heart beat as I write these words for the readers. My thoughts move like the erratic flight of a wounded bird. The terrible blow stuns the senses.

Joselito killed by a bull!

No. No. It is impossible. There are no newspapers tonight. It is surely a rumor. A serious horn wound, perhaps, and lack of information has blown it into a frightening thing, exaggerated and disfigured. Instinctive refusal to accept the report feigns optimistic assurance. But we are lacerated by the awful fact that penetrates all the avenues of hope.

Joselito killed by a bull!

Never can the agony of this incredible night be erased from memory. Madrid in those silent hours of the night—eleven to one—when the people who are not in the theatres gather as voiceless groups or walk slowly along the streets. Few taxis move. Muffled rumors. One name spoken softly. Joselito. Everyone speaks in low tones, and words come haltingly from a deep fear.

Joselito killed by a bull!

And, it is true! Four or five times we could not confirm the report. Then came the sad confirmation. It happened far away in an isolated village, just a few hours ago. But now the news has spread like a poison wind.

Joselito killed by a bull!

Oh, what an absurdity! But how can we deny the evidence? Reason tells us it is not true. But it is true! Reality permeates the people; the black wave rolls on; the black cloud envelops the city street by street, plaza by plaza, repeating the mournful echo.

Joselito killed by a bull!

There is no aficionado living who is not smothered in the emotion of this tragedy.

Joselito killed by a bull . . . Sorrowful theme of an unforgettable night and these words. Perhaps the endless repeating of this strange refrain of pure impossibility will blot out the nightmare. One must awake from this bad dream. But, no. With one swift slash, the blade of eternity severed Joselito's life. He was. He is no more. He is lost in yesterday with no tomorrow. The triumphal pathway of his life has ended. Like the stroke of a guillotine, death has cut short his splendid youth.

Where, how, who can give us the details? Who told us? To whom did we listen? Storm in Talavera? The *corrida* suspended. Why did not somebody stop him from trying to save casual, amateur impresarios? Who was it? Who said so? How did we know? The arena was a mud hole. Joselito who slipped in a cape pass, in a *muleta* pass . . . and the bull gored him, and left him dead. Rumors, rumors that seem like facts. Was this what we heard? How or where? Nobody knows. The night is full of contradictions which confuse us in a disconnected dream, full of voices from far places, mutterings of phantoms.

We know that we were at Joselito's house, and it was closed. We were at the telephone exchange which was crowded with silent people. We know that his brother, Rafael, had gone, weeping, in a car for Talavera.

And now, we see the silhouette of the bull ring rose-colored at dawn, a necropolis, where only yesterday Joselito fought, and where he is scheduled to fight tomorrow. Now there is no Joselito for tomorrow.

Why is he dead? Why does Joselito not live today? Because he was killed by a bull in Talavera de la Reina. A bull of a new breed. The debut of this breed. A promise he made to a friend. He went to Talavera; he fought in a plaza where he had never fought before, a plaza his father had dedicated. He went there and died.

It is true that Joselito is dead. It is morning and we must try to sleep, and see in the fading light a poster announcing the last *corrida* of San Isidro in Madrid, today: Six bulls of Gamero Cívico. Joselito, Belmonte, "Varelito."

This . . .

Today an era of bullfighting is ended. Joselito is the past . . . yesterday . . .

An abyss remains.

Daniel Perea

Daniel Perea, 1834–1909, was a great artistic popularizer of Spain's national fiesta, and one of the most successful artists of his time. He produced many illustrations of the ritual movements in the *corrida* and a variety of artistic contributions to books. Perea was deaf and dumb from birth and became a famed professor in the College of Deaf-Mutes, Madrid. As Goya was a pioneer in etching, Perea was a pioneer of journalistic bullfight art. The Spanish public held him in the highest admiration. This series is from his album *A Los Toros*.

Frontispiece for Daniel Perea series. The Madrid plaza in the 'nineties

Taking the fighting bulls to the arena, led by oxen

41

Delivery of the key, signifying the opening of the fight

42

The entry of the bull

The *verónica*

Cape pass, bringing the bull from behind the *matador*

Banderillas al quiebro, without moving from position

Banderillas in a quarter-circle

47

Preparing for a natural pass

48

The natural pass

49

Poised for the kill, receiving

50

This Day and Age

Joselito's death brought indescribable mourning. "Guerrita," from retirement in Córdoba, said, "Bullfighting is finished." There were probably millions who agreed with him. There is an articulate and informed writer, Nestor Luján, who wrote in *De Toros y Toreros,* Barcelona, 1947, ". . . he was right, within limits. The fiesta, as such, was finished. Another epoch had begun; the *faena* was made more elaborate; the blood was shielded as much as possible; delicacy and dexterity approached aesthetic choreography."

Luján also interpreted the death of Manuel Domínguez, "Desperdicias," 1886, as the end of classical bullfighting. Domínguez was a full disciple of Pedro Romero, who headed the first School of Bullfighting, established by Ferdinand VII May 28, 1830, in Seville. According to Luján, "He represented and gave life to Romero's teachings. This was the serious and formal tragedy. Afterwards came the accent on elegance which formed its greatest development in "Lagartijo." This plastic essence combined with human emotion became the revolution created by Belmonte. This began a taurine spectacle. The term "classic" took on a new meaning, and changed all the rules of the ritual.

The basic Romero commandments for deportment in the arena included:

1. The coward is not a man; bullfighters must be men.
2. Fear causes more wounds than the bulls.
3. The honor of the *matador* requires that he neither run nor retreat in front of the bull, as long as he has the *muleta* and sword in his hands.
4. The *matador* should never vault over the barrier after facing the bull; this is shameful.
5. The *matador* should not depend on his feet, only his hands. He should kill or die before the bull, rather than turn his back or humble himself by unworthy movement.

The basic rules multiplied into a diversified catalogue of conduct. The reaction of the purists did not conceal the fact that times changed and the bullfight took on the colorful features of its evolution, fiesta, or spectacle, or ballet of death. The crowds made the rules and paid to see them observed. Many bullfighters died under the lashes of public tongues. But the Golden Age passed by.

After the death of Joselito, Belmonte continued to fight for a few years with-

Domingo Ortega, low right-handed pass

"Manolete" and his natural of Rondeño dignity

Carlos Arruza finishes a series of cape passes

out adequate opposition. A Mexican bullfighter of great talent, versatility and renown, Rodolfo Gaona, was active in this same era, but he had the misfortune of facing the mighty Joselito-Belmonte rivalry. Nevertheless, he left an indelible record, including one of the most beautiful cape passes, the *Gaonera,* the perfection of which carried his name, as well as *banderilla* performances that included the immortal "pair of Pamplona."

There was also an extraordinary bullfighter, master *banderillero,* author and gentleman, Ignacio Sánchez Mejías, whose death in 1934 inspired one of the great dirges in Spanish literature, by Federico García Lorca. This man ignored the danger of the enemy. It was not disdain. It was not recognition. It was a relentless faith in his own purpose; if no emotion appeared in the contest between man and animal, he invented perilous maneuvers to excite emotion. There was an iron taste of death in his dark devotion. I have seen him starkly unaware of dangers that strangled spectators. I wrote of him once that this irresistible force cannot last forever; the public cannot stand it. He finally died, a

sacrifice to his ignorance of danger, seated on the *estribo,* passing the bull in impossible terrain. The threnodies of the poets covered Spain with a musical shroud.

Belmonte retired a couple of times; finally he quit for good in 1934 and occupied himself with his fighting-bull ranch and other properties. He still fought in 1956 displays with small animals and had become a fine *rejoneador* on horseback for the delight of his admirers. He has enjoyed living his legend for several years.

Belmonte once told a newspaperman, Joaquín Llizo, how he saw himself.

The newspaperman asked: "When the bull charges, your body seems to curve inward from the bull although you do not move your feet?"

"No," replied Belmonte quickly. "I do not move. I direct the bull; it may be that you get this impression but it is not true."

"You have a characteristic that when the bull charges you drop your chin on your chest. Many fighters are imitating you. You must have a reason for this. Do you fix your eyes on a constant point, such as the bull's horn, his neck, or his eyes?"

"None of these," said Belmonte. "What I do is watch the distance between the head of the bull and the cape or *muleta*. I want to keep that distance the same, so the bull thinks he is about to strike his moving enemy. It is a relationship between sight and movement. And to fight the bull well the fighter must keep that relationship between the charging animal and the man who leads him through the passes."

"That means?"

"You can condense my theory of bullfighting into one word: rhythm."

There were several excellent fighters between Belmonte and "Manolete," but none of epochal stature. Any history must include such figures as Marcial Lalanda, Domingo Ortega, Fermín Espinosa (Armillita Chico), Jesús Solórzano and others. But there were none who could symbolize an epoch. This is not a history, as such. It is primarily an anthology of writings on the bulls, with enough history to weave it together.

The next great era of rivalry came between Manuel Rodríguez, "Manolete," and Pepe Luis Vázquez. "Manolete," the Rondeño stylist, was confronted with Pepe Luis Vázquez, the magician of the Sevillana school of bullfighting.

Manuel Rodríguez, "Manolete," was born in Córdoba, July 4, 1917, the descendant of well-known bullfighters. He served a long apprenticeship, and dominated the bullfighting world between his debut and his death, August 28, 1947, on the horns of a Miura bull in Linares, a plaza that his father had helped to dedicate. "Manolete" was more than a bullfighter. He was a graceful and solemn symbol of Spanish pride and virility.

As José Gaviño, an essayist and poet, wrote me, after seeing "Manolete" fight for the first time: "This is man magnified. He is not of this world. His solemn movement is an eternity, and he holds the bull hypnotized for an interminable cadence of breathless ecstasy in the almost motionless rhythm of his *muleta*. His repertoire is confined to classic passes, and his own creations from classic forms, but he makes an entire school by a single pass. He has found a new dignity in the Rondeño majesty as if everything before had been born for him. There has never been anybody like him." Belmonte was right when he saw the boy as a *novillero* in 1937: "If he has no bad luck, this bullfighter will become the best *torero* in the arena." "Manolete" also had the climaxing ability of fine swordsmanship.

Pepe Luis Vázquez was born in San Bernardo, Seville, 1920. He developed as a versatile and superlative artist. All of the gaiety, delicacy, grace and color of the Sevillana school came to its fullest expression in this figure. This is his true style, although his basic principles came originally from Belmonte's revolution. Vázquez fought a brilliant competitive period, between 1940–1943, with "Manolete." Then he was seriously wounded.

Somewhere about this time another truly magnificent bullfighter had appeared, Carlos Arruza of Mexico, to reach the heights of rivalry with "Manolete." Arruza had everything, in the Sevillana category. He was one of the most complete bullfighters who ever lived—cape, *banderillas, muleta,* and sword. He had a gay insouciance that contrasted well with "Manolete's" aloof solemnity, slightly inelegant but sensational. They were good friends, out of the arena. These two men undoubtedly engaged in some of the most exciting fights of modern times. Arruza fought on after "Manolete's" death, but he missed the somber master. He retired, full of glory and wealth, in Mexico, in 1951. John Steinbeck and I saw the farewell *corrida.* He was superb, but lonely in the ring. His eyes had the long, dark look of great things past. This afternoon was the end of the recent era.

There were and are excellent bullfighters. Luis Miguel González, "Dominguín," born in Madrid, 1925, son of Domingo González, "Dominguín," a *matador* who became more successful as a manager and impresario. Young "Dominguín" is smart, a good actor, versatile, wise in all phases of the fight, and a good swordsman. But he is more of a craftsman than an artist. He gives the impression of being too ingenious to be sincere. He has enjoyed a wide, social, and celebrity following, but he is not an epochal fighter. "Dominguín" lacks the essence beyond the rules that distinguishes genius. His life has been easy, and he is rich from the rewards of his talents and the fact that his father controls many of the top plazas in Spain.

The greatest of the present-day bullfighters is his brother-in-law, Antonio Ordóñez, born in Ronda, 1932, son of "Niño de la Palma," who inspired the matador character in *The Sun Also Rises.* That is, he is the best when he wants to be. This young man recalls to old aficionados the ancient glories of the pure Rondeño school, with cape and *muleta.* He is not as good with the sword as he should be.

There may be somebody else, or others, coming along. But in 1957 the horizon is empty of that great competition that will excite the crowds to delirium and the reviewers to the rich resources of the rambunctious Spanish language. Ordóñez needs somebody to match his classical purity of line with the golden filigree of the graceful, joyful Sevillana tradition. However, stars will rise again, and the splendor of *la fiesta brava* will shine again for the deep response and high fulfillment the *corrida* brings to the Spanish people and those who understand the spectacle.

A Parade of Perspective

DIPLOMATS, STATESMEN, AUTHORS, INCLUDING SYMBOLISTS

There are those who apply their rules of cultural thumbs to the fiesta. Some of them are moralists and known to the public. Some indulge in polysyllabic scrutiny, looking down the nibs of very pointed pens. Others draw aside curtains on scenes of symbolism.

We present first James Russell Lowell, American literary critic, poet, and first editor of *The Atlantic Monthly,* Minister to Spain from 1877 to 1880. In late January, 1878, the young king, Alfonso XII married his cousin, Princess Mercedes. A bullfight was scheduled as one of the public spectacles in the celebration.

The following is an excerpt of Minister Lowell's report to the State Department.

The day was as disagreeable as the Prince of the Powers of the Air could make it, even with special reference to a festival. A furious and bitterly cold wind discharged volleys of coarse dust, which stung like sleet, in every direction at once, and seemed always to threaten rain or snow, but unable to make up its mind as to which would be most unpleasant, decided on neither. Yet the broad avenue to the amphitheatre was continually blocked by the swarm of vehicles of every shape, size, color, and discomfort that the nightmare of a bankrupt livery stabler could have invented. All the hospitals and prisons for decayed or condemned carriages seemed to have discharged their inmates for the day, and all found willing victims. And yet all Madrid seemed flocking toward the common magnet on foot also.

I attended officially, as a matter of duty, and escaped early. It was my first bullfight and will be my last. To me it was a shocking and brutalizing spectacle in which all my sympathies were on the side of the bull. As I came out I was nearly ridden down by a mounted guard, owing to my want of any official badge. For the moment I almost wished myself the representative of Liberia. Since this dreadful day the 16,000 spectators who were so happy as to be present have done nothing but blow their noses and cough.

And, it is easy to imagine the good Ambassador thinking it served them right, too.

Lowell, at least, did not make a diplomatic issue of his attitude.

But William Dean Howells, 1837–1920, was a different sort of fellow. He wrote a book on his Spanish travels, published in 1913. The well-known editor, novelist, playwright, commentator on social and ethical problems, was considered, in his era, as a leader of American letters. Although he had found a grammar somewhere and had had a week's instruction in London before he went to Spain, he admitted: "The truth is . . . that I was not perfect in my Spanish after quite six weeks in Spain. . . ." This shows that he was a man to be reckoned with.

About bullfighting:

. . . we had vowed ourselves in coming to Spain to set the Spaniards an example of civilization by inflexibly refusing to see a bullfight under any circumstances or for any consideration; but it seemed to us that it was a sort of public duty to go and see the crowd, what it was like, in the time and place where the Spanish crowd is most like itself. We would go and remain in our places till everybody else was placed, and then, when the *picadors* and *banderilleros* and *matadors* were all ranged in the arena, and the gate was lifted, and the bull came rushing madly in, we would rise before he had time to gore anybody, and go inexorably away. This union of self-indulgence and self-denial seemed almost an act of piety when we learned that the bullfight was to be on Sunday, and we prepared ourselves with tickets quite early in the week. On Saturday afternoon it rained, of course, but the worst was that it rained on Sunday morning and the clouds did not lift till noon. Then the glowing concierge of our hotel, a man so gaily hopeful, so expansively promising that I could not believe he was not an Italian, said that there could not possibly be a bullfight that day; the rain would have made the arena so slippery that man, horse, and bull would all fall down together in a common ruin, with no hope whatever of hurting one another.

We gave up this bullfight at once, but we were the more resolved to see a bullfight because we still owed it to the Spanish people to come away before we had time to look at it, and we said we would certainly go to Córdoba where we should spend the next Sabbath. At Córdoba we learned that it was the closed season for bullfighting, but vague hopes of usefulness to the Spanish public were held out to us at Seville, the very metropolis of bullfighting, where the bulls came bellowing up from their native fields athirst for the blood of the profession and the aficionados, who outnumber there the amateurs of the whole rest of Spain. But at Seville we were told that there would be no more bull-feasts, as the Spaniards much more preferably call the bullfights, till April, and now we were only in October. We said, never mind; we would go to a bull-feast in Granada; but at Granada the season was even more hopelessly closed. In Ronda itself, which is the heart, as Seville is the home of the bull-feast, we could only see the inside of the empty arena; and at Algeciras the outside alone offered itself to our vision. By this time the sense of duty was so strong upon us that if there had been a bull-feast we would have shared in it and stayed through till the last *espada* dropped dead, gored through, at the knees of the last bull transfixed by his unerring sword; and the other *toreros*, the *banderilleros* with their darts and the *picadors* with their disemboweled horses, lay scattered over the blood-stained arena. Such is the force of a high resolve in strangers bent upon a lesson of civilization to a barbarous people when disappointed of their purpose.

This man's writing is his own analysis, from any point of view.

On the other hand, there are the skeptical symbolists. Waldo Frank is one. This novelist and critic has written considerably on Spain and Spanish America. He takes a mystic approach to *la fiesta brava*.

In his book, *Virgin Spain*, first published in 1926, he said:

The medieval lords of Spain jousted with bulls as Amadis with dragons. The *toreo* was held in the public squares of towns, alternating possibly with *autos de-fe*. In the one sport, the actors were nobles and the victims were bulls. In the other officiated captains of the Church and the victims were Jews. In both, the religious norm was more or less lost sight of, as the spectacular appeal grew greater; but no esthetic norm had been evolved to take its place.

Frank sketched through the years when the nobles relinquished participation to the professional fighters. He symbolized the "modern, profound *corrida*" with Belmonte:

The elemental glare of Spanish sunlight makes that body, striding so quiet toward the bull, frail and helpless . . . Belmonte in this instant has already awakened in the crowd the troubling emotion of pity mixed with fear. He salutes the bull and spreads his red mantle (the *capa*) across the fragile sword.

The author means *muleta*. The *capa* and sword are not used together.

Within an instant, breathless save for the breath of the bull, something goes forth from Belmonte to the beast and marries them. The bull is the enemy and they are joined more closely, more terribly than love. . . . Back and forth they go, in rigorous dance. The *torero's* body does not break from its repose. He is as cool as sculpture; he is as fluid as music. The bloody beast is attuned by a will, hard and subtle as Belmonte's sword. His clumsy movements are molded into grace: his rage is refined into three exquisite feints. He, too, like the *torero,* leaves the plane of nature, and becomes a symbol.

As the *torero* stepped out to the sand, his role was godlike. His minions had played with the great innocent victim: fed him victory and blood: taunted him: taught him. Now he, to enact the ultimate rite of life . . . the ultimate gift of the gods . . . the only gift which they give unstintingly . . . death.

And now another change in the beauty of their locked encounter. The man becomes the woman. This dance of human will and brutish power is the dance of death no longer. It is the dance of life. It is a searching symbol of the sex act. The bull is male; the exquisite *torero*, stirring and unstirred, with hidden ecstasy controlling the plunges of the bull, is female.

The crowd acts its part. The little man is but a gleam of fire, the bull but a tongue of Dionysian act within this dark flame of ten thousand souls.

The author proceeds to describe the different phases of the fight with an unusual disregard for the ritual. He has not edited his own statements for fact. He not only mixes up the use of the instruments used in the *corrida*, but he has Belmonte killing the bull in an important style that was not part of his repertoire.

Nevertheless, Frank gets around it all by his conclusion: This is the archetype of the Spanish bullfight. It describes a masterpiece. And in an art so profound and dangerous, the masterwork is rare, even as in other esthetic fields. But if great *toreros* are rare, one actor in the play is constant and is always masterful. The crowds of Spain, against the agitation of intellectuals and of Church, hold to their dear drama. In the *corrida,* all the desires which history has bred and then denied an issue, find an issue. Conflict is the stratified peace of the Spanish soul. For too many ages has the Spaniard lived on war to be able to do without it. In war, the lusts of the world and the lust for God become one. Christ and Priapus were joined in its full ecstasy. And in this dumb show of a man and a bull, they are conjoined again.

These excerpts from Frank's analysis point the way to his mystic conception of the Spanish character. Through the frills and furbelows of his style may be glimpsed the slim body of his conceit. But it is a frail thing upon which to drape so florid a tapestry depicting a simple truth.

Ernest Hemingway took an indignant look at Frank's imagery, puffed out his purpling cheeks and blew him down in *Death in the Afternoon*, 1932. He likened Frank's prose to the

. . . unavoidable mysticism of a man who writes a language so badly he cannot make a clear statement, complicated by whatever pseudo-scientific jargon is in style at the moment. God sent him some wonderful stuff about Spain during his short stay there preparatory to writing of the soul of the country, but it is often nonsense. The whole thing is what, to make a belated entry into the pseudo-scientific field, I call erectile writing. It is well known, or not known, whichever you prefer, that due to a certain congestion or other, trees for example look different to a man in that portentous state and a man who is not. All objects look different. They are slightly larger, more mysterious, and vaguely blurred.

For a more objective analysis, we present the famed John Hay, 1838–1905, writer and statesman who closed his career as Secretary of State. He was attached to the American Embassy in Madrid during the 'sixties, and wrote a book on Spain, *Castilian Days,* first published in 1871. This observer reported on the bullfight as a purely Spanish spectacle:

It is this monopoly of the bullfight which so endears it to the Spanish heart. It is to them conclusive proof of the vast superiority of both the human and taurine species in Spain. The eminent *torero,* "Pepe-Illo," said: 'The love of bulls is inherent in man, especially in the Spaniard, among which glorious people there have been bullfights ever since bulls were, because the Spanish men are much more brave than all other men, as the Spanish bull is more savage and valiant than all other bulls.' The sport permeates the national life . . . but it has not always enjoyed the royal favor. Isabel the Catholic would fain have abolished bathing and bullfighting together. The Spaniards, who willingly gave up their ablutions, stood stoutly by their bulls, and the energetic queen was baffled.

Hay recognized the skill and danger of the performance:

I must copy the inscription on the sword which Antonio Sánchez, "el Tato," presented to "Lagartijo" as a specimen of tauromachian literature:
"If, as philosophers say, gratitude is the tribute of noble souls, accept, dear 'Lagartijo,' this present; preserve it as a sacred relic, for it symbolized the memory of my glories, and is at the same time the mute witness of my misfortune. With it I killed my last bull named Peregrino, bred by Don Vicente Martínez, fourth of the fight of the 7th of June, 1869, in which act I received the wound which has caused the amputation of my right leg. The will of man can do nothing against the designs of Providence. Nothing but resignation is left to thy affectionate friend, Antonio Sánchez (Tato)."

However, the author did not see much future for the spectacle:

Even those who most stoutly defend the bullfight feel that its glory has departed and that it has entered into the era of full decadence. I was talking one evening with a Castilian gentleman, one of those who cling with most persistence to the national traditions, and he confessed that the noble art was wounded to death. "I do not refer, as many do, to the change from old times, when gentlemen fought on their own horses in the ring. That was nonsense, and could not survive the time of Cervantes. . . . I saw the short day of the story of the ring when I was a boy. There was a race of gladiators then, such as the world will never see again—mighty fighters before the king. 'Pepe-Hillo' and 'Costillares,' Romero and Montes, the world does not contain the stuff to make their counterparts. . . . Compare them with the men of to-day, with your 'Lagartijo,' who allows himself to be gored, playing with a heifer; with your frivolous boys like 'Frascuelo.' I have seen the ring convulsed with laughter as that buffoon strutted across the arena, flirting his muleta as a *manola* does her skirts, the bewildered bull not knowing what to make of it. It was enough to make 'Pepe-Hillo' turn in his bloody grave.

"Why, my young friend, I remember when bulls were a serious matter; when we kept account of their progress from pasture to the capital. We had accounts of their condition by couriers and carrier-pigeons. . . . The fighters of that day were high priests of art; there was something of veneration in the regard that was paid them. Duchesses threw them bouquets with love notes. Gossip and newspapers have destroyed the romance of common life." The distinguished statesman-author reported this in 1871.

Just before that time two famous French writers had expressed themselves on the subject. The poet and novelist, Théophile Gautier, 1811–1872, applied his colorful talents to bullfighting in fiction and travel writings. The forerunner of the symbolists wrote, in *Gatherings in Spain:*

It has been asserted and re-asserted on all sides that the Spaniards are losing their taste for bullfights, and that civilization will soon cause the amusement to be discontinued altogether. If civilization does effect this, all I can say is that it will be all the worse for civilization, as a bullfight is one of the grandest sights that the imagination of man can conceive; but, at any rate, the time for abolition has not yet arrived, and those sensitive writers who affirm the contrary have only to transport themselves some day to Spain in order to be convinced that the taste for this *ferocious* pastime is, as yet, very far from extinct.

Gautier was a painter in his youth and his eye caught the artistic phases of the spectacle. This is how he saw the final act of the *corrida.*

The instant had come: the *espada* placed himself exactly opposite the bull. Waving his *muleta* with the left hand, and holding his sword horizontally with his right hand, and the point on a level with the animal's horns. It is difficult to convey by words an idea of the fearful curiosity, the frantic attention produced by this situation, which is worth all the plays Shakespeare ever wrote. A few seconds more and one of the two actors will be killed! Which will it be, the man or the bull?

The man has no defensive weapons, to speak of . . . a woman's pin would pierce through his satin jacket, a mere rag and a slight sword are all that he has to save his life. In this fight all the material advantage belong to the bull, who possesses two terrible horns sharp as daggers, immense force, and that animal fury which is not conscious of danger. . . .

The *muleta* was suddenly moved to one side, leaving the *matador's* body exposed to view; the bull's horns were not an inch from his breast . . . a silvery flash passed with the rapidity of lightning between the points of the lethal crescent, and the bull is on his knees with a roar. He had the hilt of the sword between his shoulders, just as the stag of St. Hubert is represented in Albert Dürer's marvelous engraving, bearing a crucifix in the midst of his branching antlers.

The only phase of the fight that he did not like was the *picadors* and their sorry horses. But that did not deter him from becoming an aficionado who could condemn the "disgusting butchery" of a bad kill, and applaud swift drama of properly placed *estocada*. He reacted very much like the Spaniards: "The public is impartial, and censures a bad kill with hisses and abuse, and applauds man and bull in exact proportion to their respective merits."

Another French novelist, Prosper Merimée, 1803–1870, author of the book from which the opera *Carmen* was derived, was not so satisfied with the spectacle in 1859. He was a long-time Spanish expert, and a devotee of Francisco Montes, noted *matador:*

I was present at a bullfight and it amused me very little indeed. I was unlucky enough to know all too early in life what a degree of excellence this sport can attain, and, after having seen Montes, I really cannot look at his degenerate successors with any degree of pleasure. The animals have degenerated, too, as well as the man.

This sentiment has a familiar refrain with the feelings of John Hay's friend. Such nostalgia will be repeated as long as men grow old.

Two of the diplomats who served in Spain, and were also professional writers, Washington Irving and Claude G. Bowers, must be included. Irving's interest in Spain is common knowledge through his classics, *The History of the Life and Voyages of Christopher Columbus, The Alhambra, The Conquest of Granada,* his diaries and other writings. Bowers, one of the finest modern political historians, was Ambassador to Spain from 1933 to 1939. He wrote two books as a result of his assignment, *My Mission in Spain,* and *The Spanish Adventures of Washington Irving.*

Bowers wrote that Irving attended bullfights as a relaxation from his heavy writing tasks:

. . . he frequently found his way to the bullfights, and it is impossible to conclude that he found these exhibitions shocking. There is evidence enough that he enjoyed them, and he came to know the names and methods of the matadors, but the people attending interested him quite as much.

"I did not know what a bloodthirsty man I was till I saw them [bullfights] at Madrid on my first visit. The first was very spirited, the second dull, the third spirited again, and afterward I hardly ever missed."

One day he went to the *toros* with a "little, round-bellied Spanish marquis, as round as a pumpkin yet pale and withered in the face," and was amused by the old roué's routine for a day of ideal pleasure. He went to the bullfight in the morning, dined at a small café, returned to the bullfight in the evening, and then went to the theatre, after which he topped off a perfect day with "a girl for the night."

This was apparently very interesting to Irving for he was an aficionado and a great theater-goer, too.

Bowers was not an aficionado himself, but he was too much of a historian to ignore the fiesta. He wrote in *My Mission in Spain*:

I had seen my first fight under a burning Madrid sky one day in June. The scene itself was thrilling—the bluest of blue skies, the scorching sun rays accentuating the blue, green, red and yellow dresses and parasols of the women in the stands. Twenty thousand people, tense, expectant. The murmur of so many voices beat upon the eardrums like the pounding of the sea. From the moment the two horsemen in the garb of the time of Philip II rode, to the sound of bugles, into the arena for the key to the bull ring, my emotions were acutely aroused, but confused. The color, gusto, bravado of the procession led by the strutting *matadors* in gorgeous uniforms, the first breathtaking charge of the bull, the grace and daring of the cape work, the skill and valor of the *matadors,* the brilliance and audacity of the *banderilleros,* the knowledge that death hovered in the air close to the bloodstained sand, would quicken the pulse of a statue. And out of it all, in the end, emerged one dominant feeling—a profound admiration and pity for the courageous, magnificent fighting bull.

"But it is not a sport," explains the Spaniard. "It is a tragedy." Do the English think it cruel? They are asked to explain the hunting of the little fox that cannot defend itself. "It seems so cruel," said an American woman, without tact. "Perhaps," replied a Spanish woman, who did not care for bullfights, quoting a Castilian saying, "perhaps, and yet we do not have to have Societies for the Prevention of Cruelty to Children."

The Ambassador did not put it in his book, but after seeing his first fight, he declared to a newspaperman:

It is uniquely Spanish and a most thrilling spectacle. It is the only ceremony left from the color and display of ancient times. The *corrida* is a spectacular contribution of Spain to living history.

This statement had two consequences: the Spaniards immediately accepted Bowers as an understanding historian, and his popularity was off on that note; President Roosevelt called him on the phone, from behind a pile of indigant telegrams on the White House desk, sent by members of the Society for the Prevention of Cruelty to Animals.

Another American diplomat is quoted for the reason that he weaseled his words about the fiesta as Sir Roger de Coverley expressed in his famous attitude, ". . . there is much to be said on both sides." H. C. Chatfield-Taylor, who had been attached to the American Legation in Spain, wrote a book, *Land of the Castanet*, Spanish sketches, 1896. He said slyly, "They presented in Madrid a *corrida* as a benefit for the Society for the Prevention of Cruelty to Animals." The Spaniards have a word, and the Conde de las Navas wrote it down, for this kind of comment, *garbanzo*, chick pea, which is an epithet of sorts.

But Chatfield-Taylor bowed later, once to the left and once to the right. "It is impossible to defend the 'national sport' of Spain. Although it is cruel, it is also fascinating, exciting and seductive. All in all, the most splendid spectacle of our time, and comparable only with the gladiatorial combats."

The English author, psychologist, and critic, Havelock Ellis (1859–1939), seems to fit into this company. He spent some time in Spain, and wrote *The Soul of Spain*, (1908). He was another author who was attracted by the symbolism of the spectacle. This is what he saw and felt during Holy Week in Seville:

It may seem a long way from the cathedral to the bull ring. In Seville one feels it is not so. The Giralda, the cathedral tower, is the one outside object that we see towering above the walls into the cloudless sky as we sit in the ring, and it introduces no dash of discord. When the *toreadors* enter —grave, lithe, handsome men, in their varied and beautiful costumes— and walk with hieratic grace and dignity of carriage to salute the president in his box, we feel at once that we are still in the presence of the same spirit —in slightly different form—which has dominated the Holy Week. One recognizes afresh that fundamental harmony in apparent opposites, which, though part of the Spanish temperament generally, may be said to reach its finest and deepest embodiment in the atmosphere of Seville. Gorgeous ceremony, elaborate ritual, solemnly accepted, we are just as much in the presence of here, as when we witnessed the Archbishop consecrating the holy oil or washing the feet of the thirteen old men. The whole process by which the death of the bull is compassed is nothing but an elaborate ritual, the detail of which the stranger is altogether unable to appreciate. In the church the ceremonies of every divine office gain their solemnity by association with the highest conceptions of the Christian faith; in the plaza the sense of solemnity is gained by the possible imminence of death. But in both cases, ceremony and a poignantly emotional background, furnish the deepest element of fascination. The bullfight is Spanish, and appeals to Spaniards, quite as much because it is a sacred ritual as because it is a sport.

As the conclusion to the parade of famous observers and commentators, it is fitting that Spaniards have the final words. After all, it is their fiesta.

José Sánchez de Neira, historian of bullfighting, 1896:

Public diversions are good or innocent depending on what the people want. Other countries have their spectacles. There is nothing more agreeable or innocent than riding a balloon. But it is a short pleasure, only a matter of minutes. And the impression on the public is a passing fancy. Man, in his desire for exhibitionism, tries the impossible. So, he conceived the idea of elevating himself in a balloon. And he did it.

Actually, this deserves some admiration and can become a side show or additional display for any public celebration, although it is not a sensation in itself. It is dangerous. The balloons have little safety. The bullfighter is much safer. He has assistants to help him if he gets into trouble. The aviator has only the good Lord.

Boxing is legal everywhere. It is an example of barbarism. *Corridas* cannot be compared in cruelty with this atrocious crime against beauty and humanity. It is degrading to see men pummel each other into hideous insensibility and death.

The fox hunting of England. This is the same country where a member of Parliament censured the Government for not punishing a man who kicked a cat, because the cat was eating a lamb chop he had planned for supper.

Whatever such people say, certain foreigners have been able to understand the importance of the *corridas*. Jean Jacques Rousseau, the famous French philosopher, in an essay on the government of Poland: "A great nation should maintain its own civil and domestic customs. . . . Public spectacles that entertain beneficially should be promoted. Others, such as gambling, which are effeminate, should be abolished. The *corridas* in Spain have contributed in no small measure to the vigor of that nation."

The Conde de las Navas, 1900:

In England, France, Holland, and other countries there are more or less cruel sports. Those peoples do not think themselves dishonored nor can the 'protective societies' in these countries kill the diversions. The zoological families have not united in rebellion.

What about the live pigeon shootings, the other small bird killing in tournaments?

What about the *foie gras* obtained from fattened geese that are enraged and killed?

What about the foxes of England?

Apparently these people believe The Supreme Creator cares more for large animals than He does for small ones.

Prudencio Iglesias, newspaperman and author, 1913:

England may be the most powerful and liberal nation in the world. But boxing is a gala British manifestation. A people that has no mixture of barbarity is in danger of extinction. The human being needs a safety valve. Bullfighting is the artistic manifestation of the streak of Latin barbarity. The man who does not, at least, twice a year feel animal urges in himself is not a man.

Ramón Pérez de Ayala, poet, novelist, essayist, ambassador to London during the late republic, is a vivacious representative of contemporary Spanish literature. He wrote in 1920:

If I were dictator of Spain I would take my pen with one stroke and suppress bullfights. But, meanwhile, so long as there are bullfights I shall attend them. I would suppress them because, in my opinion, they are socially a bad spectacle. I will continue to attend them because, esthetically, they are an admirable spectacle and because individually, for me, they are not harmful, and rather exceedingly useful as a text for the study of the psychology of the Spanish people.

The fiesta of the bulls is an alloy of sensual beauty for the eyes and vigorous emotions for the nerves, heart and lungs, and whatever intense emotion is necessarily produced as a result of an action which is frightening, unusual or brutal. In Spain, the spectacle has its detractors, foreigners as well as Spaniards. If they consider only the so-called barbaric side, the defenders do not have to answer except to express the delight of the senses and the spiritual excitement generated by this dismaying and dazzling spectacle, which they call sublime.

Between the detractors and defenders are the mediators, who, without denying the cruelty of the bullfights, are satisfied to compare them with sports in other countries which pretend to more cultural and exquisite moral standards than Spain; they declare that bullfighting is not more cruel than boxing or live pigeon tournaments.

Then, there is another aficionado, as in everything, who worships the past. Anytime in the past is better than now. But he keeps on going to the fights, to complain and fulminate against the grotesque performers, bulls the size of cockroaches, and cardboard *picadors,* as compared to the mighty conquerors, bulls as big as cathedrals, and *picadors* of Cyclopean awesomeness, in the good old days.

But Pérez de Ayala saw and thought deeper than this satirical analysis.

If the essence of art, as Schopenhauer maintains, is nirvana or nihilism, the forgetfulness of self and the liberation from daily cares become ecstasy, a little sample of eternity. Then, why is it strange that the Spaniards stand in line at the ticket windows of the *plaza de toros?*

. . . Man's tyrant is time. All the troubles of life would be lifted if we knew we were immortal. But we are not and we are in a hurry. . . . Emotion is an interlude in time. Smashing clocks does not solve anything. There is a clock in our breast with an unwinding spring, the heart. Its cadence, like the tic tac of the pendulum, tells us that time goes by, time goes by. But, at the fiesta, an emotion takes over, time pauses and for a moment, which is interminable, our heart, the merciless clock, stops and starts again. What difference does it make? We have stopped time, if only for an instant!

The Verónica, the Natural, and the Estocada

The basic elements of the *corrida* are the *verónica,* the *natural,* and the *estocada.* These were the original phases of what has since become a complicated and colorful ritual. They remain in all their serenity and dignity as the classic fundamentals of the art. No matter how many passes of punishment, grace and daring dexterity are invented, they all add up to filigree in the face of the simple, majestic composition of the *verónica,* the *natural,* and the *estocada.*

I
The Verónica

The *capa* was a large article of apparel, and an old Spanish costume for men. It was close around the collar but spread out in long flowing fullness, and opened in front. The knightly lancers wore their capes on horseback in the arena, and it was the first article of defense used in fighting on foot. It is frequently called the *"capote,"* but José María de Cossío, authority on all phases of the fiesta, states in *Los Toros:* ". . . this is not strictly correct, except by habit, because the *capote* was actually a shorter cape while the *capa* used in bullfighting is as long or longer than the regular cape men wore." The cape-wearing custom is, unfortunately, dying out in Spain. There has never been an overcoat that can replace the flowing beauty of the gentleman's cape.

"The *capa* became a primary part of bullfighting on foot from the beginning, because it served for defense, as a means of citing the bull to charge, and, draped on the arm as a shield, it held the bull's attention in the act of killing when the sword was first used, and before the *muleta* had been designed. It was originally made of light wool and red in color. But, it was found through experience that another textile was necessary because the wool caught easily on the bulls' horns. Raw silk became the material. Now two colors are used, but one side is always red ranging to magenta, and the other generally yellow. The evolution of bullfighting has changed its manner of use but not its shape."

The *verónica* is credited to "Costillares," and, in the *Tauromaquia* of "Guerrita," it is called the most valuable as well as the most colorful of cape passes. His version: ". . . the bullfighter takes his position with his side toward the bull. He cites the enemy with the cape in both hands so that the bull will charge parallel to the barrier. As the animal charges from his right side, he moves the cape first ahead of the bull stretching out his left arm and bringing his right hand to his left side. The opposite is true when the bull charges from the left. In this pass, when the bullfighter stands with his side to the bull, rather than facing it, it is easier to repeat the pass in a series from side to side without moving the body from the waist down.

"When the *verónica* is performed facing the bull, the bullfighter must move or turn on his heels to link a series of passes. The nature of the bull determines whether the pass should be started from long or short range."

The *capa de brega* is not to be confused with the *capote de paseo,* which is actually a *capote,* and is entirely ornamental, used only for the entrance parade. This is of fine silk and embroidered with gold or silver or other fancy designs.

The basis of cape work with the bulls is the movement facing the animal with both hands holding the capa. When the bull charges, the *matador* holds him through the pass, by his body, and ends it either with the cloth high or low, depending on the characteristics of the animal.

"Pepe-Hillo" called this pass, in his *Tauromaquia,* "Suerte de frente o la verónica," frontal movement, or *verónica.*" The name veronica came from religious art showing St. Veronica holding a cloth in both hands to wipe the face of the Savior.

"Pepe-Hillo" described the pass: ". . . this is done holding the cape in front of the bull, with the bullfighter erect in his position. It is the most beautiful and composed of all passes, and the rules of its execution depend on the nature of the enemy. The noble, lively bull should be allowed to approach the cape close enough to follow its movement around the body. The *matador* must not move his feet until the bull is under the control of the cape and passes by ready to be brought around for another pass. If the bull is foot-loose, the *matador* should prepare for the pass at a distance. If the bull is slow, the fighter should work from a shorter distance. He should be always on guard, otherwise the bull may stop just before or during the pass and endanger him." The master of this pass wrote a detailed study of the way it should be done with all types of bulls.

Amós Salvador, in *Teoría del Toreo:*

The customary way to hold the cape is to grasp it on both sides of the collar, catching it with the forefingers and the middle fingers extended. Facing the bull squarely, the *torero* marks out a pathway for the bull in his preliminary pass outside, so that when he terminates the series back and forth he can finish between the bull and the *barrera* and the animal will be toward the center, his own *querencia.* The bullfighter must keep his feet still and close together, or move one foot forward, on the side of the charge and following the movement of the cape, if the bull requires an open termination of the pass.

Verónica by Jesús Solorzano

Verónica by "Cagancho"

The *verónica* is finished off by holding the arms level, as if lifting a curtain over the face of the bull, and turning on the heels in a half circle to continue the series.

The finale of the pass is made by the regular *verónica* movement until the bull reaches the cape, then whipping it around the hips sharply instead of following through, causing the bull to wheel and stop as the cape settles quietly around the man's body.

The pass has changed over the years and has many variations now, as well as related maneuvers. Some are more spectacular and complicated but the simple *verónica* still retains its classical purity and breath-taking beauty.

II
Pase Natural

The basic pass of the *muleta* is the *pase natural*. It has long been a subject of controversy with violent partisans among the critics and aficionados over one point. Can it be made with the right hand as well as the left hand? This editor is not impartial. He believes that the only natural pass is made with the muleta in the left hand and the sword in its proper hand, the right hand. The pass of similar movement with the right hand is aided, or *ayudado,* by the sword which gives the *muleta* an unnatural spread. Hereafter are quoted the statements of famous authorities, and a poet.

José María de Cossío
in Los Toros

José María de Cossío, in *Los Toros,* printed different opinions on the natural or regular pass, then climbed right up on the *barrera* and sat there, working both his hands as rightful wielders of the *muleta.* This attitude has its misleading aspects. Two passes with different employment of the *muleta* and sword cannot be the same. The movement has to be different, also, because the sword broadens the spread of the *muleta* and the tempo changes with the heavier weight of the sword, balanced by an empty left hand. No aficionado would depreciate the beauty and value of the right-handed passes, the foundation of many modern *muleta* innovations. But how can it be denied that the original, natural way to fight a bull in the basic pass of the *faena* was with the *muleta* in the *muleta* hand and the sword in the sword hand, naturally?

Cossío said:

It appears certain that in the old times, as Montes declared in his textbook on the ritual, the right-hand passes were maneuvers of resourcefulness, depending on the characteristics of the bull. However, in modern bullfighting these passes are normal and often primary features of the *faena.*

He is correct in that statement; many modern *faenas* have little or no

Natural by Marcial Lalanda

Natural by Félix Rodríguez

left hand, and aficionados are gradually losing their appreciation of the danger and the difference because the modern ritual is one of rippling rhythm and shimmering color. It is difficult to see the living statue through the silken kaleidoscope.

Amós Salvador
in Teoría del Toreo

The natural pass is executed with the *muleta* in the left hand and the sword in the right hand. The fighter usually cites the bull full-face. Then he leads the bull by his body so that the bull will follow the *muleta* as he spins slowly prepared for another pass. The bull should be passed from head to tail and the fighter should turn his left foot slowly in time with the *muleta* movement, bringing his right foot around in a repetition of the original position.

The pass *con la derecha* is similar to the left-hand movement but the sword spreads the *muleta* as both are in the right hand.

José Sánchez de Neira
in Gran Diccionario Taurómaco

The natural or regular pass is made by the left hand of the matador, who faces the bull. Without moving his feet, he holds the *muleta* fan-like waving it slightly backward. Then he turns in a semicircle so that the bull follows the *muleta* and wheels ready for another change. A continuation of these passes is called *en redondo*. No single pass can be turned *en redondo*.

A similar pass with the right hand, holding both sword and muleta, can be called a natural, but it has neither the merit nor dexterity of the left-handed movement.

José Delgado ("Pepe-Hillo")
in Tauromaquia (1796–1804)

The *matador* takes the *muleta* in his left hand. For the pass, he holds it spread at his side as he faces the bull. Standing in the bull's terrain, he provokes the attack which he takes in the *muleta,* controls the bull's speed and direction without moving his feet.

Francisco Montes
in Arte de Torear

To pass the bull with the *muleta,* the fighter stands facing the animal as he does in a *verónica.* He has the *muleta* in his left hand, toward the center of the arena. The bull is called and must be led by the fighter until the pass is completed, either with the *muleta* hand high or low, just as the *verónica* may be performed high or low.

If the bullfighter is on the outside of the bull, toward the center of the ring, he can change the *muleta* to the sword hand but it is not so graceful.

Rafael Guerra ("Guerrita")
in Tauromaquia

The natural pass can be made with either hand, but the *matador* must remember it is most effective and artistic, as well as more dangerous, with the left hand. In the right-hand pass, the *matador* has more cloth of the *muleta* in the bull's face because it is spread by the sword. Right-hand passes of this kind should only be used on the bulls that hook to the left.

Felipe Sassone
In Casta de Toreros

The natural pass? With the *muleta* in the left hand, the sword in the right hand, and the heart in between. That is the way it is, and the only way it is.

The Natural
by Armando Vilches Cano

The *muleta*
In the left hand, the heart hand,
And the sword
In the right hand, the knight hand;
A black storm, the raging form
That plunges
Like thunder through the shadow on the sand.
Where stands a man,
Slim, alone, forlorn,
Between his destiny and death.

There is a movement, and music,
As he sways
With the dark and deadly cloud,
To a sombre rhythm,
In a tragic grace.
And a statue is born in the sun.
The flick of an instant, an hour;
The agony is endless,
Till the multitude can breathe in ecstasy,
For the man, slim and alone,
Who seems so small
Between his destiny and death.

III
The Estocada

The *estocada* is the supreme moment of the spectacle, *la hora de verdad;* the time of truth where life and death are joined in the flash of a steel blade wielded

Estocada by Nicanor Villalta

by a man moving through a stately ritual. The climax of the *corrida* is performed with solemn rhythm as the hushed spectators pay their respects to mortality. If the final act is accomplished courageously and well, the plaza echoes a hoarse exultation for man's victory. But man must prove worthy to receive this vociferous accolade. Less than courage and dexterity brings violent criticism and abuse. A simple and swift death for the bull is the purpose of all that has gone before, and the crowd demands this reward for their emotion and their money.

There are three fundamental ways of killing the bull practiced since bullfighting on foot began.

In the first, known as receiving, *recibiendo,* the matador profiles, erect, facing the bull, with the *muleta* low in his left hand and the sword extended high toward the bull in his right hand. He lifts the left hand, and may advance the left foot, slightly to attract the animal. Then he awaits the charge, without changing position and aims the sword between the bull's shoulders at a 45 degree angle to cut the artery that leads into the heart. He directs the bull's horns by his body with a slow sweep of the *muleta* to the right as he crosses the sword arm high over the horns for penetration between the tops of the shoulder blades. Then he pivots slowly alongside the animal's body.

The second style begins the same way, but the bull and man move toward each other at the same time. This is called *a un tiempo,* at one time.

The third way of killing, the *volapié,* flying feet, is the one universally used today.

Joaquín Rodríguez, "Costillares," has the credit for changing the style from receiving, also called *by the rules,* to *volapié* or flying feet, about the middle of the eighteenth century. He was probably not the first to kill bulls by moving over the horns, but he was the first to make a practice of it. There was even a Spanish proverb current at that time, "If the bull does not charge you, charge him." The *volapié,* undoubtedly started out as a resourceful way to dispatch bulls that refused to charge. Francisco Montes, in his *Tauromaquia,* gives the strictest rules for its pure performance. The bull must be well fought and come to the death ceremony tired enough to charge slow and straight, rather than be capable of unexpected fury. His front feet should be even and close together, which will cause him to hesitate slightly as he moves into attack. The *espada* should take up his position relatively close, not more than three or four paces in front of the animal. Then, just before the bull moves, the *matador* should go forward and plant the sword over the horns as the bull charges, with his head following the *muleta* to the left and low. This enables the *matador* to escape.

The old way of *recibiendo* is rarely seen any more. The legitimate *volapié* is not generally practiced. A variation of the *volapié* called *arrancando,* or running toward the bull before he can actually charge, is in more general usage, but it all, as a rule, comes under the heading of *volapié* these days, which is a modification of the truth, to say the least.

Belmonte's Epilogue to His Autobiography

The late Manuel Chávez Nogales was a highly capable newspaper writer and editor when I knew him more than twenty years ago in Madrid. He not only mixed his knowledge of the bulls and politics in a most natural manner but he wrote well on both subjects. Belmonte told him the story of his life, and Chávez Nogales put it down well. The book was translated into English by Leslie Charteris, best known, perhaps, for his mystery and crime fiction, and published by Doubleday, Doran, New York, 1937, titled *Juan Belmonte, Killer of Bulls.* The epilogue to Belmonte's autobiography, as Charteris translated it, is presented here.

I am a bad theorizer. I don't know how to describe what I do to a bull, and I shall not attempt to put forward a comprehensive theory of bullfighting which any of the expert judges of the art could certainly do better than

I. But having come to the end of these memoirs of mine I feel bound to say something about the way I understand and practice my art.

Bullfighting is one of the few activities in Spain which can allow itself the luxury of maintaining a perfected system of criticism. The theorist and the doctrinaire of the art of bullfighting exist in greater profusion perhaps than those of the art of painting or literature or music. The explanation is simple: Bullfighting is a business which commands a greater popular interest than the beaux arts, and its social and economic prosperity is able to support highly paid critics and theorists.

This is not to say that bullfighting critics are necessarily venal. The venality of reviewers who frankly mould their criticisms according to how much the bullfighter pays them, and the nuisance of publicity agents with their modern methods of propaganda, are secondary considerations which have nothing to do either with art or criticism. The only problem they present is that they are ruinous for the *torero;* and a time will come—I believe it has come already—when bullfighting will no longer be a paying business.

Criticism is something else. There may be certain critics who are mercenary; but I have not known any of them. I have systematically refused to meet them. Personally, I have never been capable of bribing anyone, and no one can ever say that I have ever done so.

I remember one occasion when it was suggested to me that I ought to give a certain sum of money to an influential critic. I refused. If he was really an honest man who wrote what he sincerely felt, I needn't attempt to bribe him. If he was only another of the reviewers who write what you want at so much a line, he could come to terms with my manager or the *mozo de espadas.* I have never recognized the existence of a man to whom one has to give money on the sly; but I have had to resign myself to my manager's reports that one man or another wanted his palm greased. What I object to is only hypocrisy. In the case I am referring to, Juan Manuel told me that the critic in question was one of those who accepted subsidies, but on condition that it be kept dark.

"When you go to San Sebastián," said Juan Manuel, "he will be there. You'll pretend to meet him by accident and give him so much."

"I wouldn't have the nerve to do it," I answered. "It may offend him, and it would certainly offend me."

"Nonsense. You've nothing to be afraid of."

"But didn't you say that this fellow is supposed to be an honest man?"

"Don't be so innocent. He's like all the others. The only difference is that he wants to swim and keep his clothes dry."

"Then look here," I said. "If he's really an honest man I can't bribe him, and if it's a matter of dealing with some sort of polite blackmailer, that's what I keep you for. So you look after it yourself."

Apart from corruptions like this, which I have mentioned only to avoid leaving my memoirs with any pretended ignorance of what goes on behind the scenes of bullfighting, I must repeat my high esteem of the real theorists of the art. Thanks to them, it has reached a state of perfection which would be difficult to surpass. I believe that bullfighting has acquired a literature of its own which deserves appreciation; and anything that I, being only a practicing *torero,* can say about it has nothing but the limited value of one man's personal experience.

Many laymen and, what surprises me more, certain professionals have cast doubts on what I have referred to in this book as bullfighting in the country; so I should like to be a little more particular about this technique. These remarks may be well timed, because I am told by some rancher friends of mine that by describing my days in Tablada in this biography I have helped to revive the practice among the lads of Sevilla after it had been almost forgotten for many years. So although my friends may not thank me for it, I should like to tell the boys of today how it is done, or at least how we used to do it.

It is a fact, as everyone ought to know, that the bull in the open country does not attack a man. The only bull which attacks is the outcast rogue who has left the herd after losing a fight with another bull. Cows which have recently calved will also nearly always charge. But the normal thing is that the free bull is not naturally ferocious.

The bull decides to charge only when it is obliged to, when it is cornered and has no other way out, or when it is tired of running away. Therefore in order to make it fight you must first tire it and then convince it that its only chance of escape is to attack. Naturally, to tire a bull by chasing it over the open country is practically impossible for one man alone, because he will always tire before the bull. In order to overcome this difficulty, you resort to strategy.

When you are walking through the country and you meet a suitable bull, all it does is to turn round and retreat in the direction which its instinct indicates. We would stop it by spreading ourselves out in open formation along the line which we thought it would take, forming a kind of human wall along its chosen route. When the first lad got in its way, the bull would make a detour to try and avoid him and continue its escape in the same direction. But when it got back onto its line of retreat, it would meet the second boy, who forced it to turn aside again. So they would go on appearing one after another along the whole length of the bull's retreat. Meanwhile the first boy, as soon as he had performed his task of turning the bull aside, would turn diagonally back and overtake the bull while it was eluding the others; so that when the bull had evaded the last lad in line it would meet the first again. Thus we formed a human chain which allowed us to chase the bull all the way across the pasture without exerting ourselves. When the animal at last became tired and annoyed and made up its mind to fight, the boy whom it charged had to stand his ground empty-handed and keep avoiding its attacks until we had all caught up with him and could begin fighting. Sometimes, if the animal was small and not very fierce, one could seize it by the head and twist its neck until it fell, holding it down like this until the others arrived. If you take hold of a bull in a certain way it loses all its strength and falls easily, and you can keep it down with quite a moderate effort. Then we would form a ring and play it until it was worn out and refused to charge any more.

Our technique in this sport became almost perfect. I remember that one of the guards of Tablada, who thought he knew all about bulls, refused to believe that we could play them in the open country, and in order to see it proved he allowed us to give an exhibition one day under his very nose.

All the same, I don't think that we invented anything. That pursuit of the animal by men with no other advantages than the speed of their legs, the strength of their arms, and their superior intelligence, is probably the same procedure which was followed by the caveman who hunted the bull, barefooted and naked like ourselves, to kill and eat it. It must have been the origin of bullfighting itself as it may well have been practiced by the mythical inhabitants of Atlantis.

Now, thousands of years later, we all eat the bull, and naturally bull-fighting has come to a stage of decadence. Everything that can be achieved has been done. The bull of today has no more interest: it has been domi-nated and conquered.

Of course it is not a matter of mastering the bull in order to eat it, but of mastering it in order to play gracefully with its blind instincts and thus produce a spectacle of beauty and emotion. And yet even this has been achieved so perfectly that the *corridas* are less interesting every time. The mastery has been reached by successive stages. Perhaps I was one of them. After me, there have been others. Each stage leaves the bull more com-pletely dominated. The *torero* does what he likes with it. If one bullfighter, after a few passes, grasps the bull by the horn, another bullfighter comes after him and seizes it by the horn without having played it first, when the animal has just come out of the pen in its full freshness of vigor. Later on comes someone else who seizes it by the ear, and finally someone appears who holds it by the nose. Every day somebody goes a step further, so that about the only thing left is for the *torero* to take bites out of the bull and eat it alive. Progressing in this direction, the fight is doomed to become more like a circus performance. It will be emasculated. The beauty of the fiesta will still be there; but the drama, the emotion, the supreme anguish of the savage struggle will have been lost. Already the fiesta is decadent.

The technique of bullfighting goes on becoming more nearly perfect; every day men are fighting better, more artistically, closer to the bull, with a skill that has never been seen before. Today there are many *toreros* of un-surpassable merit, any two of whom would make a pair of stars worthy to rank with the famous names who thrilled the public thirty or forty years ago. And yet the bullfight goes on losing interest.

On the same scale as the art of bullfighting has been evolving and per-fecting itself in the sense of giving more beauty to the fiesta, the bull, which in the beginning was unplayable and lacking in all the indispensable qualities on which the bullfighter could exercise his art as we understand it today, has also been evolving. We might say that the bull has been learning how to be fought. It is as highly cultivated, as completely trained in the specialty for which destiny has ordained it, as a university professor is for his vocation; as different from its ancestor in the prehistoric swamps of the Guadalquivir as the *torero* of today is different from the caveman who went out naked and unarmed to hunt the beast for food.

The fighting bull of today is a product of civilization, a standardized industrial article like Coty perfumes or Ford cars. The bull is manufactured according to popular demand. Thanks to a slow and painstaking process of selection, the breeders have succeeded in meeting the wishes of the public by turning out bulls which are perfect instruments for the fight. I think that in the manufacture of bulls the Stradivarius has already arrived.

This does not mean that the bulls are inferior in danger or power or courage to those which used to be fought. To say that the bulls of today are harmless is nothing but pretentious blah. It is not true that the breeder has contrived with his selections and crossed strains to eliminate danger: what he has done is to polarize it in the direction which the fight requires.

The bull has lost none of its strength; it has as much strength today as it had half a century ago. Aficionados who sadly recall those *corridas* of bygone days in which a bull would knock over and disembowel six or eight horses in the arena forget that the protective padding which is insisted on by our present laws, and which does positively save the lives of the poor brutes, also prevents the bull from attacking the horse with the same facility as before. They think that the bull is less powerful because when it charges the horse it doesn't knock it over easily; but the fact is that what used to bring down the horse was not so much the impact of the bull as the wound which the bull's horn used to open in its stomach. In other days, fighting bulls were reared on grass, not on grain as they are now. Thus it happened that in the month of May:

> Cuando los toros son bravos,
> Los caballos corredores . . .
> (When bulls are brave
> And horses swift . . .)

as the song says, the bull was very strong and powerful; but for the rest of the year, the animals that came out in the arena could hardly carry their tails. With the diet on which it is reared today, the bull which comes out to fight in the arena in November is stronger than the bulls which were fought in May thirty years ago.

The bull is just the same fierce and well-armed wild animal that it was before; but its development has been one-sided towards making the fight more pleasing to the eye. It is not true that it has lost courage. The modern bull charges much more often than the old one, although it is true that it does less damage. I doubt whether one of the bulls which were fought years ago could stand the strenuous *faenas* of today, with the number of passes with the cape which the public demands, the padded horses, the inevitable *quites*, and the amount of work which is now usually done with the *muleta*. Its courage has not been taken away, but its spirit has. The spirit only serves to make the fight more difficult, and fighting is what the spectator is most concerned to see.

The objective has been to breed a bull which will provide more brilliant but no less dangerous *corridas*. Something similar occurs with the aging of the bull. A three-year-old bull is as dangerous as a five-year-old, but it is more adapted to be played with brilliance. The public does not want unplayable bulls. I have seen all the spectators rise in a body and call me a suicide because I insisted on fighting an animal which in their judgment did not combine the necessary qualities for the fight. The breeders who made themselves famous for the difficulty with which their bulls were fought have disappeared, not because the *torero* rejects them, but because the public does not want them either. What aficionado would go today to see a *corrida* of Palha bulls? Isn't it significant enough that the herds of Santa Coloma have been sold for meat? What has happened to the breeds of Parladé, Saltillo and so many others?

The public wants a bull which is easy to play, and for this reason it prefers the three-year-old. The reason is obvious. The three-year-old bull lends itself better to the art simply because it charges straight. Until it gets old, the bull's horns have not opened completely, and it has not learned to hook. In the *novillo*, the horns point straight ahead, and for this reason it is accustomed to wound with a straight forward movement. Later on, when it has lived longer in the pasture and has learned more about fighting from its battles with other bulls, when it knows how to hook to right and left and has learned to defend itself with something more than uncontrolled instinct, it gores in quite a different manner. But the old and expert bull is of no use for the kind of fight which the public taste demands.

In my opinion there are only two solutions. Either the public must go on being satisfied with *corridas* which are pretty to see and full of accurate and consistent fancy fighting, which is what they have become; or we must go backwards, give the enemy some weapons, and multiply the difficulties instead of reducing them. Let us fight old, tricky, savage, unplayable bulls. Perhaps then the fiesta would awaken again the old passionate enthusiasms; but at the same time it would mean good-by to the technique of today, good-by to the fancy figures and the marvelous patterns of bullfighting. We should return to the days when you hunted the bull as best you could.

I don't know whether the aficionado of today would enjoy watching anyone fight as "Pepe-Hillo" fought. I sincerely believe that he wouldn't. I also believe that the bullfighters of today would find it hard to fight bulls like those which "Pepe-Hillo" killed, and moreover that the public would send them back to the corrals as unplayable.

This, as I honestly know and understand it, is the present situation of the art of bullfighting. The public will say which it prefers, and the *toreros* will go on risking their lives to win its applause in the circumstances and conditions which the public taste demands. This is what has always happened and will go on happening.

As far as I am concerned, apart from these technical questions, the most important thing in the fight, on whatever terms it takes place, is the personal accent which the fighter gives it. That is to say, his style.

The style is the bullfighter. It is the color which the spectacle of the struggle between man and beast, old as the world, takes from a personal temperament, a type of character, an individual spirit. One fights according to what one is. That is what matters. One man's inward emotion must shine through the mechanical movements of the fight. When the bullfighter ends his *faena,* the tears should come to his eyes, or his lips should be touched with that smile of spiritual fulfilment which a man feels each time that the exercise of his art, however lowly and humble it may be, has made him aware of its divine inspiration.

The seasons of 1934 and 1935 are so near that I cannot see them in their true perspective. I am still too hot from the struggle to be able to speak of them dispassionately. Last year I fought thirty-odd *corridas* and was gored fourteen or fifteen times. It was a hard battle. The circumstances in which I fight today are as unfavourable as they can be. The public treats my appearances as if each of them were an epoch-making event, and comes expecting to see something almost supernatural, so that whatever I do must be inferior to what they have imagined. I have never found any satisfactory explanation of these popular reactions. In these days I hardly know why I am being applauded or why I am being shouted at.

So I pay no attention. Sometimes it seems to me that they are excessively severe, at other times that they are too enthusiastic; but I go on fighting at the dictation of that inward faith which will always take me back to the arena again and again to go on with my life work. I finished the season of 1934 in this state of mind; and at the beginning of 1935 a bull caught me in Palma de Mallorca and split my collarbone. The following day a friend rang me up.

"I'm very sorry that the bull split your right collarbone," he said. "And I'm just as sorry that it didn't split your left collarbone at the same time and your breastbone as well. Maybe that would make you stop fighting."

My family and certain other friends held the same hope, which gave me the impression that my craving to go on was making me a bit of a bore, and that I was simply being obstinate about keeping up a struggle which I ought to have given up long ago. This time I thought that I had really reached the end. I decided to finish the season, completing the obligations for which I was already contracted, and then to go quietly home.

I set out with this resolution to fight my last *corridas;* but as if fate were determined to upset my plans, or perhaps because my subconscious mind rebelled against the certainty of a definite retirement, I experienced in those last fights, at which I thought I was only appearing because I had to, a triumphant revival which culminated in the *corrida* of September twenty-second in Madrid. This *corrida* and the one which I fought afterwards in Sevilla were like the breaking of a new dawn. And they gave me the unspeakable happiness of ending as I had begun, and leaving me room to dream that I was only just beginning. For the truth is that I was born only this morning.

All these old stories which it has given me pleasure to recall pale and fade away in the clear light of this morning which is stealing through the windows. Everything I have related is so old, so remote and strange to me, that even I can hardly believe that it happened. I am no longer that desperate little boy of Tablada, nor that ambitious young *novillero,* nor that dramatic rival of Joselito, nor that conscientious and embittered maestro of the later years. . . .

The truth, the only truth, is that I was born this morning.

Death of Manolete

by BARNABY CONRAD

Barnaby Conrad has a bewildering virtuosity. He lived through a time in his youth as secretary to the pyrotechnical genius, Sinclair Lewis. As a friend of the immortal Redhead, I can testify that this, alone, was an achievement only shared by one other writer I know, John Hersey. Undismayed, Conrad went on to Spain, and the comparative quiet of learning to fight bulls with Belmonte. Then came a kaleidoscopic career as a diplomat, a writer, a painter, a pianist, a restaurateur, a lecturer and a man-about-the-world. His writings on bullfights did a lot to stimulate the recent American interest in the spectacle, *Matador, La Fiesta Brava,* a must for any library, numerous articles, and the English version of Arruza's autobiography, "My Life as a Matador." Except for an unpredictable knee, he might have become an extraordinary *matador.* He lives in San Francisco, where his restaurant, El Matador, is a magnet for aficionados from everywhere, and Conrad holds forth for his friends as a host and as an authority on some of the most interesting aspects of life, including painting, and writing, and bullfighting, and the almost lost art of conversation. I include in this book his "The Day I Fought with Belmonte," and his introduction to *La Fiesta Brava*.

On August 28, 1947, a multimillionaire and a bull killed each other in Linares, Spain, and plunged an entire nation into deep mourning. The bull's name was Islero, and he was of the Miura strain. The man's name was "Manolete," and he was the essence of everything Spanish. His story is the embodiment of *la fiesta brava*.

It's hard for Americans to understand why all this fuss about one bullfighter. But he wasn't just a bullfighter to the Spaniards. He was their only national and international hero. Yet when he was killed, he died such a beautiful dramatic Spanish death that I swear, in spite of the great funeral, the week of national mourning, the odes, the dirges, the posthumous decorations by the government, that in his heart of hearts every Spaniard was glad that "Manolete" had died. They, the Spaniards themselves, murdered him.

He looked quixotic. Ugly in photos, cold and hard in the bull ring, he had tremendous magnetism, warmth, and gentle humor among his friends. Once, in Peru, I took a blasé American college girl to watch "Manolete" in the ceremony of preparing for a fight, though she protested she had no interest in a "joker who hurts little bulls."

"Excuse me, señorita, if I don't talk much," he said with his shy smile as they worried his thin frame into the skintight uniform, "but I am very scared."

After that he didn't say more than ten words to her. But she walked out of the room dazed. "That," she announced, "is the most attractive man in the world."

An hour later he had her weeping with emotion as he calmly let the horns of a giant Fernandini bull graze the gold braid on his costume time after time. The fear he spoke of was nowhere in evidence.

"To fight a bull when you are not scared is nothing," another bullfighter once said, "and to not fight a bull when you are scared is nothing. But to fight a bull when you are scared—that is something."

"Manolete" told me, "My knees start to quake when I first see my name on the posters and they don't stop until the end of the season."

But there was never any real end of the season for him. In 1945, for example, he fought ninety-three fights in Spain in six months, about one every other day. This meant body-racking travel, for he would fight in Barcelona one day, Madrid the next, and then maybe Lisbon the day after. He would snatch some sleep in the train or car and sometimes had to board a plane with his ring outfit still on. Then followed Mexico's season and Peru's season, and when he got through with those it was March again and time for the first fights in Valencia. It would be grueling even for a very strong man, and "Manolete" was frail to the point of appearing tubercular. Yet he kept driving, driving.

What, then, made him run? What made him The Best?

Money was the obvious thing. In his eight years as a senior *matador* he made approximately four million American dollars. In his last years he was getting as high as $25,000 per fight, about $400 for every minute he performed, and he could fight where, when, and as often as he liked. His yearly income was abetted by such things as a liqueur called Anís Manolete, dolls dressed in costume with his sad face on them, testimonials for cognac ads, songs about him, and a movie called "The Man Closest to Death."

Yet it wasn't the money; people seldom risk their necks just for money. It was that he needed desperately to be someone—something great.

He was born Manuel Rodríguez in Córdoba, Spain, in 1917, in the heart of the bullfighting country. His great-uncle, a minor-league bullfighter, was killed by a bull, one of the dreaded Miura breed that years later was to kill Manuel. His mother was the widow of a great *matador* when she married Manuel's father, also a bullfighter. He began to go blind, kept fighting as long as he could distinguish the shape of the bull, and finally died in the poorhouse when Manuel was five years old.

The family was always hungry-poor. Manuel was a frail child, having had pneumonia when a baby, and could contribute little to his mother's support. But he started carrying a hod as soon as he was big enough to tote one.

His two sisters stood the hunger as long as possible, and then they started making money in a profession even older than bullfighting. This was the secret of the driving force behind Manuel. He never got over it. He resolved to make enough money somehow so that his family would never have to worry again, and to become an important enough person so that his sisters' shame would be blurred. Bullfighting is the only way in Spain for a poor boy to become great. "*Matadors* and royalty are the only ones who live well," they say. Young Manuel decided to become the greatest bullfighter who ever lived.

He was twelve and working as a plasterer's assistant on the Sotomayor ranch when he got his first chance. They raised fighting bulls, that special savage breed of beast originally found only on the Iberian peninsula, that can easily kill a lion or tiger. Little Manuel begged so persistently to be allowed to fight that finally the Sotomayors put him in the corral with a cape and a calf. Manuel, an awkward, skinny kid in short pants, was knocked down every time he went near the little animal. If the calf had had sharp horns instead of stubs, he would have been killed twenty times; instead he was just a mass of bruises by the time he limped out of the ring. He decided to go back to plastering.

But he couldn't stay away from the bulls. In the next few years he got out with the calves every time he could, even after he had been badly wounded, at thirteen, by a young bull.

There always are back-seat bullfighters around a ranch, and they told him some of the mistakes he was making. He learned fairly fast but he was no genius. He was awkward and tried to do the wrong kind of passes for his build. However, he was brave and took it so seriously that he finally persuaded someone to give him a fight with small bulls in Córdoba's big *plaza de toros,* under the *nom de taureau* of "Manolete," a diminutive of Manuel.

In his debut he was clumsy, but so brave and obviously trying so hard that the home folks applauded the sad-faced gawk. It was the greatest day of his life. Flushed with success, he and two other boys scraped their money together, formed a team called the Cordovan Caliphs, and set out to make their fortune. They wangled some fighting at night and in cheap fairs. "Manolete" was almost the comic relief of the outfit. The crowds would laugh at his skinny frame, made more awkward by the fancy passes he was trying. His serious, homely face and his earnestness made it all the funnier.

"He looks as dreary as a third-class funeral on a rainy day," they'd say. But they couldn't laugh at the way he killed. He was so anxious to do well that when it came time to dispatch his enemy, "Manolete" would hurl himself straight over the lowered head, the horn missing his body by inches, to sink the sword up to the hilt between the shoulders.

"He's going to get killed that way someday," said the experts.

His career, if you could call it that at this point, was interrupted by his being drafted into the army. After his discharge a year later he resumed fighting without the other two Caliphs. Then came the turning point in his life, for Camará spotted him.

José Flores Camará, a bald, dapper little man of thirty-five with omnipresent dark glasses, might have become the greatest bullfighter of all time except for one thing: he was a coward. He displayed more grace and knowledge of bull psychology than anyone had ever seen before. He had the build and he knew all about the different fighting habits of bulls and the rest of the complicated science of tauromachy. The only thing he couldn't do was to keep his feet from dancing back out of the way when the bull charged, which is the most important thing in bullfighting.

When he saw "Manolete" gawking around a small-town ring, he knew that here was someone who could be everything that he had failed to be. With his expert eye he saw what the crowd didn't, that the boy wasn't really awkward, but that he was trying the wrong passes for his build and personality. Camará figured that with his brains and "Manolete's" blood they could really go places. He signed up the astonished young man for a long, long contract.

Camará remade "Manolete." He took him out to the ranches and showed him what he was doing wrong. He made him concentrate on just the austere classic passes, none of the spinning or cape-twirling ones. With the cape he showed him how to do beautiful slow *verónicas,* finishing with a half-*verónica.* It was the only pass, of the dozens that exist, that "Manolete" would ever do again with the cape. With the small *muleta* cape used with the sword, Camará let him do only four passes. He showed him how to hold himself regally, how to give the classic passes with a dignity never before seen in the ring.

When Camará thought "Manolete" was ready, he launched his protégé. It took a little while for people to appreciate what they were witnessing, but soon they came to realize that here was a revolutionary, a great artist. His repertory was startlingly limited, but when he did the simple *verónica* the cape became a live thing in his hands, and the easy flow of the cloth, the casual way it brought the bull's horns within a fraction of an inch of his legs, was incredibly moving. Heightening the effect was the serious mien and the cold face, which gave a feeling of tragedy every time he went into the ring.

No one laughed at him now. Camará had made a tragic genius out of a clown. And always the nervous little man with his dark glasses was behind the fence while his protégé was out with the bull, watching every move and saying: "Careful, Manolo, this one will hook to the left," or "Take him on the other side, he has a bad eye," or "Fight him in the center, he swerves when he's near the fence." And "Manolete" kept learning and learning.

If his first year was successful, his second was sensational. It seemed as though Spain had just been waiting for his kind of fighting. His honest and brave style showed up the fakery that the cape-twirlers had been foisting upon the public. In 1939 he took "the alternative" and became a senior *matador*, fighting older and larger bulls. From then on his rise was dizzying, for every fight and every season seemed better than the last one.

By 1946 he was the king of *matadors* and Mexico beckoned with astronomical contracts, the highest prices ever paid a bullfighter. Spectators thought they were lucky to get a seat for $100 for his first fight in Mexico City. It was the greatest responsibility a *matador* ever had, and he gave them their money's worth, although he was carried out badly wounded before the fight was half over. He came to as they were carrying him to the ring infirmary, shook off the people who tried to stop him, and lurched back into the ring to finish the bull, before collapsing.

After he recovered he went on to fight all over Mexico and South America. When I saw him in Lima he was exhausted. Most bullfighters can give a top performance one day and then get away with a few safe, easy ones. But not "Manolete." To preserve his fabulous reputation he had to fight every fight as though it were his first time in the Madrid plaza.

But the machine was wearing down. Though he was only twenty-nine, he looked forty. He was drinking a lot; not mild Spanish wine but American whisky. His timing was beginning to go off. I remember once in Peru he took nine sword thrusts to kill a bull, and he left the ring with tears running down his cheeks.

Even Camará, who enjoyed having his wallet filled through risks taken by someone else, thought it was time to quit. But the public makes an idol and then it tires of what it has made and it destroys the idol. When "Manolete" returned to Spain and announced that he was going to retire, he found he had slipped from public grace. The people were now saying that he dared to fight only small bulls and that this new young Luis Miguel, "Dominguín," was better and braver. "Manolete" had been on top too long. They wanted someone new. They amused themselves by changing the words of the once popular eulogizing song, "Manolete," to "Manolete, you couldn't even handle a robust field mouse if confronted by one in the bathroom."

"Quit," Camará advised him. "Quit," said Luis Miguel, who would then be cock of the roost. "Quit," said the other bullfighters, who then wouldn't look so clumsy and cowardly.

"Manolete" had too much pride to quit under fire. He said he would have one last season, just a few short months, with the largest bulls in Spain, and fighting with any fighters the promoters wished to bill him with. He wanted to retire untied and undefeated.

His first fight was in Barcelona, and the critics said he had never been greater. Then Pamplona, and he was even better than at Barcelona. It looked as though everyone was wrong, that he was in his prime.

Then, on July 16, he was wounded in Madrid. The wound wasn't serious, but he left the hospital too soon to go on a vacation in the mountains with Antonia, his mistress. He began fighting again long before he should have; it was as though he were afraid that if he missed any of these last contracts there would always be some people who would remain unconvinced that he was still The Best.

The next fights were not good. He just wasn't up to it physically, and he wasn't helping himself by the way he was drinking. He would stay up all night with a bottle of whisky, not go to bed, and try to fight the next afternoon. They say he drank because of Antonia, because he knew she was a girl "of a bad style" and a gold digger, but that he loved her and couldn't break off with her and hated himself for loving her. A friend of his said, "She dragged poor Manolo through the Street of Bitterness with her cheapness."

Also the crowd's new attitude toward him was intolerable, not because of egotism but because of his professional pride. Now they were always prone to applaud the other *matadors* more, no matter how close "Manolete" let death come.

"They keep demanding more and more of me in every fight," he complained to me. "And I have no more to give." People want heroes, need heroes, but the "Manolete" myth had outgrown the real "Manolete," and the people were angry at him instead of at themselves for having created it.

Then came August twenty-eighth and the fight in Linares. It was extremely important to him that he be good this afternoon. First, because it was near his home town; second, because Luis Miguel, "Dominguín" was on the same program; third, because the bulls were Miuras, the famous "bulls of death" that have killed more men than any other breed in existence. People claimed that "Manolete" was scared of Miuras and had always avoided fighting them.

Since it was midsummer and the sun shines till nine in Andalusia, the fight didn't begin until six thirty. It began, like any other of his fights— the stands jammed with mantilla-draped señoritas and men with the broad-brimmed sombreros cocked over one eye. There was an excitement in the air because of the Miuras and the rivalry between "Dominguín" and "Manolete." The stylish gypsy Gitanillo de Triana completed the bill.

Gitanillo did well by the first bull and received applause and handkerchief-waving, which meant the audience wanted him to be granted an ear of the dead bull as a token of a good performance. But the president of the arena was hard to please and refused to grant it.

The second bull was "Manolete's." It was dangerous and unpredictable, but "Manolete" was out to cut an ear. He made the animal charge back and forth in front of him so closely and gracefully that even his detractors were up out of their seats, yelling. But when it came time to kill, he missed with the first thrust. The second dropped the bull cleanly and the crowd applauded; but he had lost the ear; they were demanding perfection today.

The trumpet blew, and it was Luis Miguel's turn. This was an important fight to him also. He wanted to show up the old master in his own province. He wanted to show them who could handle Miuras better than anyone in the world.

He strode out into the arena, good-looking, smug, twenty-one years old. "Manolete" was through—here was the new idol, here was the king of the rings!

He had the crowd roaring on the first fancy, twirling passes with the big cape. He put in his own *banderillas* superbly, to win more applause. With the *muleta,* the little cape that is draped over the sword for the last part of the fight, he unfurled all of his crowd-pleasing tricks, dropping to his knees for two passes and even kissing the bull's forehead at one moment. He lined the bull up, thrust the sword in between the withers halfway up to the hilt, and the animal sagged down dead. The crowd cheered and waved their handkerchiefs until the president granted "Dominguín" an ear.

"Manolete" had watched the entire performance from the passageway, with no change of expression. Those tricks and cape twirls were not his idea of true bullfighting. He would show the crowd what the real thing was if it killed him.

After "Gitanillo's" mediocre performance with his second animal, "Manolete" saw the toril gate swing open and the last bull of his life came skidding out of the tunnel. It was named Islero. The moment Camará saw it hooking around the ring, he sucked in his breath and said to "Manolete": *"Malo*—bad, bad. It hooks terribly to the right." That is a dread thing, for a *matador* must go over the right horn to kill. "Stay away from this one, chico!"

But "Manolete" was determined to give the best performance of his life. He caught the collar of the cape in his teeth and held it while he got the big magenta cloth right in his hands. Then he slid through the opening in the fence and called the bull.

"*Toro*, hah, toroooo!" he called in his deep voice, holding the cape out in front of him and shaking it.

The animal wheeled at the voice, its tail shot up, and it charged across the ring. As it reached the cloth the man did not spin or swirl the cape around him or dance about the way that Luis Miguel had done. He merely planted his feet and swung the cape slowly in front of the bull's nose, guiding the great head with the tantalizing cloth so that the left horn went by his legs ten inches away. Without moving his feet, he took the bull back in another charge and the right horn stabbed six inches away from his thighs. Five more perfect classic *verónicas,* each closer than the other, finishing with a half-*verónica* that was so close that the bull's neck hit him and nearly knocked him off balance. He turned his back on the bewildered animal and looked up at the crowd that was cheeringly deliriously.

With the *muleta* cape, his forte, he worked in even closer, until the crowd was shouting, "No, no!" Camará was shouting with them, for "Manolete" was passing the animal just as closely on the dangerous right side as the left. But the man didn't pay any attention. He did the Pass of Death and his own pass, the dangerous *"manoletina."* He did fifteen suicidal "natural" passes, the one where the sword is taken out of the cape and only the limp bit of rag is used to divert the bull's charge away from the body. Then he did his famous trade-mark—the fantastic pass where he looked disdainfully away from the bull up into the stands as the animal thundered by. It seemed as though the bull couldn't miss, but it did. By now the crowd was hoarse from cheering the domination that the man had acquired over the beast.

It was time to kill. As he was lining up the Miura so that the feet would be together and the shoulder blades open, Camará and his *banderilleros* were yelling: "Stay away from him, man! Off to the side and get away quick!"

But "Manolete" had to finish this one right. He wasn't going to spoil the performance by running off to the side and stabbing it in the lungs. He was going to head in straight, get the sword in, give the bull a fair shot at him, and hope to God it wouldn't hook to the right.

He stood in front of the Miura, sighted down the blade, rose on the toes of one foot, and as the bull lunged forward, "Manolete" hurled himself straight over the lowered right horn. The sword was sinking in, the horn cutting by him. But suddenly the bull wrenched its head to the right and drove the horn deep into the man's groin. "Manolete" was flung high into the air, trying to fight the horn out of his body, and then was slammed to the sand. The bull spiked at him twice on the ground and then staggered, choked, and flopped over dead, the sword up to the red hilt between its shoulder blades.

The pool of blood on the sand told them the man was mortally wounded. Camará and the *banderilleros* picked up the unconscious form and rushed him down the passageway to the ring infirmary. He regained consciousness on the operating table and gasped weakly, "Did it die?"

"*Sí, chico, sí,*" said Camará, tears raining down his cheeks.

"It died and they didn't give me anything?" "Manolete" said, trying to raise himself from the table.

"They gave you everything, *Matador*," said a *banderillero*, putting his cigarette between the wounded man's lips. "Everything—both ears and tail."

He smiled and lay back.

At five in the morning he moaned, "Doctor, I can't feel anything in my right leg." The doctor assured him he would be well in no time. Then, "Doctor, I can't feel anything in my left leg." He gave a cry and said, "I can't see!" and he was dead.

An old *banderillero,* staring at the corpse, said dully, "They kept demanding more and more of him, and more was his life, so he gave it to them."

Manolete

by TÍO CARLOS

Carlos Septien García, "Tío Carlos," was one of the most brilliant young Mexican newspapermen and bullfight critics until his untimely death in 1953. A volume of his opinions and reviews was published in 1948, *Crónicas de Toros*. A selection from his article on "Manolete," republished here, appeared first in *El Universal* of Mexico City.

Spain was not born crying—Spain had no fragile infancy. Spain was not rocked in a soft cradle, nor was her childhood covered with linen and perfume. Spain was raised austere, lean and grave, the soul forged in indomitable maturity; with her idea of the world sharply outlined. Spain was—long before nations existed—an unbreakable attitude. Because Spain was created in hurricanes to the music of thunder; because Spain was born on its wild earth—and the hoarse voices of oceans sounded its maternal lullabies; because Spain was developed through the blood and toil and glory of mighty champions and queens who were female captains; because Spain was mistress of her own fate, servant of ideals, intrepid conqueror of horizons, since she breathed the breath of life and since her lean and flowing figure rose over the isolated parapets of her castles and the flowering meadows of her southern plains.

Hardly had Spain sprung from robust Roman roots when her spirit was first defined, by a philosopher, and from Córdoba. Seneca declared, "So live that, whatever they say about you, they say you are a man."

What splendid heritage for Santiago, the son of thunder. Recaredo, the golden Goth. Ruy Díaz, the Cid Comprador. The imperial Isabel; Philip, the Latin defender of the faith, Hernando Cortez, the conquistador, and a long line of mighty personages who illuminated the centuries and changed the face of the world.

What a wonderful heritage that, here, on the sand of the arena, there rose the lean, grave silhouette of bullfighting Spain in the person of Manuel Rodríguez, "Manolete."

The scene is unforgettable.

Above him, the irresponsible paid masqueraders abusing the bullfighter. Below, the bullfighter who had truly fought his first bull. Above, the cowardly anonymous mob. Below, the austere silence of danger, the gravity of the drama enacted between sun and shadow of life and of death. Above, the inconscience of ignorance. Below, the full consciousness of his perilous art.

The bullfighter took his *muleta* and his sword. In his Grecolike hands, he carried the black hat of his profession to the bleachers of abuse. He walked slowly and his face was calm; there was neither provocation nor theatrical posture; there was neither hysteria nor compromise. It was a man and a bullfighter who walked toward the disturbers. He did not act for publicity purposes nor because of agitation, he acted like a man and a bullfighter. He arrived at the place where he could see the calumniators. He lifted his hat, and cited the bull to charge.

A dark and horned avalanche plunged toward him. The slim figure lifted his arm. And again, like Pelayo, or the Cid, or Philip or Isabel, the tempest, with a pagan face and lethal horns, crashed toward him and fell at the feet of Spain. The clamor of combat, the roar of an ocean, and a moment of history was made.

The bullfighter turned and walked step by step to the place of the disturbers. He lifted his black hat of his profession to venal ignorance. He inclined his head with a slow, ascetic smile.

Then, ignorance fell at his feet and the ampitheater trembled with the roar of the humiliated spectators.

"So live that whatever they say about you, they say you are a man."

"What a man! What a bullfighter! What a Spaniard! Manuel Rodríguez, 'Manolete'!"

Carlos Arruza

by VERDUGUILLO

Don Rafael Solano, "Verduguillo," brilliant and respected Mexican bullfight critic and newspaperman, is a friend whom I met in Spain almost twenty-five years ago. He is a ranking editor now of the distinguished newspaper, *El Universal,* of Mexico City. Although he does not write much of the bulls nowadays, because of his executive duties, no book of mine on the subject would be complete without a selection from his wisdom. Herewith is presented a sketch of Carlos Arruza, the epochal Mexican, which is also a provocative analysis of the spectacle.

During my forty years as a bullfight critic, specially on *El Universal* and *El Universal Gráfico,* Mexico City, I have always been a partisan of "the complete bullfighter." The term "complete bullfighter" is understood by aficionados to describe the performer who can execute all phases of the fight with mastery, elegance, and color.

Some analysts have established the difference between "long bullfighters" and "short bullfighters," characterizing a fighter as "long" who performs all the phases of repertory, and "short" those who only use their specialties.

I have never been in agreement with this division in definition. I call a bullfighter "long" who can fight the greatest number of bulls, who has resources and technique to cope with all kinds of bulls. I consider a bullfighter "short" who can fight successfully only the easy bulls.

Let us take a base of one hundred bulls. The "long" bullfighter, in my opinion, can cut the ears of ninety; the "short" performer only fifteen.

Actually, the great "Manolete" exemplified the defective, arbitrary division in definition. I considered "Manolete" a "long" bullfighter because he could and did fight effectively ninety per cent of his bulls. Some critics called him a "short" bullfighter because he used only a few of the many movements of the *corrida.* Nevertheless, "Manolete" reached the highest plane of contemporary bullfighting.

I favor the "complete" bullfighter over the detailed specialist. For this reason I have always admired Carlos Arruza. I saw him when he first appeared in the arena. I followed his career attentively because his progress interested me. He had excellent training from a fine artist, Samuel Solís. Carlos learned and perfected his style, refined his cape work, timed his *banderillas* better, and developed masterful control of his *muleta*. Improvement with the sword was not so noticeable, because a good swordsman is born not made.

When Carlos Arruza returned from Spain, after the controversy between Spanish and Mexican fighters over permissions was settled, he had become a master. He was in the fullness of his art. He had great elegance and finished grace with the cape. He had become a master of the *muleta*, in domination, in variety, and artistry.

I must say, however, that Arruza had to work harder for ovations than some others. The art and valor of Arruza aroused Mexico, his native land, where even now there is some hassling about his merit and his place among the great bullfighters of the world.

In the competition with "Manolete," he was uniformly successful but his modesty kept him a little behind the Monster of Córdoba. A bull, well fought, well *banderilleado,* and well killed by Arruza left the spectators with a sensation of having seen art fulfilled. "Manolete" left the same deep satisfaction. But Arruza had a wider range of wizardry, and left the crowd limp beyond desire.

I stated in a review that Arruza was better than "Manolete." This provoked bitter controversy in Spain. But Mexico appreciated the analysis. The retirement of Arruza means that the spectacle lost one of its greatest figures.

The Capital of the World

by ERNEST HEMINGWAY

Ernest Hemingway is a man who deserves a special place in any book on the bulls, not only because he is a writer of tremendous influence, but also because he changed the attitude of many people toward the fiesta by his writings. He was not a St. Paul, nor any kind of missionary. He was not the first British or American writer to take up the subject of bullfighting. These things made no difference to Hemingway. He proceeded to write more about it than any non-Spanish writer, up to that time.

One of his most unusual and poignant stories of this phase of Spanish life, "The Capital of the World," is included in this book.

Gertrude Stein said that Hemingway heard about bullfighting from her. And this was at a time when he was not so active, apparently, in outdoor activities. She wrote in *The Autobiography of Alice B. Toklas:* "I have always loved Spanish dancing and Spanish bullfighting. He used to recount to Gertrude Stein the conversations he afterwards used in *The Sun Also Rises . . . "*

Hemingway, a man of mighty talent, saw significance in the spectacle and he did something about it, by extraordinary short stories, a novel, a book on bullfighting, and historic conversations as spectacular as the art that inspired them. But his conversations, like those poetic sculptures of motion, passed into memory at the end of the day. In Hemingway's words: "I know no modern sculpture, except Brancusi's, that is in any way the equal of the sculpture of modern bullfighting. But it is an impermanent art as singing and the dance are, one of those that Leonardo advised men to avoid, and when the performer is gone, the art exists only in the memory of those who have seen it and dies with them. Looking at photographs, reading descriptions, or trying to recall it too often can only kill it in the memory of an individual. If it were permanent, it could be one of the major arts, but it is not and so it finishes with whoever makes it, while a major art cannot even be judged until the unimportant physical rottenness of whoever made it is well buried. It is an art that deals with death and death wipes it out. But it is never truly lost, you say, because in all arts all improvements and discoveries that are logical are carried on by someone else; so nothing is lost, really, except the man himself."

Although the *corrida* and the conversations live only in the memory of those who saw and heard them, the writings remain as a testament of his understanding. I was a correspondent in Spain at the same time Hemingway lived there, and our seats at the bull ring were not far apart. He was a very active aficionado and more intransigent than I on more than one phase of the spectacle. He really felt cheated if a bullfighter did not have a few spangles torn off his jacket and a blood smear or two from the bull. He had his favorites and nobody was going to show him any different. I shall say he was a friendly but emphatic controversialist. I insisted that the man who wrote "Hills Like White Elephants," a great short story of mood, could not demand that the *matador* kill himself to make him a poem. Hemingway's attitude was that a poem is what he paid for, and that is what he wanted.

Enough dramatic poetry of the *corrida* soaked into him to inspire a book that would explain the fiesta. That was *Death in the Afternoon* 1932, the first book in English of such nature.

A few strange characters wandered willy-nilly through this discursive forest, and that may puzzle some readers, but the effect was achieved of some shock treatments, a sexual aberration, a love affair with the subject of bravery, and a lot of old-fashioned straightforward information about death, especially in the afternoon. All this in one book.

But Hemingway stated his objective in the opening lines, and, no matter how he meandered around, he always came back to the highway of his intent.

"At the first bullfight I ever went to I expected to be horrified and perhaps sickened by what I had been told would happen to the horses. Everything I had read about the bull ring insisted on that point; most people who wrote of it condemned bullfighting outright as a stupid brutal business, but even those that spoke well of it as an exhibition of skill and as a spectacle deplored the use of horses and were apologetic about the whole thing. The killing of the horses in the ring was considered indefensible. I suppose, from a modern moral point of view, that is, a Christian point of view, the whole bullfight is indefensible; there is certainly much cruelty, there is always danger, either sought or unlooked for, and there is always death, and I should not try to defend it now, only to tell honestly the things I have found true about it. . . ."

Then, he said later: "The bullfight is not a sport in the Anglo-Saxon sense of the word, that is, it is not an equal contest or an attempt at an equal contest between a bull and a man. Rather it is a tragedy; the death of the bull, which is played, more or less well, by the bull and the man involved and in which there is danger for the man but certain death for the animal."

That is what he saw. What he did not see was symbolism on the sand. Indeed he had short shrift for those who wove figures of rhetorical fancy over the fiesta. Hemingway slapped them down with his muscular prose.

It is unfortunate for bullfighting history that he did not live in Spain during the era of a great competition. I have often wondered which perfection he would have chosen, the Sevillana or the Rondeño, if he had seen the best, hand to hand. Wherever he was, he would have been heard.

One could say that Hemingway owes a lot to bullfighting. He took to Spain a few more or less fictional expatriates from the Paris atelier of Gertrude Stein and bistros on the Left Bank and made a great novel out of them. The bullfighter and the bullfighting atmosphere gave *The Sun Also Rises* an exotic flavor that seasoned its basic ingredients to the popular taste. The author became a redoubtable fellow overnight in the literature of the 'twenties. He had just written the history of an era in a short novel.

One must say bullfighting owes a lot to Hemingway, as far as the English reading public is concerned. Although *Death in the Afternoon* is a highly opinionated miscellany of facts, prejudices, snatches of history, extraneous interludes, and sound technical information, it is a volume of courageous presentation and has had a continuing influence on those who wish to see and understand the *corrida*.

It also has won many English-reading persons to the ranks of aficionados. It is neither the fault of the author nor the book that some maudlin converts fondle it under cashmere sleeves in Hollywood, on Broadway, or at the switch-hitting parties of New York and London.

These are not typical of the British and American interest in bullfighting. They represent only the fringes of exhibitionists, headline hunters, celebrity leeches, unskilled laborers in prose, and gushing votaries of exotic themes. The real understanding comes from average people who have better than average chances to travel and to understand the customs of other nations. It is, certainly, necessary to have some understanding of the *corrida* in order to reach any understanding of Spain. It may be that Hemingway wrote larger than he realized. He did excite new sensations in many authors, artists, and general readers. This intoxication produced incoherency in many who got lost in their figures of speech, wild delight in others who danced rigadoons over Hemingway quotations. But he did not lend personal approval to this new cult. He is safe and serene in his Cuban Olympus, with no visible recognition of the taurine sycophants. It has been a long time since Hemingway lived in Spain. He visited Pamplona a couple of years ago and saw the son of the hero of *The Sun Also Rises*. That is a privilege of age. Hemingway has been to Spain since I have, but I am sure both of us get a similar chuckle from the words of the Duke of Veragua, descendant of Columbus and mighty breeder of fighting bulls, about fifty years ago: ". . . bullfighting is not what it used to be . . . the virile old style is dying out . . . the customs and distinctive dress are disappearing as the profession becomes industrialized . . . open to people who are looking for a life of leisure and pleasure . . . the tendency of the bullfighters is to stay away from the natural hazard of the profession . . . when they lower the standards of prudence, they lower the prestige of the spectacle."

Nobody, perhaps, should outlive more than one generation of bullfighting, without recognizing the fact he is an old fogy no matter what he says. It has such impact on spectators that only youth can take it without comparisons, and most people are in love with youth, whether it be their own or that of somebody else.

It is high tribute to Hemingway that he compared Antonio Ordóñez favorably with his father, "El Niño de la Palma." I wonder if he remembers the afternoon in Vista Alegre, more than twenty-five years ago, when the father, Cayetano, fought a bull all by himself from the time it came out of the *toril* until he killed it *recibiendo,* with a perfect *estocada.* Only the *picadors* and their horses, and "Niño de la Palma" sculpturing a masterpiece. Cape, *banderillas, muleta* and sword. Cayetano alone.

Madrid is full of boys named Paco, which is the diminutive of the name Francisco, and there is a Madrid joke about a father who came to Madrid and inserted an advertisement in the personal columns of *El Liberal* which said: Paco, Meet Me at Hotel Montana Noon Tuesday. All is forgiven. Papa, and how a squadron of Guardia Civil had to be called out to disperse the eight hundred young men who answered the advertisement. But this Paco, who waited on table at the Pension Luarca, had no father to forgive him, nor anything for the father to forgive. He had two older sisters who were chambermaids at the Luarca, who had gotten their place through coming from the same small village as a former Luarca chambermaid who had proven hardworking and honest and hence given her vil-

Niño de la Palma at the height of his career

lage and its products a good name; and these sisters had paid his way on the auto-bus to Madrid and gotten him his job as an apprentice waiter. He came from a village in a part of Extramadura where conditions were incredibly primitive, food scarce, and comforts unknown and he had worked hard ever since he could remember.

He was a well-built boy with very black, rather curly hair, good teeth and a skin that his sisters envied, and he had a ready and unpuzzled smile. He was fast on his feet and did his work well and he loved his sisters, who seemed beautiful and sophisticated; he loved Madrid, which was still an unbelievable place, and he loved his work which, done under bright lights, with clean linen, the wearing of evening clothes, and abundant food in the kitchen, seemed romantically beautiful.

There were from eight to a dozen other people who lived at the Luarca and ate in the dining room, but for Paco, the youngest of the three waiters who served at table, the only ones who really existed were the bullfighters.

Second-rate *matadors* lived at that pension because the address in the Calle San Jerónimo was good, the food was excellent and the room and board was cheap. It is necessary for a bullfighter to give the appearance, if not of prosperity, at least of respectability, since decorum and dignity rank above courage as the virtues most highly prized in Spain, and bullfighters stayed at the Luarca until their last *pesetas* were gone. There is no record of any bullfighter having left the Luarca for a better or more expensive hotel; second-rate bullfighters never became first-rate; but the descent from the Luarca was swift since any one could stay there who was making anything at all and a bill was never presented to a guest unasked until the woman who ran the place knew that the case was hopeless.

At this time there were three full *matadors* living at the Luarca as well as two very good *picadors,* and one excellent *banderillero.* The Luarca was luxury for the *picadors* and the *banderilleros* who, with their families in Seville, required lodging in Madrid during the spring season; but they were well paid and in the fixed employ of fighters who were heavily contracted during the coming season and the three of these subalterns would probably make much more apiece than any of the three *matadors.* Of the three *matadors* one was ill and trying to conceal it; one had passed his short vogue as a novelty; and the third was a coward.

The coward had at one time, until he had received a peculiarly atrocious horn wound in the lower abdomen at the start of his first season as a full *matador,* been exceptionally brave and remarkably skillful and he still had many of the hearty mannerisms of his days of success. He was jovial to excess and laughed constantly with and without provocation. He had, when successful, been very addicted to practical jokes, but he had given them up now. They took an assurance that he did not feel. This *matador* had an intelligent, very open face and he carried himself with much style.

The *matador* who was ill was careful never to show it and was meticulous about eating a little of all the dishes that were presented at the table. He had a great many handkerchiefs which he laundered himself in his room and, lately, he had been selling his fighting suits. He had sold one, cheaply, before Christmas and another in the first week of April. They had been very expensive suits, had always been well kept and he had one more. Before he had become ill he had been a very promising, even a sensational, fighter and, while he himself could not read, he had clippings which said that in his debut in Madrid he had been better than Belmonte. He ate alone at a small table and looked up very little.

The *matador* who had once been a novelty was very short and brown and very dignified. He also ate alone at a separate table and he smiled very rarely and never laughed. He came from Valladolid, where the people are extremely serious, and he was a capable *matador;* but his style had become old-fashioned before he had ever succeeded in endearing himself to the public through his virtues, which were courage and a calm capability, and his name on a poster would draw no one to a bullring. His novelty had been that he was so short that he could barely see over the bull's withers, but there were other short fighters, and he had never succeeded in imposing himself on the public's fancy.

Of the *picadors* one was a thin, hawk-faced, gray-haired man, lightly built but with legs and arms like iron, who always wore cattle-man's boots under his trousers, drank too much every evening and gazed amorously at any woman in the pension. The other was huge, dark, brown-faced, good-looking, with black hair like an Indian and enormous hands. Both were great *picadors* although the first was reputed to have lost much of his ability through drink and dissipation, and the second was said to be too head-strong and quarrelsome to stay with any *matador* more than a single season.

The *banderillero* was middle-aged, gray, cat-quick in spite of his years and, sitting at the table he looked a moderately prosperous businessman. His legs were still good for this season, and when they should go he was intelligent and experienced enough to keep regularly employed for a long time. The difference would be that when his speed of foot would be gone, he would always be frightened where now he was assured and calm in the ring and out of it.

On this evening every one had left the dining room except the hawk-faced *picador* who drank too much, the birthmarked-faced auctioneer of watches at the fairs and festivals of Spain, who also drank too much, and two priests from Galicia who were sitting at a corner table and drinking if not too much certainly enough. At that time wine was included in the price of the room and board at the Luarca and the waiters had just brought fresh bottles of Valdepeñas to the tables of the auctioneer, then to the *picador* and, finally, to the two priests.

The three waiters stood at the end of the room. It was the rule of the house that they should all remain on duty until the diners whose tables they were responsible for should all have left, but the one who served the table of the two priests had an appointment to go to an Anarcho-Syndical-ist meeting and Paco had agreed to take over his table for him.

Upstairs the *matador* who was ill was lying face down on his bed alone. The *matador* who was no longer a novelty was sitting looking out of his window preparatory to walking out to the café. The *matador* who was a coward had the older sister of Paco in his room with him and was trying to get her to do something which she was laughingly refusing to do. This *matador* was saying, "Come on, little savage."

"No," said the sister. "Why should I?"

"For a favor."

"You've eaten and now you want me for dessert."

"Just once. What harm can it do?"

"Leave me alone. Leave me alone, I tell you."

"It is a very little thing to do."

"Leave me alone, I tell you."

Down in the dining room the tallest of the waiters, who was overdue at the meeting, said, "Look at those black pigs drink."

"That's no way to speak," said the second waiter. "They are decent clients. They do not drink too much."

"For me it is a good way to speak," said the tall one. "There are the two curses of Spain, the bulls and the priests."

"Certainly not the individual bull and the individual priest," said the second waiter.

"Yes," said the tall waiter. "Only through the individual can you attack the class. It is necessary to kill the individual bull and the individual priest. All of them. Then there are no more."

"Save it for the meeting," said the other waiter .

"Look at the barbarity of Madrid," said the tall waiter. "It is now half-past eleven o'clock and these are still guzzling."

"They only started to eat at ten," said the other waiter. "As you know there are many dishes. That wine is cheap and these have paid for it. It is not a strong wine."

"How can there be solidarity of workers with fools like you?" asked the tall waiter.

"Look," said the second waiter who was a man of fifty. "I have worked all my life. In all that remains of my life I must work. I have no complaints against work. To work is normal."

"Yes, but the lack of work kills."

"I have always worked," said the older waiter. "Go on to the meeting. There is no necessity to stay."

"You are a good comrade," said the tall waiter. "But you lack all ideology."

"*Mejor si me falta eso que el otro*," said the older waiter (meaning it is better to lack that than work). "Go on to the *mítin*."

Paco had said nothing. He did not yet understand politics but it always gave him a thrill to hear the tall waiter speak of the necessity for killing the priests and the Guardia Civil. The tall waiter represented to him revolution and revolution also was romantic. He himself would like to be a good Catholic, a revolutionary, and have a steady job like this, while, at the same time, being a bullfighter.

"Go on to the meeting, Ignacio," he said. "I will respond for your work."

"The two of us," said the older waiter.

"There isn't enough for one," said Paco. "Go on to the meeting."

"*Pues, me voy,*" said the tall waiter. "And thanks."

In the meantime, upstairs, the sister of Paco had gotten out of the embrace of the *matador* as skillfully as a wrestler breaking a hold and said, now angry, "These are the hungry people. A failed bullfighter. With your tonload of fear. If you have so much of that, use it in the ring."

"That is the way a whore talks."

"A whore is also a woman, but I am not a whore."

"You'll be one."

"Not through you."

"Leave me," said the *matador* who, now, repulsed and refused, felt the nakedness of his cowardice returning.

"Leave you? What hasn't left you?" said the sister. "Don't you want me to make up the bed? I'm paid to do that."

"Leave me," said the *matador,* his broad good-looking face wrinkled into a contortion that was like crying. "You whore. You dirty little whore."

"*Matador,*" she said, shutting the door. "My *matador.*"

Inside the room the *matador* sat on the bed. His face still had the contortion which, in the ring, he made into a constant smile which frightened those people in the first rows of seats who knew what they were watching. "And this," he was saying aloud. "And this. And this."

He could remember when he had been good and it had only been three years before. He could remember the weight of the heavy gold-brocaded fighting jacket on his shoulders on that hot afternoon in May when his voice had still been the same in the ring as in the café, and how he sighted along the point-dipping blade at the place in the top of the shoulders where it was dusty in the short-haired black hump of muscle above the wide, wood-knocking, splintered-tipped horns that lowered as he went in to kill, and how the sword pushed in as easy as into a mound of stiff butter with the palm of his hand pushing the pommel, his left arm crossed low, his left shoulder forward, his weight on his left leg, and then his weight wasn't on his leg. His weight was on his lower belly and as the bull raised his head the horn was out of sight in him and he swung over on it twice before they pulled him off it. So now when he went in to kill, and it was seldom, he could not look at the horns and what did any whore know about what he went through before he fought? And what had they been through that laughed at him? They were all whores and they knew what they could do with it.

Down in the dining room the *picador* sat looking at the priests. If there were women in the room he stared at them. If there were no women he would stare with enjoyment at a foreigner, *un inglés,* but lacking women or strangers, he now stared with enjoyment and insolence at the two priests. While he stared the birthmarked auctioneer rose and folding his napkin went out, leaving over half the wine in the last bottle he had ordered. If his accounts had been paid up at the Luarca he would have finished the bottle.

The two priests did not stare back at the *picador.* One of them was saying, "It is ten days since I have been here waiting to see him and all day I sit in the ante-chamber and he will not receive me."

"What is there to do?"

"Nothing. What can one do? One cannot go against authority."

"I have been here for two weeks and nothing. I wait and they will not see me."

"We are from the abandoned country. When the money runs out we can return."

"To the abandoned country. What does Madrid care about Galicia? We are a poor province."

"One understands the action of our brother Basilio."

"Still I have no real confidence in the integrity of Basilio Alvarez."

"Madrid is where one learns to understand. Madrid kills Spain."

"If they would simply see one and refuse."

"No. You must be broken and worn out by waiting."

"Well, we shall see. I can wait as well as another."

At this moment the *picador* got to his feet, walked over to the priests' table and stood, gray-headed and hawk-faced, staring at them and smiling.

"A *torero,*" said one priest to the other.

"And a good one," said the *picador* and walked out of the dining room, gray-jacketed, trim-waisted, bow-legged, in tight breeches over his high-heeled cattleman's boots that clicked on the floor as he swaggered quite steadily, smiling to himself. He lived in a small, tight, professional world of personal efficiency, nightly alcoholic triumph, and insolence. Now he lit a cigar and tilting his hat at an angle in the hallway went out to the café.

The priests left immediately after the *picador,* hurriedly conscious of being the last people in the dining room, and there was no one in the room now but Paco and the middle-aged waiter. They cleared the tables and carried the bottles into the kitchen.

In the kitchen was the boy who washed the dishes. He was three years older than Paco and was very cynical and bitter.

"Take this," the middle-aged waiter said, and poured out a glass of the Valdepeñas and handed it to him.

"Why not?" the boy took the glass.

"*Tú,* Paco?" the older waiter asked.

"Thank you," said Paco. The three of them drank.

"I will be going," said the middle-aged waiter.

"Good night," they told him.

He went out and they were alone. Paco took a napkin one of the priests had used and standing straight, his heels planted, lowered the napkin and with head following the movement, swung his arms in the motion of a slow sweeping *verónica*. He turned and advancing his right foot slightly, made the second pass, slow, perfectly timed and suave, then gathered the napkin to his waist and swung his hips away from the bull in a *media-verónica*.

The dishwasher, whose name was Enrique, watched him critically and sneeringly.

"How is the bull?" he said.

"Very brave," said Paco. "Look."

Standing slim and straight he made four more perfect passes, smooth, elegant and graceful.

"And the bull?" asked Enrique standing against the sink, holding his wine glass and wearing his apron.

"Still has lots of gas," said Paco.

"You make me sick," said Enrique.

"Why?"

"Look."

Enrique removed his apron and citing the imaginary bull he sculptured four perfect, languid gypsy *verónicas* and ended up with a *rebolera* that made the apron swing in a stiff arc past the bull's nose as he walked away from him.

"Look at that," he said. "And I wash dishes."

"Why?"

"Fear," said Enrique. "*Miedo*. The same fear you would have in a ring with a bull."

"No," said Paco. "I wouldn't be afraid."

"*Leche!*" said Enrique. "Every one is afraid. But a *torero* can control his fear so that he can work the bull. I went in an amateur fight and I was so afraid I couldn't keep from running. Every one thought it was very funny. So you would be afraid. If it wasn't for fear every bootblack in Spain would be a bullfighter. You, a country boy, would be frightened worse than I was."

"No," said Paco.

He had done it too many times in his imagination. Too many times he had seen the horns, seen the bull's wet muzzle, the ear twitching, then the head go down and the charge, the hoofs thudding and the hot bull pass him as he swung the cape, to re-charge as he swung the cape again, then again, and again, and again, to end winding the bull around him in his great *media-verónica*, and walk swingingly away, with bull hairs caught in the gold ornaments of his jacket from the close passes; the bull standing hypnotized and the crowd applauding. No, he would not be afraid. Others, yes. Not he. He knew he would not be afraid. Even if he ever was afraid, he knew that he could do it anyway. He had confidence. "I wouldn't be afraid," he said.

Enrique said, *"Leche,"* again.

Then he said, "If we should try it?"

"How?"

"Look," said Enrique. "You think of the bull but you do not think of the horns. The bull has such force that the horns rip like a knife, they stab like a bayonet, and they kill like a club. Look," he opened a table drawer and took out two meat knives. "I will bind these to the legs of a chair. Then I will play bull for you with the chair held before my head. The knives are the horns. If you make those passes then they mean something."

"Lend me your apron," said Paco. "We'll do it in the dining room."

"No," said Enrique, suddenly not bitter. "Don't do it, Paco."

"Yes," said Paco. "I'm not afraid."

"You will be when you see the knives come."

"We'll see," said Paco. "Give me the apron."

At this time, while Enrique was binding the two heavy-bladed razor-sharp meat knives fast to the legs of the chair with two soiled napkins holding the half of each knife, wrapping them tight and then knotting them, the two chambermaids, Paco's sisters, were on their way to the cinema to see Greta Garbo in "Anna Christie." Of the two priests, one was sitting in his underwear reading his breviary and the other was wearing a nightshirt and saying the rosary. All the bullfighters except the one who was ill had made their evening appearance at the Café Fornos, where the big, dark-haired *picador* was playing billiards, the short, serious matador was sitting at a crowded table before a coffee and milk, along with the middle-aged *banderillero* and other serious workmen.

The drinking, gray-headed *picador* was sitting with a glass of Cazalas brandy before him staring with pleasure at a table where the *matador* whose courage was gone sat with another *matador* who had renounced the sword to become a *banderillero* again, and two very houseworn-looking prostitutes.

The auctioneer stood on the street corner talking with friends. The tall waiter was at the Anarcho-Syndicalist meeting waiting for an opportunity to speak. The middle-aged waiter was seated on the terrace of the Café Alvarez drinking a small beer. The woman who owned the Luarca was already asleep in her bed, where she lay on her back with the bolster between her legs; big, fat, honest, clean, easygoing, very religious and never having ceased to miss or pray daily for her husband, dead, now, twenty years. In his room, alone, the *matador* who was ill lay face down on his bed with his mouth against a handkerchief.

Now, in the deserted dining room, Enrique tied the last knot in the napkins that bound the knives to the chair legs and lifted the chair. He pointed the legs with the knives on them forward and held the chair over his head with the two knives pointing straight ahead, one on each side of his head.

"It's heavy," he said. "Look, Paco. It is very dangerous. Don't do it." He was sweating.

Paco stood facing him, holding the apron spread, holding a fold of it bunched in each hand, thumbs up, first finger down, spread to catch the eye of the bull.

"Charge straight," he said. "Turn like a bull. Charge as many times as you want."

"How will you know when to cut the pass?" asked Enrique. "It's better to do three and then a *media*."

"All right," said Paco. "But come straight. Huh, *torito!* Come on, little bull!"

Running with head down Enrique came toward him and Paco swung the apron just ahead of the knife blade as it passed close in front of his belly and as it went by it was, to him, the real horn, white-tipped, black, smooth, and as Enrique passed him and turned to rush again it was the hot, blood-flanked mass of the bull that thudded by, then turned like a cat and came again as he swung the cape slowly. Then the bull turned and came again and, as he watched the onrushing point, he stepped his left foot two inches too far forward and the knife did not pass, but had slipped in as easily as into a wineskin and there was a hot scalding rush above and around the sudden inner rigidity of steel and Enrique shouting, "Ay! Ay! Let me get it out! Let me get it out! and Paco slipped forward on the chair, the apron cape still held, Enrique pulling on the chair as the knife turned in him, in him, Paco.

The knife was out now and he sat on the floor in the widening warm pool.

"Put the napkin over it. Hold it!" said Enrique. "Hold it tight. I will run for the doctor. You must hold in the hemorrhage."

"There should be a rubber cup," said Paco. He had seen that used in the ring.

"I came straight," said Enrique, crying. "All I wanted was to show the danger."

"Don't worry," said Paco, his voice sounding far away. "But bring the doctor."

In the ring they lifted you and carried you, running with you, to the operating room. If the femoral artery emptied itself before you reached there they called the priest.

"Advise one of the priests," said Paco, holding the napkin tight against his lower abdomen. He could not believe that this had happened to him.

But Enrique was running down the Carrera San Jerómino to the all-night first-aid station and Paco was alone, first sitting up, then huddled over, then slumped on the floor, until it was over, feeling his life go out of him as dirty water empties from a bathtub when the plug is drawn. He was frightened and he felt faint and he tried to say an act of contrition and he remembered how it started but before he had said, as fast as he could, "Oh, my God, I am heartily sorry for having offended Thee who art worthy of all my love and I firmly resolve . . .," he felt too faint and he was lying face down on the floor and it was over very quickly. A severed femoral artery empties itself faster than you can believe.

As the doctor from the first-aid station came up the stairs accompanied by a policeman who held on to Enrique by the arm, the two sisters of Paco were still in the moving-picture palace of the Gran Via, where they were intensely dissappointed in the Garbo film, which showed the great star in miserable low surroundings when they had been accustomed to see her surrounded by great luxury and brilliance. The audience disliked the film thoroughly and were protesting by whistling and stamping their feet. All the other people from the hotel were doing almost what they had been doing when the accident happened, except that the two priests had finished their devotions and were preparing for sleep, and the gray-haired *picador* had moved his drink over to the table with the two houseworn prostitutes. A little later he went out of the café with one of them. It was the one for whom the *matador* who had lost his nerve had been buying drinks.

The boy Paco had never known about any of this nor about what all these people would be doing on the next day and on other days to come. He had no idea how they really lived nor how they ended. He did not even realize they ended. He died, as the Spanish phrase has it, full of illusions. He had not had time in his life to lose any of them, nor even, at the end, to complete an act of contrition.

He had not even had time to be disappointed in the Garbo picture which disappointed all Madrid for a week.

Steinbeck

John Steinbeck is one of the most influential writers on the evolutionary American scene. His sensitivity to people and their places in the moving stream of history is unique in our time. He has traveled widely and wisely, but he has remained an American writer in the highest sense of the words.

He and I have seen the bulls together, in the plaza and on the ranch. This brief and powerful essay is his first writing on the subject.

I have heard people say they love the bullfights. I have also seen them pilfer a vicarious courage from the exhibition, satisfy a destructive sadism, or indulge in thoughtless empathy with the bull.

I know experts who achieve critical satisfaction in the deadly ballet of the *faena.* Also I have gone to the *ganaderías,* the bull ranches whose owners never look at the bullfighter but only search for perfection or its lack in the bull.

No I do not love the bullfight. I go to the ring with the knowledge and feeling that I am about to witness ritual tragedy. I do not love Oedipus Rex either nor Othello nor the Black Goyas.

One combs many galleries to find a great picture and sits uncomfortably in hundreds of theater seats before triumphant theater is born on stage. When a great bullfight develops out of the disciplined form, it is no less tragic but as with other art forms, there is a fullness, a satisfaction and a justification beyond personal triumph.

I am sad and sorry that man for his soul's safety must test himself, his control and courage against this most ferocious and clever of all beasts but I am filled with a kind of elation, not that he must, but that he can and does. In so doing he grafts a little greatness on his audience.

A great bullfight brings the exaltation great music does and great poetry. One carries for a time afterwards the satisfaction and the knowledge that man is no weakling in a dreadful world—that by his bravery, his versatility and his merits he has and can survive anything the world can bring against him.

That small, unshielded, soft-fleshed, inferior-muscled figure, clad in penetrable silk, armed only with a triangle of woolen cloth and a tooth pick of steel can and does face and dominate and kill the ever reborn force of evil, and fear is the greatest and most poisonous evil we know.

No, I do not love the bullfight, but I love the bull, and I love the man who reassures to us that we are of the race of men.

Don Quixote

The most famous knight of fact or fiction, Spain's Don Quixote, was feasted on his travels by some village folks enjoying a picnic dressed as shepherds and shepherdesses. He expressed his thanks by proclaiming a holiday for them. This became one of the incidents of his adventures, and is of interest in this book because it has to do with fighting bulls. This version is from the translation by Samuel Putnam. The illustrations are by the French artist, Gustave Doré, 1832–83.

"O ye travelers and wayfarers, knights and squires, those on foot and those on horseback, who pass along this road within the next two days,

Don Quixote challenges the bulls

know that Don Quixote de la Mancha, knight errant, stands here to maintain that the nymphs who inhabit these groves and meadows excel in beauty and in courtesy all others in the world, leaving aside the lady of my heart, Dulcinea del Toboso. And so, let anyone who holds the contrary come on, for I await him on this spot."

Twice he repeated these same words and twice there was no adventurer to hear them. But fate, which was guiding his affairs from better to better, ordained that shortly afterward he should descry down the road a large number of men on horseback, many of them with lances in their hands and all riding hard, in close formation. No sooner did those who were with Don Quixote catch sight of the horsemen than they turned and withdrew some distance from the road; for they knew very well that if they stayed they might incur some danger. Don Quixote alone stood his ground, while Sancho shielded himself behind Rosinante's crupper.

The troop of lancers came on, and one of them who rode ahead of the others cried out to the knight, "Out of the way, devil take you, or these bulls will trample you to pieces!"

"Ha, rabble!" replied Don Quixote, "bulls mean nothing to me, even though they be the fiercest that Jarama breeds upon its banks. Confess at once, ye scoundrels, that it is the truth I have here proclaimed or be prepared to do battle with me!"

The animals crash over the challenge

The herdsmen had no time to reply and the knight did not have time to get out of the way if he had wished to do so, and as a result the wild bulls and the tame leading oxen and all the many drovers and others who were taking the animals to be perused in a village where the bulls were to be fought the following day—the entire troop, in short, both man and beast, passed over Don Quixote and over Sancho, Rosinante and Sancho's grey ass as well, knocking them all down and sending them rolling. Sancho was badly mauled, his master was frightened, the ass was battered, and Rosinante was far from sound; but they all finally got to their feet, and, stumbling here and falling there, Don Quixote ran after the herd as fast as he could.

"Stop, scoundrelly rabble!" he shouted. "It is a single knight who awaits you . . ."

But the drovers in their haste did not stop . . .

The knight of the sorrowful consequence

The Bullfight of Gazul

The English translation of *Ancient Spanish Ballads,* J. G. Lockhart, London, 1856. "The Romance of Gazul" was a popular folk song before the sixteenth century, and published in Madrid in one edition, 1589. This is an excerpt from the long narrative poem. It is published here primarily to show there is little new under the sun. Almost all loyal American Westerners think they have a monopoly on the phrase "biting the dust" as applied to their Indian exploits.

> King Almanzor of Granada, he hath bid the trumpet sound,
> He hath summoned all the Moorish lords from the hills and
>   plains around;
> From Vega and Sierra, from Betis and Xenil,
> They have come with helm and cuirass of gold and twisted
>   steel.
> 'Tis the holy Baptist's feast they hold in royalty and state,
> And they have closed the spacious lists beside the Alhambra's
>   gate;
> In gowns of black with silver laced, within the tented ring,
> Eight Moors to fight the bull are placed, in presence of the
>   king.
> Eight Moorish lords of valor tried, with stalwart arm and
>   true.
> The onset of the beasts abide, as they come rushing through;
> The deeds they've done, the spoils they've won, fill all with
>   hope and trust—
> Yet, ere high in heaven appears the sun, they all have bit
>   the dust.

114   The Bullfight of Gazul

Excerpt from In the Heart of Spain

by THOMAS EWING MOORE

Thomas Ewing Moore was a member of the American Diplomatic Service. He wrote a book, *In the Heart of Spain,* 1927, which included an excerpt from a French book published in 1700, describing a bullfight. Mr. Moore did not like the fiesta, but he shall have his say reprinted because he was thoughtful enough to include the interesting French commentary in his volume.

While bullfighting has been denounced in no uncertain terms by writers in many countries, and justly denounced, there are not a few unenlightened individuals who hold that this indignation might with equal justice be directed against fox-hunting and stag-hunting. Fox-hunting is certainly a far less sanguinary diversion than bullfighting, nevertheless it does not seem to present a particularly strong argument, from the standpoint of fair play, in favour of the one as against the other. The torments that the bulls and horses have to undergo, and their inevitable death, have been spoken of above, and the numbers engaged against the bull have been emphasized to show that he is not given fair-play. The same might be said with equal justice as to the chances of the fox, were it not for his being at liberty in the open, and were he not, fortunately, endowed with the great cunning wherein lies his chance of safety. But the comparison is a far-fetched one. The one sporting chance the bull has, is not, alas, that of saving his life, but that he occasionally takes a toll of a too-sluggish opponent. This is denied the fox, for we fail to remember of ever having heard of one turning on a Master of Fox Hounds and rending him asunder. It would seem a pity that foxes have not horns.

One thing that may be said in favour of the Spaniards is that the pretty thought has not yet occurred to them of having the *espada* cut off the head and hoofs of the bull in order to present them to the most enthusiastic young ladies "in at the kill." It is true, however, that the *espada* sometimes receives an ear of his victim to commemorate an especially daring fight.

Custom and familiarity largely govern the point of view where sport is concerned. It may not always prove profitable to look too far from home, but this cannot possibly apply to bullfighting. The more we consider it, the more we are disposed to condemn it, and the more we write against it, the better for humanity.

Shortly after leaving Spain we discovered in a little town of the French Hautes-Pyrénées an old book of travels entitled *Voyages faits en divers temps en Espagne.* This narrative, printed in the year 1700, at Amsterdam, as was the case with so many French books of the period, has a foreword by the author that is as ingenuous as it is worthy of acceptance as a model for the guidance of all truthful recorders of the scenes and incidents of travel. We have been tempted to reproduce it, as containing in its opening paragraph the very maxims which we set ourselves to observe in writing this book.

The author of the *Voyages* styles himself "A Gentleman of the Court" (of France) who left Paris in November, 1669, for the travels in Spain which he describes with much spirit. The translation of his witty and sarcastic foreword reads as follows: "One need search here for nothing but a simple and unaffected narrative, without other ornament than that of the Truth, which will be found with all exactitude in these travels; thus differing from certain others which have appeared, written by people whose only travels have been in their libraries, or at most in the *Dictionnaire de Moreri;* or by those again who have preferred romance and the marvellous to a bare statement of facts."

A very slight acquaintance with the literature of travel is sufficient to convince one that the number of those writing books on this subject who have only journeyed around their libraries is as great now as when our author nearly three centuries ago made this disdainful reference; yet records of travel should be governed by the same reverence for the truth as those of history herself, for are they not verily the little sister of history?

As these *Voyages* contain an early description of the ancient manner of fighting bulls with the *rejón,* it is given here as an interesting contemporary account of a seventeenth-century *rejóneo* held for the Court at Madrid. The old-time French courtier writes of it:

"Sunday the fifteenth of June (1670) went to the Segovia bridge to see the bulls which had been fetched from the *casa del campo* (country estate) to the *toril* (bull-pen), as the place is called where they are kept confined.

"The next day everyone flocked to the great square of Madrid, where gentlemen armed with long lances attacked the bulls. The more curious were already there at daybreak; some of whom had cause to repent not having found places secure from these beasts which always knock down, or even kill, some of the spectators. As for those with lances mounted on horses, they are neither in danger nor peril.

"As the time approached to attend the fête we left our lodgings for the balcony which we had reserved. The combat did not commence until four o'clock, so I had time to consider the preparations. This is the description of what I remarked.

"The square is situated in the centre of Madrid and is called the Plaza

Mayor; it is 434 feet long, 334 feet wide, and 1536 in circumference. It is surrounded by 136 houses, all alike, which have five stories, with as many balconies, as is the custom in Spain, and which requires a great quantity of iron. It is said that more than four thousand people inhabit this square, and that on the days of the bull-fights it contains more than sixty thousand. A promenade extends around the place under a gallery sustained by columns. The square is used as a market where the men come to buy their household provisions, as the women do not occupy themselves with this as in France.

"The proprietors of the houses are not masters of them during this day, being dependent on the King to place whomever he pleases in them. All the officers of the Council and the royal household have their places gratis. Several give theirs to their servants, who make money thereby; some of the balconies are let for rent. All around the square, wooden stands are built for the public. These belong to the city and produce a large sum.

"These fêtes are announced two or three days in advance, in order to give time for all the preparations. The evening before, the grand promenade is filled with the throng, and nothing is heard but the sounds of guitars, harps and castanets; of games and laughter; all sorts of buffoon cries are permitted that at other times would result in blows or the stab of a poignard.

"It must be admitted that the spectacle [bull-fight] has something of grandeur, and it is agreeable to see the great number of people on the balconies, where all is covered and adorned with beautiful tapestries. It recalls the fêtes of ancient Rome.

"I considered with pleasure all the different incidents which ordinarily occur. From the highest to the lowest, none fails to find a place, and no gallant on this day fails to provide his lady with a balcony and to serve her with water, sweets and all the best that the season affords.

"About four o'clock the Company of the Spanish Guards, clad in yellow velvet with plumed hats, arrive and take their place, their captain and lieutenant in embroidered doublets, hats with white aigrettes, mounted on very beautiful horses magnificently caparisoned and with flowing ribbons hanging from mane and tail almost to the ground. After having made the tour of the square with the accustomed gravity of their nation, they post themselves beneath the balcony of the King. This company is a hundred strong, and was formed in 1504.

"A few minutes afterwards the German Guards, also dressed in gala attire for the fête, arrive and post themselves with the others. The Flemish Guards come last, these, otherwise known as the Archers of the Conchilla, properly form the royal bodyguard and march immediately in front of Their Majesties. They were created by Philip I.

"Those who have chariots drive two or three times around the square before going to their balconies.

The Plaza Mayor of Madrid

Excerpt from "In the Heart of Spain"

"The ladies take pains to don all their ornaments.

"The King and Queen take their seats on their balcony with the Duke of Pastrance, called the *Infantado,* the richest lord of all Spain, who for five or six months has been Mayor Domo Mayor, which we in France call Grand Master. He stands behind the King, covered most of the time, his rank of Grandee giving him this privilege. To the right of this balcony are the ladies of honour of the Queen, while all about are placed the Councils and those who are attached to the Court, forming not the least beautiful part of this fête.

"The Nuncio and the Ambassadors have their balconies on the other side of the square, facing the King.

"A quarter of an hour after his arrival the King makes a sign with his handkerchief that the square shall be cleared of the rabble, which walks about and disturbs the beauty of the scene.

"The guards promptly expel these unimportant people, who tumble one over the other. After the square is sprinkled with water the Captain of the Archers appears before the King on one of the most beautiful black horses I have ever seen, and converses with the King and Queen, making his horse perform hundreds of evolutions. During this time the *toreadors* enter the square mounted on very fine horses and accompanied by many servants in rich liveries. The latter are more or less according to the expense their masters will undertake. One named Saavedra had fifty servants dressed in green livery at this fête. I was told that the grandees who fought bulls during the time of Philip IV would not enter the square with less than one hundred of these attendants, all magnificently clad.

"The fighters have a sabre at their side and carry a recon (*rejón*) in the hand, while their attendants carry several, because it is with this arm they pierce the bulls. This *recón* is like a pike, and has a wooden shaft about four and a half feet long pointed with iron. This troop makes the tour of the arena, saluting profoundly Their Majesties and all the assembly. All these ceremonies completed, only the two who are to fight the bulls remain in the square, with a number of their attendants and four *algousils* (*alguaciles*) who are there to give command to remove the bulls that are killed, or to give their horses to *toreadors* whose mounts are wounded.

"All being ready, the Duke of Pastrance throws the key of the *toril* to the first alguacil, who rides at full pace to let in the bulls while trumpets sound. The bulls appear, bounding with impetuosity, because they have been pricked with irons to render them more furious. If they appear cool and without vigour, the attendants animate them by whistling and gesticulating with their hats and capes to drive them to their masters, who await them with a *rejón,* endeavoring to strike them at a certain point between the horns. But few find the place; mostly they strike near by it. If the stroke is successful, the shaft should remain in the hand, and the iron point of the spear fixed in the bull, which often receives five or six hits before succumbing.

"The proper manner to fight is to approach slowly, pass by his side, plant the *rejón* and put spur to the horse to pass the bull, because the bull never turns. A *toreador* who kills a bull with one stroke receives great praise; the ladies wave their handkerchiefs, and all cry *'vitor,'* which means 'victory.' "

The Lady Who Wasn't There

Madame d'Aulnoy, a noble lady of Normandy, published a book about the court of Spain, 1690, and a book about travels in Spain, 1691, English translation, 1692. She was one of the most widely read and popular authors of her time. These two books became source material for many writers on Spain. It was not really for more than a hundred years that scholars began to feel some caution in using her material. Skepticism grew with scholarship. Finally thorough investigations came to a climax in 1926 when the famous French scholar, M. Foulché-Delbosc, published his commentaries on her work.

The lady appears in these pages because she wrote a colorful description of a Madrid bullfight in her travel book. She had the most glittering details and ladylike reactions. The only thing wrong about it was, apparently she was not there. That detracts little from the graphic description, which, according to Foulché-Delbosc, came verbatim from writings mostly by Carel de Sainte-Garde, published in 1670, with an assist from Antoine de Brunel, 1665.

Furthermore, the French scholar claimed she not only did not attend the bullfight, but she did not go to Spain at all. Research has proved that her books on Spain were compilations of writings and items from the publication in Paris, *Gazette,* which had an official status and correspondents abroad. She was adroit in weaving her information into narrative, and disguising its origin.

Foulché-Delbosc said of her: "Very few literary fakes have had such good fortune . . . this fake is in a large part made up of downright theft and borrowings from some of the most celebrated books on Spain."

An English edition of the French writer's analysis, with the 1692 English translation, was published by George Routledge & Sons, London, 1930.

Foulché-Delbosc declared: "Madame d'Aulnoy describes a bullfight, but her description is that of Carel de Sainte-Garde, whose letter she has copied from beginning to end; a few details are also taken from Brunel. The bullfight described by Carel de Sainte-Garde took place at the Plaza Mayor, so it is at the Plaza Mayor that Madame d'Aulnoy places her own and she dates it May 22, 1679, having doubtless seen in the *Gazette* that there was a fight on May 22nd. Unluckily the bullfight to which the *Gazette* refers had taken place at the

Royal Palace of Buen Retiro and on May 22nd there was no bullfight either at the Plaza Mayor or at Buen Retiro, or anywhere else."

The King had a mind to divert himself, and ordered a bull-feast to be on the twenty-second of this month. I was very glad of it, for though I had heard much talk of them I never saw any yet. And the young Count de Conismark, who is a Swede, would taurice, or bait the bull, for a young lady of my acquaintance, so that I was the more eager to go to the Plaza-Mayor, where my kinswoman, as she was a *titulada* (titled lady) of Castile, had her balcony set up with a canopy, a carpet, and cushion of state. To give you a particular account of all that passes at these feasts, I must tell you that after the King has appointed one of them, there are some cows, which they call mandarines, led into the forests and mountains of Andalusia. It is known that the most furious bulls are in these places, and as they are trained up for this purpose, so they run into the wood; the bulls spy them out and eagerly court them, those fly, and these pursue them and so are decoyed into certain palisades set on purpose along the way, which is sometimes thirty or forty leagues in length. Several men are armed with half-pikes, and well mounted hunt these bulls and hinder them from coming back, but it is not seldom that they are forced to fight them within these pales, and frequently they are killed or wounded.

There are people placed all along the road which bring advice when the bulls will arrive at Madrid, and there also they set palisades in the street to prevent any mischief.

The mandarines, who are real traitors, go constantly before, and the poor bulls quietly follow after, into the very place designed for baiting them, where there are great stables built on purpose with shutters contrived to keep them in. There are sometimes 30, 40, or 50 together. This stable has two doors, the mandarines go in at one and escape at the other, and when the bulls think to follow them still they are hindered by a trap, in which they are caught.

After they have rested a few hours, they are one after another let out of the stable into the great place, where there are a great many young, lusty, strong, peasants, some of which take the bull by the horns, and others by the tail, and because they mark him upon the buttock with a hot iron, and slit his ears, they call them Heradores. This is not so easily done, for there are frequently divers persons killed, and this is the beginning of the show which always mightily delights the people, whether it be upon the account that blood is shed, or else that they love to see something extraordinary and at first sight surprising, and which afterwards furnishes with matter for long reflections. But though unlucky accidents do happen at these feasts, yet it does not appear that they take any warning from them, for they are still forward to expose themselves at every baiting that's made.

The bulls are fed, and the best of them are picked out for the baiting. They can even distinguish those that are either sons or brothers of those bulls which made a great slaughter in former feasts. They tie to their horns a long ribbon, and by the colour of that everybody knows them again, and recites the history of their ancestors; that the grandsire or even great grandsire of these bulls bravely killed such and such a one, and they expect no less from those that then appear.

When they have sufficiently rested, the Plaza Mayor is covered with sand, and round it are placed bars as high as a man, upon which are painted the arms of the king and his kingdoms. I fancy this place to be larger than the Place Royal at Paris. It is longer than it is broad, and about it are houses built upon pillars and arches, like towers, five stories high, and to each a row of balconies into which there are great glass doors. The King's stands more forward than the rest, is more spacious and all gilt. It is in the middle of one of the sides, with a canopy over it. Over against it are the ambassadors' balconies, who have place when the King goes to chapel, that is, the Nuncio, the Emperor's ambassadors, that of France, of Poland, the Venetian, and that of Savoy; those of England, Holland, Sweden, Denmark, and other Protestant princes have none there. The Councils of Castille, Aragon, the Inquisition, Italy, Flanders, the Indies, the Orders, War, and the Finances are on the right hand of the King; they are distinguished by their arms upon their crimson velvet carpets, which are all embroidered with gold. After these, are placed the city companies, the judges, the grandees and titulados, according to their several degrees, and at the King's charge, or else at the city's, who hire these balconies of private persons that dwell there.

For all those I have now named the King makes a collation, and it is given in very neat baskets to the women as well as the men. It consists of fruits dried, sweetmeats, and water cooled with ice, of gloves, ribbons, fans, pastilles, silk stockings, and garters, insomuch that these feasts always cost above a hundred thousand crowns, and this expense is defrayed out of the fines and forfeitures adjudged to the King or to the city. This is a fund which must not be meddled with though 'twere to save the kingdom from the greatest danger; the doing of it might cause a sedition, so bewitched are the people with this kind of pleasure.

From the level of the pavement to the first balcony there are scaffolds made for the rest of the people. They give from fifteen to twenty pistoles for a balcony, and there is not any but what are let, and adorned with rich carpets and fine canopies. The people are not seated under the King's balcony; that place is filled with his guards. There's only three gates open into it, through which the persons of quality pass in their richest coaches, and particularly the ambassadors and they make several turns round it a little before the King comes. The cavaliers salute the ladies, who stand in the balconies without being covered with their mantles or veils; they are decked out with all their jewels and whatever they have that's finest. One can see nothing but extreme rich stuffs, with tapestry, cushions and carpets all of raised work in gold. I never saw anything more glorious. The King's balcony is hung round with green and gold curtains which he draws when he will not be seen.

The King came about four o'clock, and immediately all the coaches went out of the place. Generally the ambassador of France is the most taken notice of, because he and all his train are dressed after the French mode; and he is the only ambassador that has this privilege here, for the others are in the Spanish dress. There's five or six coaches go before the King's, in which are the officers, the gentlemen, and pages of his chamber. The coach of honour, in which there goes nobody, marches immediately before his majesty's own, whose coachman and postilion are always bareheaded, a footman carrying their hats. The coach is surrounded with foot-guards. Those which they call the Life-Guards have partisans, and march very near the coach, and next the boots go a great many of the King's pages, clothed in black and without swords, which is the only mark to know them from other pages. As the ladies that are designed to be about the young queen are already named, so they all came, under the conduct of the Duchess of Terra Nova, in the King's coaches; there march by the boots men of the highest quality, some on foot that they might be nearer, others mounted on the finest horses in the world, trained up for that purpose, and which they call "horses of motion." That they may perform this piece of gallantry they must have leave from their mistresses, otherwise 'tis a great blemish to their reputation, and even engages the ladies' kindred in trouble, for they take their honour to be concerned in this liberty. But when she approves of it, they may practice all the pleasant humours for which these sort of feasts minister occasion. But though they need fear nothing from the ladies they serve nor their relations, yet they are not freed from all uneasiness, for the duennas, or women of honour, of which there's too great a provision in each coach, and the guardadamas which go on horseback are troublesome observers. Hardly can one begin to discourse but these old hags will draw the curtain, and the guardadamas will tell you that that love which is fullest of respect is the most discreet, so that very often one must be content to let the eyes speak and to sigh so loud that one may be heard at a distance.

All things being thus disposed, the captains of the guards and the other officers, mounted upon very fine horses, enter the place at the head of the Spanish, German, and Burgundian Guards. They are clothed in yellow velvet or satin, which is the livery of the King, trimmed with tufted crimson galloon mixed with gold and silver. The yeomen of the guard, which I call the Life-Guard, wear only a short cloak of the same livery over black clothes. The Spaniards wear breeches tucked up after the old way. The Germans, which are called Tudesques, wear them like the Switzers, they stand in ranks near the King's balcony. While the two captains and the two lieutenants, who carry each of them a staff of command in their hands and are followed by a great many in liveries, march all four in a rank at the head of the guards, several times round the place to give the necessary orders and to salute the ladies of their acquaintance, their horses curvet and bound continually; they are covered with knots of ribbons and embroidered housings; they are called pissadores for distinction. Upon this day every one of these Lords affect to wear that colour which their mistresses love most.

When the people are come without the bars, and are seated upon their scaffolds, the place is watered with forty or fifty tons of water which is brought thither in little carts. Then the captains of the guards come back and take their posts under the King's balcony, where all the guards are likewise placed, and make a sort of a fence, standing very close together. And although the bulls are sometimes ready to kill them, yet they must not go back nor stir from their place; they only present to them the point of their halberds, and so with a great deal of hazard defend themselves.

I do assure you that this strange number of people for every place is full, even the tops of the houses as well as the rest, the balconies so richly set out, and so many beautiful women in them, this great Court, the guards, and in a word, the whole place makes one of the finest shows that I ever saw.

As soon as the guards are possessed of the quarter where the King is, six alguazils, or city door-keepers, enter the place, each holding a white rod. Their horses are excellent, harnessed after the Morisco fashion and covered with little bells. Their habit is black, they wear plumes of feathers, and put the best looks on they can in so much danger as they are in, for they are not allowed to stir out of the list; and 'tis their business to fetch the knights that are to fight.

I should tell you, before I proceed any further in this short description, that there are certain laws established for this sort of baiting, which are called *duelo,* that is "duel," because one knight assaults the bull, and fights him in single combat. These are some of the things which are observed: one must be a gentleman born, and known for such, that he may fight on horseback. It is not allowed to draw the sword upon the bull unless he has insulted over you; they call it insulting when the bull breaks or forces the garrachon or lance out of the hand, or if he make your hat fall off, or your cloak, or has wounded you or your horse or any of your company. In this case the knight is obliged to push his horse directly upon the bull; for this is an *empeño,* that is to say, an affront that engages one to be revenged or to die; and he must give him *una cuchillada,* or a back stroke upon his head or neck. But if the horse upon which the *caballero* rides refuses to go up to the bull, then immediately he alights, and courageously marches up a-foot to this fierce animal. The sword is very short and about three fingers broad. The other knights which are there to fight are also obliged to alight off their horses and accompany him, that is under the *empeño;* but they do not second him so as to assist him in the least against his enemy. If they all march up in this manner towards the bull, and he flies to the other end of the place instead of tarrying for them, or meeting them, after they have pursued him some time, they have satisfied the laws of duelling.

If there be in the town any horses that have been at a baiting and are dexterous at it, though they do not know the owners yet they'll borrow them; nay, though they do not desire to sell them, nor the others in a condition to buy them, yet they never refuse them. If, by mischance, the horse is killed and they offer to pay for him, it is not accepted because to receive money upon such an occasion would not be agreeable to the Spanish generosity. Nevertheless, it would vex a man to have a horse that he had taken pains to breed up, without any more ado taken from him by the first stranger, and through his means killed. This sort of combat is reckoned so dangerous that indulgences are exposed in several churches for those days, because of the great massacre that is then made. Several popes would have quite abolished such barbarous fights, but the Spaniards begged the Court of Rome so earnestly to let them continue that their humour has been complied with, and to this day they are tolerated.

The first day I was there, the alguazils came to the gate, which is at the end of the list, to fetch the six knights (of whom the Count de Conismark was one) which offered themselves to combat. Their horses are handsome to admiration, and most richly harnessed. Besides those they ride on, they had each of them a dozen led by grooms, with as many mules loaded with *rejones* or *garrochones,* which are, as I have said, lances made of very dry fir, about four or five foot long, painted and gilt, and the iron-work very well polished; and the mules were covered with velvet cloths of the same colour of the combatants, with their arms embroidered in gold. This is not practised at all feasts. When the city orders one, there's far less magnificence, but as the King commanded this, and it was upon his marriage, nothing was omitted.

The caballeros were dressed in black, embroidered either with gold and silver, silk or bugles. They had white plumes of feathers spotted with several colours, and a rich knot of diamonds with a hatband of the same. They had scarves, some white and others crimson, blue, and yellow, embroidered with gold. Some wore them round their waist, others over their shoulders like a belt, and others about their arms. These last were narrow and short: without doubt their mistresses presented them, for commonly they run to please them and to show that there's no danger to which they would not expose themselves for their diversion. They had also a black cloak which wrapped them about, but the ends being thrown behind them, it did not hinder their arms. They wore little white buskins, with long gilt spurs, which have only one sharp point after the Moors' fashion; they also sit a horse like them, which is called *cavalgar a la jineta.*

The caballeros were handsomely mounted, and looked gracefully enough for this country; they were nobly born, and every one had forty footmen, some clothed in gold mohair trimmed with lace, others in carnation-coloured brocade, striped with gold and silver, and the rest in some other fashion. Every one of them was dressed like a stranger, whether 'twas Turk, Hungarian, Moor, Indian, or wild people. Several of the footmen carried a bundle of these *garrochones* I have mentioned, and this looked very well. Thus with all their train they crossed the Plaza Mayor, conducted by the six alguazils, and the trumpets sounding. They came before the King's balcony and made a profound reverence to him, and desired leave of him to fight the bulls, which he granted them, and wished them victory. Then the trumpets everywhere began to sound again, and this is done, as 'twere, in defiance of the bulls. All the people fall a shouting, and repeat *Viva, viva los bravos caballeros.* After this they separate and salute the ladies of their acquaintance. All the footmen go out of the list, except two for each knight which are left to carry their *rejónes;* they keep close to their masters, and 'tis very seldom that they forsake them.

Several young men enter into the place, and they come a great way off to fight on these days. These I now speak of are afoot, and not being nobly born they use no ceremonies with them. Whilst one caballero is fighting, the rest withdraw, but not out of the bars; and they do not assault that bull which another has undertaken to fight unless he makes at them. The first to whom the bull comes when they are altogether is he that fights him. When he has wounded the knight, they cry out, *fulano es empeño,* that is to say, it is an obligation upon such a one to revenge the affront he has received from the bull. And, indeed honour engages him either on horseback or afoot, to attack the bull and give him a cut with his sword, as I have said, either upon his head or throat, without striking him in any other part. Afterwards he may fight him as he will, and strike him where he can, but in doing this one's life is a thousand times in danger. When this blow is given, if the knights are afoot, they may mount their horses.

When the King thought it was time to begin the baiting, two alguazils come under his balcony, and he gives to Don John the keys of the stable where the bulls are secured; for the King keeps the key, and when it must be thrown, he delivers it into the hands of a Chief Minister, as a favour. Immediately the trumpets sound, the timbrels and the drums, the fifes and the hautboys, the flutes and bagpipes make a noise round the place one after another; and the alguazils, who are naturally great cowards, go trembling to open the doors where the bulls are kept. There was a man hid behind the door, who shut it as fast as he could and then by a ladder climbed up to the top of the stables. For 'tis usual with the bull, in coming out, to look behind the door and to begin his expedition by killing, if he can, the man that stands there: after that he falls a-running with all his might after the alguazils, who spur their horses to save themselves, for they are not allowed to stand upon their defence and their best play is to run away. Those men which are on foot throw at him arrows and very sharp darts, which are trimmed with cut paper. These darts stick in him in such a manner, that the pain causing him to stir much, makes the iron enter deeper; besides when he runs the paper makes a noise, and being on fire, vexes him extremely. His breath looks like a thick mist about him, his eyes and his nostrils are like fire, he runs swifter than a race-horse, and holds it much better; to speak truth, he strikes terror. The knight who is to fight him comes near him, takes a *rejón*, holds it like a poniard. The bull makes up to him, he declines his blow, and thrusts his *garrochón* at him; the bull so thrusts it back that the wood, being weak, it breaks. Immediately his footmen, who hold ten or twelve dozen, present him with another, which the caballero thrusts also into his body; with this the bull falls a-bellowing, grows angry, runs, leaps, and woe be to them that stand in his way. And if at any time he is ready to run at a man, a cloak or a hat is thrown at him, and this stops him; or else, one falls down on the ground and the bull, in running, passes over him. They have also great figures made of pasteboards, with which they deceive him, and so gain time to escape. That which helps them further is that the bull constantly shuts his eyes just before he pushes with his horns, and they are so quick in that moment to avoid the blow, but yet this is not so certain but that a great many perish.

I saw a black, with a short poniard, go directly to the bull when he was in the height of his fury, and between his horns thrust it into the very seam of his skull, which is a place very soft and easy to be pierced, but withal, very small to hit. This was one of the boldest and most dexterous blows that can be imagined. The bull fell down dead upon the spot; and presently the trumpets sounded, and several Spaniards ran with their swords in their hands to cut in pieces the beast that was no longer able to hurt them. When a bull is killed, four alguazils go out to fetch four mules, which some grooms, clothed in yellow and carnation-coloured satin, lead in. They are covered with feathers and little silver bells; they have silken traces, with which they tie the bull, and so draw him away; upon which the trumpets and people make a prodigious noise. There were twenty baited the first day. There came out a furious one which very dangerously wounded Count Conismark in his leg, and yet the force of the blow did not light upon him but upon his horse, whom it burst. He quickly got off him, and though he is no Spaniard yet he would not be excused from any of the laws. It would have drawn pity from anybody to see one of the finest horses in the world in such a condition; he ran violently about the place, striking fire with his feet, and killed a man with a blow upon his head and breast. The great rail was opened for him and he went out. As for the Count, as soon as he was wounded a very fine Spanish lady who believed that he fought for her sake, stood forward in her balcony and with her handkerchief made several signs, in all likelihood to encourage him, but he did not seem to need being animated. And although he had lost abundance of blood and was forced to lean upon one of his footmen, who held him up, yet with great fierceness he advanced with his sword in his hand, made a shift to give a very great wound to the bull on his head, and then presently turning himself towards that side where this young lady, for whom he fought, was, he kissed his sword and suffered himself to be carried away by his people half dead.

But you must not think that these sort of accidents interrupt the feasts.

The Lady Who Wasn't There   **127**

'Tis said that it will not end but by the King's order; so that when any knight is wounded, the others accompany him to the bars and immediately they return to fight. There was a Biscayneer so bold as to throw himself off his horse upon the back of the bull, held him by his horns, and in spite of all the endeavours of the animal to throw him off, yet the Biscayneer set upon him for above a quarter of an hour and broke one of his horns. If the bulls defend themselves too long, and that the King would have others come out (for fresh ones afford more delight, because every one has his particular manner of fighting), they turn loose some English dogs. These are not so big as is generally seen there, but 'tis a breed something like those the Spaniards carried into the Indies when they conquered them; they are small and low, but so strong, that when they once seize the throat you may sooner cut them in pieces than make them let go their hold. They are very frequently killed: the bull takes them upon his horns and tosses them up in the air like footballs. Sometimes they hamstring the bull with certain irons made crosswise, which they put at the end of a long pole, and this they call *jarretar al toro*.

There was another caballero under the *empeño*, because in fighting his hat fell off. He did not alight but drew his sword and pushing his horse upon the bull which expected him, gave him a wound in the neck; but as it was a slight one, so it served only to enrage him the more. He tore up the earth with his feet, he roared, and he leapt about like a stag. I cannot well describe to you this combat, nor the acclamations of everybody, the clapping of hands, nor the multitude of handkerchiefs which are thrown up in the air for an expression of admiration, some crying out, *Víctor, Víctor*, and others *Ha Toro, Ha Toro*, the more to excite the bull's fury. Neither can I tell you my particular disturbance, and how my heart failed me every time I saw these terrible creatures ready to kill those brave caballeros: these things are equally impossible to me.

There was a Toledan, both young and handsome, which could not avoid being wounded by the horns of the bull, who tossed him up very high: he immediately died. There were two others mortally wounded, and four horses either killed or desperately hurt. And yet everybody said it had not been a fine baiting because there was so little bloodshed; and to have been such there should have been at the least ten men killed upon the spot. It is hard to describe the dexterity of the caballeros in fighting, and that of the horses in avoiding the bull. They'll turn sometimes an hour about him, and though they be not a foot distant from him, yet he is not able to touch them but when he does hit them he wounds them cruelly. The King threw fifteen pistoles to the black that killed the bull with his poniard, and he gave as much to one that had subdued another, and said he would remember the knights that had fought.

I observed a Castilian, who knew not how to defend himself, jump upon a bull as nimble as a bird. These feasts are fine, great and magnificent, 'tis a noble sight, and costs abundance. One cannot give a just description of it, it must be seen to be well understood. But I assure you that all this did not please me. Do but think if a man that is very dear to you should be so rash to go and expose himself against a furious beast, and that for your sake (for generally that's the motive), you see him brought back weltering in his blood, and half dead. Is it possible, I say, for you or any one, to approve of such actions and these customs? Nay, suppose one had no particular concern, would one desire to be present at such sports that cost the lives of so many men? For my part, I wonder that in a kingdom where their king bears the name of Catholic, there should be such barbarous diversions permitted. I am satisfied that 'tis very ancient, because they derive it from the Moors; but yet methinks this, as well as divers other customs which they have from those infidels, ought to be entirely abolished.

Don Fernand observing me very much disturbed and uneasy during the baiting, and taking notice that I was sometimes as pale as death, I was so much frighted to see some of those killed which fought, said to me in smiling:

"What would you have done, Madam, if you had seen what had happened some years ago? A caballero of worth, passionately loved a young woman, who was only a jeweller's daughter, but a perfect beauty, and was to have a great estate. This caballero, having understood that the most furious bulls of the mountains were taken, and thinking it would be a very glorious action to vanquish them, resolved to taurize as they call it, and for that end desired leave of his mistress. She was so surprised at the bare proposal only which he made that she swooned away, and by all that power which he had given her over himself, she charged him not to think of it, as he valued his life. But in spite of this charge he believed he could not give a more ample proof of his love, and therefore privately caused all things necessary to be got ready in order thereunto. But as industrious as he was to hide his design from his mistress, she was informed of it, and used all means to dissuade him from it. In fine, the day of this feast being come, he conjured her to be there, and told her that her very presence would be sufficient to make him conquer and to acquire a glory which would render him yet more worthy of her. 'Your love,' says she, 'is more ambitious than 'tis kind, and mine is more kind than 'tis ambitious. Go where you think glory calls you. You have a mind I should be there; you will fight before me: well, I do assure you that I will be there, but yet perhaps my presence will afford you more matter of trouble than emulation.'

"However, he left her, and went to the Plaza Mayor, where there was already a mighty assembly. But scarce had he begun to defend himself against a fierce bull which assaulted him, when a country youth threw a dart at this terrible creature, which pierced him so deep that it put him to a great deal of pain. He immediately left the caballero that was fighting him, and roaring run directly after him that wounded him. This youth thus frighted would have saved himself, when his cap which covered his head fell off, and then the loveliest and the longest hair which could be seen appeared upon his shoulders, and this discovered it to be a maid of about fifteen or sixteen years of age. Fear had put her in such a trembling that she could neither run nor in any way avoid the bull. He gave her a desperate push on the side. At the same instant her lover knew that it was she, and was running to assist her. Good God! what a grief it was for him to see his dear mistress in this sad condition! Passion transported him, he no longer valued his life and grew more furious than the bull, and performed things almost incredible. He was mortally wounded in divers places. On this day certainly, the people thought the baiting fine. They carried these two unfortunate lovers to her unhappy father's house. They both desired to be in the same chamber, and though they had but a little time to live, yet begged the favour they might be married. Accordingly they were married, and since they could not live together, yet at least were they buried together in one and the same grave."

The Bulls

by ANGEL DE SAAVEDRA, the Duke of Rivas

The author of this poem was Angel de Saavedra, the Duke of Rivas, 1791–1865, who was exiled from Spain for some time, because of his political and literary liberalism, living in France and England. He wrote the poem of a *corrida* held in 1638, during the reign of Philip IV. Conditions at that time inspired the blend of pageantry and satire on court life. The duke wrote many important poems and plays, including the famous *Don Alvaro,* a drama of verbal magnificence which excited theater-goers who were fed up with routines of their current productions.

It was the Plaza Mayor,
Madrid in festival
Of honor to the reign
Of Philip IV, the king.

His majesty and queen,
With nobles of the palace,
Royal box festooned,
In tapestry and silk

The balconies in damask,
Coats-of-arms, brocade,
Grandees with their ladies,
And royal courtiers.

Bright with noble costumes,
Plumes and richest velvet.
Ladies, and their gentlemen
Filled the upper tiers.

The multitude was gay
In balustrades and windows,
Like a windswept garden
Rippled many colors.

Before the Royal canopy,
The King's box underneath,
Their backs against the barrier
And facing the arena.

The Teuton guard on file
Became a woven wall
Of lacquered jade and crimson
With cornices of faces.

Over the waving plumage
Like trembling border hedges,
The halberds shone respendent
In the May day sun.

The bailiffs of the castle,
With lances poised and ready,
Astride their modest horses,
Stood stiffly at the sides.

The King, the Queen, and grandees,
The ladies and the courtiers
The royal guard and bailiffs,
The crowd within the plaza

Turned their eyes, inquiring,
To the gateway of Toledo
Where from the entrance rode
A calm and noble horseman.

He saw in the arena,
A Fury breathing terror,
Eyes like burning coals
And horns be-smeared with blood.

The strong hooves pawing dust
In billows; this dark beast,
The bravest from Jarama,
And its enchanted plains.

Although there was no mark
Of wounds upon his shoulders,
Neither had he attacked
A single time in vain.

Among the scattered *capas*
And the dying horses,
He moved in mighty pride,
A warrior with his laurels.

Amidst the fallen banners,
Over the broken walls,
This avalanche of power
Seemed an emblem and a sign.

But a fiery dapple,
Bred from an African mare,
Spotted its breast plate and shoulders
With a shower of snow-white foam

Prancing, it struck the earth,
In rhythm with its hoof-beats,
Proud under purple fringes
Of rich caparison.

The mane a tossing banner
On his head a crest,
The bridle and the reins
Of red and golden tassels.

Mounted on this stallion,
Glistening from mane to tail,
Rode the gallant horseman
To battle with the bull.

He wore a cape and doublet
Of gleaming snow-white velvet,
Edged with gold and pearls
And intricate embroidery.

The slashes of doublet and lining,
The cuffs and the belt of crimson,
The breeches and buskin were strapped
In mahogany colored sheen.

The collar and wrist-ruffles laced;
From his breast reflected the fire
And the pride of flashing rubies
Of the Cross of Santiago.

A hat with a diamond band
Held six white waving plumes
And the sunlight of the day
Shone on his noble grace.

His left hand on the reins
In his right a javelin,
Pointed with a hand-long blade,
He rode toward the raging bull.

On the ground were his two pages
One to left and right,
Held high their crimson mantles
Awaiting the sudden battle.

Behind him were the squires
And a squadron of his footmen
Who, in respect for ritual,
Watched the bull with care.

Into the quiet plaza
This handsome noble rode,
Bowed to the king and queen
With a genteel ease of honor.

The king replied serenely
To this unexpected gesture
Meanwhile the waiting people
Roared their mass approval.

Here was the great Don Juan
Of Tarsis, courtier,
Count of Villamediana
Of Madrid, and beloved in Spain,

For his illustrious name
And his generous deportment
For his courage, true and tested,
And his discreet behavior.

Great favor, it is said,
Although secret, he enjoyed
In the palace, but the gossips'
Rumors should be forgot.

Bold Villamediana
Caught his reins and advanced
His lance to the threatened danger
As the enemy lowered its head.

Shook its horns and bellowed,
Pawed the ground and paused,
To choose the wicked moment
Of its deadly charge.

The page on the right hand waited,
With grace and skillful passes,
Aroused the bull and called him
With floating streams of color.

The bull lunged, the horseman parried
And passed it at an angle,
As the left hand page, with a flourish,
Attracted the bull and turned him.

Again the animal waited.
The Count determined to strike him
Head on, as the storm from Jarama
Wheeled to meet him, with a roar.

That moment, horse and horseman
Leaped, it seemed, on wings,
Across the plunging shadow
And then the bull stood still.

And swaying on his balance
The blood sprang from a neck wound
Where the lance had struck him;
A red lake stained the sand.

Half the spear was buried,
The other in the hand
Of the bold and valiant noble
Who faced the crowd in triumph.

From the balconies and the platforms,
The windows of the plaza,
Waved a mass of handkerchiefs
Like a snow-white cloud

"Viva!" cried the people;
The gentlemen yelled, "Bravo!"
"How gallant!" smiled the ladies,
Their palms spoke approbation.

The queen, who was scarcely breathing,
Forced her eyes from horse and horseman,
Turned anxiously, distrait,
And spoke almost in whispers,

"How well the noble lances."
"Very well," the courtiers answered.
But the king responded gravely,
"Lances well, but strikes quite high."

The sovereign turned his head
And contemplated the queen
As she blushed and all the courtiers
Repeated the royal remark;

Their opinion was an echo
Of a shred of conversation
Repeated, without thinking
What their sovereigns had meant

So, wishing to agree supinely
The courtiers following their custom,
"He lances well, but better
Keep his lancing somewhat lower."

Two more bulls were fought by horsemen
Whose boldness and whose skill
Showed bravery and ritual
But not like the elegant count.

It was mid-day as the bells
Of Santa Cruz rang the hour
And the sovereigns left for the palace
In their coach of chivalry.

After them went all the courtiers
And the mighty multitude
Emptied from the great arena,
Left the plaza desolate.

They poured through the gates and arches
Like a compact force, but later,
In the streets, the moving masses
Dispersed into groups toward homes.

Perhaps in this manner a marsh land,
A mass till the flood-gates are opened
Pours out in sudden freedom
With noisy, torrents of water,

That make a network of rivers
Which divide in diminishing streams,
Through brooklets to vanishing trickles,
And finally are lost in the plains.

Epilogue

There is a sequel to the poem. During that night, after the spectacle, the Count of Villamediana's body was found pierced by sword wounds on the vestibule of the Church of St. Philip, according to Aurelio Pérez, "Villamelón," in his *Origins of the Fiesta Brava*. The murderer was not found, but an expression of the time was: "the stroke was sure, and the motive supreme." The count had paid for his regal romance.

The African

Manuel Bellón was a well-known bullfighter of the late eighteenth century, one of the first of the fighters on foot. He was haunted by bad luck in his personal life. Bellón was called "The African" because he spent several years in that country. He was a strange, silent man, and the subject of many stories. While the authors, Leopoldo Vázquez, Luis Gandullo, and Leopoldo López de Saa, were gathering material for the *Tauromaquia* of "Guerrita," they came upon one of the most bizarre of these stories, talking with a descendant of Bellón. This is my version and translation of the story.

I

Triana is an ancient and crowded section of Seville. It is noisy and colorful by day but melancholy at night. Along its dark streets and from the shuttered houses echo mournful songs saturated with the special poetry of the Andalusian people. Here is a refuge for strange neighbors; women with silken eyelashes over eyes that can kill; wit that can please or blister; love phrases that can infatuate or assassinate. The scene is in this heterogeneous mass of luxury and misery, of incense and evil perfume. The story started one night in 1780.

A man walked heavily down a tortuous street. Low ramshackle buildings leaned on curves and corners. There were no lights and the pale moon formed grotesque shadows on the narrow space between the hunched buildings. It was a place for dark purposes and silent with the oppressive, intangible presence of danger. The man stopped at a wretched house, and entered the door noiselessly.

A voice, hoarse with age and too much brandy, grated from the shadows.

"What evil brings you here?"

"Is that you, Aunt Bibiana?"

"Don't you know?"

"Well, it is only that you and your son sound alike."

"Oh, come on in. The lazy good-for-nothing is the one who sent for you. He's inside."

"What for?"

"How do I know? Something to do with his heart and a woman. I wish you could get it out of his windpipe. He is the only support I have and I am not getting it."

"Is that him?" a voice grated from the other room.

"Yes, and what's keeping you?" his mother muttered.

"Nothing, Mother, I didn't know whether you were saying hello to somebody or talking to yourself again. Come in, Galiba, and pay no attention to her nonsense."

"Have you noticed? How he treats his mother!" The old lady pretended a great pain and leaned against the wall, dragging herself along, before collapsing on a rickety chair.

A curtain, that might have been clean at one time, served as a door. The visitors walked into the adjoining cubbyhole of a room, as poorly furnished as the first. A man slouched over his crossed legs in a chair. He looked older than believable, as he lifted his head. His face was marked with smallpox, and a malicious smile.

"God protect you," said the visitor.

"Galiba," replied the other without preamble, "I have called you on an important matter."

"What?"

"Can I get your cart and mules tomorrow night?"

"You?"

"Yes me. Why not?"

"Okay. What for?"

"For several hours."

Galiba looked at the fellow and then, slowly, glanced around the miserable room. Before he could open his mouth, he heard, "The person who will pay for this could put gold tires on your cheap carriage, and silver bells on your underfed mules."

"Really."

"Look, Galiba, let's cut all this out. Are you a man who can keep a secret?"

"It can be done."

"Okay. Then swear by the Virgin of the Macarena."

"It is done. Now, what is the point of all this?"

"Okay. And you, Mother?"

"By the Virgin of the Helpless, you know, Son, I can keep my mouth shut."

"Well, there is a woman in Seville who travels in the highest circles, and is full of social stuff. There is not a female who does not hate her, nor a male who does not want her. She could dry up a river with the fire in her eyes. And when she talks a heavenly bell rings. This woman is a lady by birth, and her father is big power in the city.

"Now there is a man who is dying for her. He is a much better man than I am. And that gives me a lot of satisfaction. He talks to her and she flirts outrageously with him, but with me that is another matter. She's got a yen for me. He is handsome and brave. I am ugly and a coward. But she would like to have me. And what do you know, Galiba, I am just ruffian enough to take her, with all her ladylike unfaithfulness."

"You have my curiosity up," said Galiba. "Who is the woman?"

"Remember your oath?"

"Yes, go ahead."

"The quality call her Lady Carmen Salices, others, Carmelita, but I call her the Carmela."

"The daughter of the judge?" exclaimed Galiba.

"Yep, that's the gal."

Aunt Bibiana sat abruptly, horror-struck at this shocking statement. Galiba could not speak for a moment, and then, stammered, "But she is the sweetheart of Manuel Bellón, the bullfighter."

"That's right. What's the matter? What's your price by the hour? I don't want to hassle over this."

Galiba was convinced. "All right," he asked, "where and when?"

"At midnight, by the bank of the river tomorrow."

"All right."

"Okay, good night."

The coachman wrapped himself in his cloak and went out, while Petote turned to the old woman.

"And you, Grandmother, what's the matter, you got St. Vitus dance or something?"

"Son, I'm thinking about how I can get you out of this terrible thing. You have got to get away from this woman."

"Who says so?"

"I say so, and I'm going to tell you a secret. After that, let's see. Listen, thirty years ago I was a pretty woman."

Petote looked at his mother narrowly.

"Devils tempted me to love a man who abandoned me."

"So what?"

"Haven't you ever been curious to know who your father was?"

"And . . .?"

"Well, you may as well get ready to tremble. My lover and your father is also the father of Carmen."

Petote erupted a gust of laughter that froze the old woman with its frightfulness.

"I don't believe you," he shouted.

Aunt Bibiana was quiet with a dignity that sat strangely on her withered and frozen face. Then, suddenly, she tore the faded kerchief from her head, and stretched out her arms to the lithographed Virgin on the wall, crying, "I swear by your sacred image that I am telling the truth!"

Petote gazed scornfully at the ceiling, pursed his lips, and scratched his nose.

"Okay. Then, by this image I swear that I am going to take this woman out of her house."

The old woman writhed with the horror of the thing. Finally she quieted down, and Petote busied himself repairing a hole in his trousers.

While this was going on, the coachman stumbled through the dark of the entire Triana maze of streets. He finally reached a tavern frequented by all elements of the night life. And there was the object of his search. A tall, handsome, dark, and bold man. He was expensively dressed in green trimmed with black silk. His deep eyes were framed by slim sideburns.

"Here I come, Don Manuel," said Galiba as he entered.

"I thought you were not coming and I was about to walk home, for a change," replied the man courteously.

"Waiter!" called the coachman. "The cards and a bottle of wine."

"So, we shall have a short play before leaving?"

The coachman nodded, and they began to play. Two or three times, Galiba tried to relieve his mind but he did not know how to begin. Finally, he blurted out, "Don Manuel . . ."

The bullfighter looked up and confused him. So he changed his tone. "They say Sr. Romero and Felix Palomo are going with you to fight bulls in Madrid."

"Francisco Romero may not go. I do not know what Palomo's plans are. As for me, I am not leaving Seville. You know, I'm not looking for anything away from here."

"Ah, who knows! And I always think a man should travel. If I were a fine bullfighter such as you are I would not stay here an hour. They tell me there are many beautiful women in Madrid. What more do you want?"

"What I have here. I would rather flirt with her at midnight, as my heart beats against the bars of her window."

"What a shame! You should be appreciated."

"More than here?" the bullfighter asked carefully.

Galiba knew the moment had come.

"Perhaps," he said hesitantly.

"What are you saying, Galiba?" shouted the bullfighter.

"You are my friend?"

"And you are mine, or are you one of those people who can ruin everything with a careless word? Do I have to kill you?"

"I am your faithful friend. And I have to prove to you that I will not have thieves and wicked women playing with you."

He spoke with such sincerity that Manuel sensed something strange. His heart filled his throat, and a hot wave swept through his brain. Then he collapsed slowly in a paralysis of despair. He raised his head heavily.

"Look," he said. "A bull's horn in the breast either kills, or is cured and forgotten. But this is a wound that will bleed as long as I live because it is in the heart."

He crossed his arms on the table, and said calmly, "All right tell me the story."

II

Judge Salices was a man of reputation, conservative routine, and high regard for the conventions. His daughter, Carmela, was a vestal, in his eyes. She was the center of his existence. The judge had two friends, his money and the canon of the cathedral. The canon was having chocolate with him when the talk turned to women.

"I had only one woman," the judge said, "my sainted Angustias who is in Heaven." He gazed at the ceiling as if he were offering a prayer for her soul.

Just then the door opened and the servant announced a poor old lady wanted to see him on an urgent matter. The judge thought of saying no, but feared that the priest would think him lacking in benevolence.

"Come in, my good woman, and what can we do for you?"

Aunt Bibiana craned her withered neck at the fine furnishings of the house. "Ah, it *is* you, my good judge," she said gaily.

The priest almost dropped his tenth piece of cake, and the judge gulped.

"Ah, a priest!" exclaimed the old woman. "I am very glad. I have a lot of sins to get rid of, if you please."

"Who are you and what do you want?" asked the judge sternly.

"You don't know me now, your honor? But your hot little Triana girl has changed. You don't remember the promises you made and broke with me? That's the way men are. Then, you were a lawyer without clients. And I had big eyes and a slim body. You deceived me and I forgave you, but God punishes."

The canon blushed, as the judge stuttered, "This woman is mad."

"No, I am not mad," Aunt Bibiana replied. "I was living very badly but very peacefully until today. Now that is all changed. I had to come here to prevent a tragedy. Our son——"

"Our son!" roared the judge. "This is too much!"

"No it is not too much. You abandoned him, and me. Then you went on to get rich and have a daughter, who is flirting with every wolf around town."

"This is infamous."

"Finally she has got around to our son, and that *is* too much."

"What a scandal!" murmured the priest.

"A doctor! I'm dying!" cried the judge.

"Die, if you will, but first do something about our son and your daughter. Because they are planning to elope tomorrow night t-o-g-e-t-h-e-r—do you understand what that means!"

The judge's hand closed over her mouth. "Who would have thought after thirty years," groaned the judge.

"Who has not had a youthful fling?" said the priest.

"But now we have to think . . ." whispered the judge.

III

It was midnight by the cathedral clock. The fragrance of orange blossoms drifted over the exclusive residential section of the city. There was no sound from the patios of the great houses. Far away on the Guadalquivir River drifted the voice of an occasional boatman. Along the streets echoed the calls of night watchmen, announcing the hours. The stars had disappeared in the clouds. The few city lamps burned low and barely marked the street intersections.

About the middle of the block on Bustos Tabera Street, a man had his face against the grilled window. His tall, handsome form and his clothing showed that it was Manuel Bellón, the bullfighter, whispering with his love. A small white hand was visible between the vines of the grill.

"Carmela, Carmela," entreated the bullfighter, "if you do not love me, please, do not deceive me. Tell me. Whatever you say I will understand. Tell me I'm not worthy of you, if you must. I swear that I will bear the pain inside. Just so I can say to my conscience that if you could not love me, at least, you were honest about it."

"There was a pause, and a sigh was heard in the shadows.

"You don't answer me, Carmelita?" urged the bullfighter.

"What do you want me to say?" replied the beguiling voice. "What can I say? You know what I am doing for your love. Disobeying my father, when all the world is asleep, I open my window to you. And what for? You and your dangerous profession. If you should look for some less risky business, who knows what would happen? Have patience, have patience."

"I'm always having patience, and waiting. It looks to me like you do not want the future to arrive."

"It will not come if we are so violent."

"Well, what can we do? Are you willing to prove your love?"

"Do you doubt me, Manuel?" she whispered tenderly.

His doubts cleared away under her spell, and he thought of killing Galiba.

"Would you," he murmured, "would you go away with me?"

"Manuel!"

"It's the only way we can be together forever."

"What things you say, and so suddenly too. That I . . ."

"You what?"

"I don't know how to answer."

"But can't you decide?" insisted the bullfighter.

The cathedral bell tolled one.

"Oh, it's awfully late, Manuel. Go away quickly before somebody sees you. Tomorrow we shall talk quietly. Come early, hear? I'll be waiting."

"Carmela, it may be that we shall not see each other tomorrow."

"You have to come. Otherwise I'll believe. . . ."

"Believe what?"

"That somebody has taken you away from me."

"Do not worry. But guard yourself. There are thieves about."

"I have these bars."

"They can be broken."

"In that case, I'll call you."

"*Adiós,* Carmela."

The shutters clicked softly shut. Manuel stood a moment watching the window and turned away. He did not go far before turning sharply and hiding in a doorway.

A few minutes later, two men came out of the door of the house he had just left. One was the judge and the other his manservant. They passed close to Manuel's hiding place.

"Could you hear well, Camilo?" asked the judge softly.

"Oh, yes, they were talking about eloping."

"The devil they were. Then the old woman was right. How could she deceive me? A convent will straighten her out. But the woman said she was escaping tonight. I see nobody."

"For the moment. It must be a later date."

"Very well. You go find a policeman. Tell him it is a secret mission for me. You know where I will be. Bring him there. Damiana will watch here."

"Do you think it is wise, sir, to trust a woman to watch a woman?"

"Don't worry. I selected her because she can scream louder than anybody I know."

"What about the noise and scandal, sir?"

"That is what we are trying to avoid. The other is only a frightened serenader at a window."

The shapes disappeared in the dark and Manuel was about to follow them when another form approached the house. He went to the door and tapped three times lightly. Then he whistled softly the partridge mating call.

A few minutes passed, and then, the window opened. That familiar, tender voice murmured, "It's you?"

"Yes," answered the man.

"I'll be right out," she said.

The bullfighter was seized with a spasm of fury, and he grasped the dagger in his belt. There was only one way to avenge his honor.

The door opened slowly and a woman's face appeared, but only for an instant. She screamed, and the door slammed shut.

The bullfighter leaped on the intruder and grasped him by the throat. Petote unclasped his jackknife and they slashed away at each other. Finally Manuel's knife pierced Petote's chest and he let out a gurgling moan. Then his body sprawled in the street.

The noise aroused the neighborhood. Manuel crossed his arms across his chest to await the police. But he was pushed roughly forward and a voice said quickly, "Hurry up. This is real."

"Oh, Galiba!" exclaimed the bullfighter from his distraction. He followed the coachman meekly.

"I knew what was going to happen, and I brought my carriage along."

He sang as he drove away about having no silver bells for his mules but he had silver bells in his heart. They arrived on the water front.

"You don't worry, Manuel. Very shortly a ship sails to Africa. All I want you to remember is I was your friend."

Manuel reached out his hand firmly to his friend. Later he sat alone and wept. He did not know whether it was the sadness or anger or deceit that caused his anguish. Who knows?

A few days later, the bullfighter sailed for Africa seeking forgetfulness for the only thing a man should never mourn—the deceit of a woman.

IV

Seville was in festival. There were no clouds in the sky. The cafés were full of frolicking people. Through the streets rolled the carriages overflowing with youth and beauty.

The crowds poured into the bull ring. The flirtations, the mutual toasts from goatskins, manganilla bottles, the aroma of sausages, the fragrance of flowers, the gay dresses of the women and the somber formality of the men.

A trumpet sounded and the procession filed across the sand. At the head walked the matadors. One was Francisco Romero, with his long, sallow face. The other was Manuel, copper-colored and stern. Now he was called simply "The African."

He had been twelve years away from home. Living had not been easy, longshoreman, exerciser of horses, herder of cattle, hunter of wild animals, conqueror of wild men. Thus passed his exile. Now he was back again on the banks of the Guadalquivir. The afternoon of the bulls revealed a new man, with a supreme contempt for life. His serenity before those deadly horns was incredible. Even Francisco Romero was astonished. He said the bulls stopped, startled at the boldness and calmness of the man.

The acclaim of the crowd reverberated like a pounding surf, unceasingly. When the delirium was at its height, the matador took a cape and draped it from his left arm. He lifted the sword in his right hand. Standing three paces from the bull, he cited it to charge. The bull did not move, undoubtedly frightened by this madman. So, he swept his cape in a low arc across to his right side and launched himself over the horns burying the steel in the bull's mighty shoulders. It tumbled down, dead.

A hurricane of applause swept him onto the backs of fanatic aficionados. This had never been seen before, and they say that "Costillares" got his idea for the *volapié* from this man of iron and implacable will.

At the end of the corrida, as the bullfighters retired from the ring, a coachman came out of the crowd and embraced The African. It was Galiba.

"Wonderful, master!" he said breathlessly. "I would give my mules and carriage to be like you!"

Manuel smiled sadly.

"Look, this is the reward. Applause, fame, and even the envy of good men such as you. It means nothing, my friend. She died. The past died. But my heart lives. And the wound, that you know about, is still bleeding."

Manuel Bellón lived on with his dark despair. But his name is high on the pages of posterity, with Francisco Romero, in the history of the arena. His heartbreak brought him eternal fame.

Selections from "Childe Harold"

by LORD BYRON

Lord Byron, 1788–1824, great and erratic British poet, recorded in "Childe Harold" his reactions to the bullfight. He traveled in Spain during his youth. Byron's genius was complicated and often contradictory in expression. Sometimes his intellect overcame natural emotions, and he did not employ subtlety on broad themes. The bullfight fascinated him, but he could not reconcile this tragic drama with his conservative British adolescence which had not reached intellectual or poetic maturity. However, this selection from Byron is important because it was distilled in the mind of a major poet in the English language.

> The Sabbath comes, a day of blessed rest;
> What hallows it upon this Christian shore?
> Lo! it is sacred to a solemn feast;
> Hark! heard you not the forest-monarch's roar?
>
> The lists are oped, the spacious area clear'd
> Thousands on thousands piled are seated round;
> Long ere the first loud trumpet's note is heard,
> Ne vacant space for lated wight is found.
> Here dons, grandees, but chiefly dames abound,
> Skill'd in the ogle of a roguish eye,
> Yet ever well inclined to heal the wound;
> None through their cold disdain are doomed to die,
> As moon-struck bards complain, by Love's sad archery.

Hush'd is the din of tongues; on gallant steeds,
With milk-white crest, gold spur, and high-poised lance,
Four cavaliers prepare for venturous deeds,
And lowly bending to the lists advance;
Rich are their scarfs, their charges featly prance:
If in the dangerous game they shine today,
The crowd's loud shout and ladies' lovely glance,
Best prize of better acts, they bear away.
And all that kings or chiefs e'er gain their toils repay.

In costly sheen and gaudy cloak array'd,
But all afoot, the light-limb'd Matadore
Stands in the centre, eager to invade
The lord of lowing herds; but not before
The ground with cautious tread is traversed o'er,
Lest aught unseen should lurk to thwart his speed:
His arms a dart, he fights aloof, nor more
Can man achieve without the friendly steed—
Alas! too oft condemn'd for him to bear and bleed.

Thrice sounds the clarion; lo! the signal falls,
The den expands, and Expectation mute
Gapes round the silent circle's peopled walls.
Bounds with one lashing spring the mighty brute,
And, wildly staring, spurns with sounding foot
The sand, nor blindly rushes on his foe:
Here, there, he points his threatening front, to suit
His first attack, wide waving to and fro
His angry tail; red rolls his eye's dilated glow.

Sudden he stops; his eye is fix'd: away,
Away, thou heedless boy! prepare the spear:
Now is thy time, to perish, or display
The skill that yet may check his mad career.
With well-timed croupe the nimble coursers veer;
On foams the bull, but not unscathed he goes;
Streams from his flank the crimson torrent clear:
He flies, he wheels, distracted with his throes;
Dart follows dart; lance, lance; loud bellowing speak his
    woes.

Again he comes; nor dart nor lance avail,
Nor the wild plunging of the tortured horse;
Though man and man's avenging arms assail,
Vain are his weapons, vainer is his force.

One gallant steed is stretch'd a mangled corse;
Another hideous sight! unseam'd appears,
His gory chest unveils life's panting source;
Though death-struck, still his feeble frame he rears;
Staggering, but stemming all, his lord unharm'd he bears.

Foil'd, bleeding, breathless, furious to the last,
Full in the centre stands the bull at bay,
Mid wounds, and clinging darts, and lances brast,
And foes disabled in the brutal fray:
And now the Matadores around him play,
Shake the red cloak, and poise the ready brand:
Once more through all he bursts his thundering way—
Vain rage! the mantle quits the conynge hand,
Wraps his fierce eye—'tis past—he sinks upon the sand!

Where his vast neck just mingles with the spine,
Sheathed in his form the deadly weapon lies.
He stops, he starts, disdaining to decline;
Slowly he falls amidst triumphant cries,
Without a groan, without a struggle dies.
The decorated car appears, on high
The corse is piled—sweet sight for vulgar eyes;
Four steeds that spurn the rein, as swift as shy,
Hurl the dark bulk along, scarce seen in dashing by.

Such the ungentle sport that oft invites
The Spanish maid, and cheers the Spanish swain . . .

Excerpt from Gatherings in Spain

by RICHARD FORD

Richard Ford, 1796–1858, has long been one of the most influential writers in English on bullfighting. He has probably been quoted more over the years than any English writer on the subject; there is scarcely a book that does not refer to Ford in some way. He knew what he was writing about, having lived for several years in Spain and he had a following for his travel stories. Ford was also a painter, who wrote on Spanish art, a lawyer, who wrote on the political policy of England in Spain, and an understanding observer of foreign customs. The extensive selection from his *Gatherings in Spain,* London, 1846, is printed here because his observations had such an effect on many writers who bolstered up their brief encounters at the *corridas* with generous borrowings from Ford, and some still do.

Our honest John Bulls have long been more partial to their Spanish namesakes, than even to those perpetrated by the Pope, or made in the Emerald Isle; to see a bullfight has been the emphatic object of enlightened curiosity, since Peninsular sketches have been taken and published by our travellers. No sooner had Charles the First, when prince, lost his heart at Madrid, than his royal father-in-law-that-was-to-be, regaled him and the fair inspirer of his tender passion, with one of these charming spectacles; an event which, as many men and animals were butchered, was thought by the historiographers of the day to be one that posterity would not willingly let die; their contemporary accounts will ever form the gems of every tauromachian library that aspires to be complete.

These sports, which recall the bloody games of the Roman amphitheatre, are now only to be seen in Spain, where the present clashes with the past, where at every moment we stumble on some bone and relic of Biblical and Roman antiquity; the close parallels, nay the identities, which are observable between these combats and those of classical ages, both as regards the spectators and actors, are omitted, as being more interesting to the scholar than to the general reader; they were pointed out by us some years ago in the *Quarterly Review,* No. CXXIV. And as human nature changes not, men when placed in given and similar circumstances, will without any previous knowledge or intercommunication arrive at nearly similar results; the gentle pastime of spearing and killing bulls in public and single-handed was probably devised by the Moors, or rather by the Spanish Moors, for nothing of the kind has ever obtained in Africa either now or heretofore. The Moslem Arab, when transplanted into a Christian and European land, modified himself in many respects to the ways and usages of the people among whom he settled, just as his Oriental element was widely introduced among his Gotho-Hispano neighbours. Moorish Andalucía is still the headquarters of the tauromachian art, and those who wish carefully to master this, the science of Spain par excellence, should commence their studies in the school of Ronda, and proceed thence to take the highest honours in the University of Seville, the Bullford of the Peninsula.

By the way, our boxing, baiting term bullfight is a very lay and low translation of the time-honoured Castilian title, *Fiestas de Toros,* the feasts, festivals of bulls. The gods and goddesses of antiquity were conciliated by the sacrifice of hecatombs; the lowing tickled their divine ears, and the purple blood fed their eyes, no less than the roasted sirloins fattened the priests, while the grand spectacle and death delighted their dinnerless congregations. In Spain, the Church of Rome, never indifferent to its interests, instantly marshalled into its own service a ceremonial at once profitable and popular . . . (The love for killing oxen still prevails at Rome, where the ambition of the lower orders to be a butcher, is, like their white costume, a remnant of the honourable office of killing at the Pagan sacrifices. In Spain butchers are of the lowest caste, and cannot prove "purity of blood." Francis I never forgave the "Becajo de Parigi" applied by Dante to his ancestor; it consecrated butchery by wedding it to the altar, availing itself of this gentle handmaid, to obtain funds in order to raise convents; even in the last century Papal bulls were granted to mendicant orders, authorising them to celebrate a certain number of *Fiestas de Toros,* on condition of devoting the profit to finishing their church; and in order to swell the receipts at the doors, spiritual indulgences and soul releases from purgatory, the number of years being apportioned to the relative prices of the seats, were added as a bonus to all paid for places at a spectacle hallowed by a pious object. So at the taurobolia of antiquity, those who were sprinkled with bull blood were absolved from sin. Protestant ministers, who very properly fear and distrust papal bulls, replace them by bazaars and fancy fairs, whenever a fashionable chapel requires a new blue slate roofing. Again, when not devoted to religious purposes, every bullfight aids the cause of charity; the profits from the chief income of the public hospitals, and thus furnish both funds and patients, as the venous circulation of the mob thirsting for gore, rises to blood heat under a sun of fire, and the subsequent mingling of sexes, opening of bottles and knives, occasion more deaths among the lords and ladies of the Spanish creation, than among the horned and hoofed victims of the amphitheatre.

It is a common but very great mistake, to suppose that bullfights are as numerous in Spain as bandits; it is just the contrary, for this may there be considered the tip-top aesthetic treat, as the Italian Opera is in England, and both are rather expensive amusements; true it is that with us, only the salt of the earth patronises the performers of the Haymarket, while high and low, vulgar and exquisite, alike delight in those of the Spanish fields. Each bull-fight costs from £200 to £300, and even more when got up out of Andalucía or Madrid, which alone can afford to support a standing company; in other cities the actors and animals have to be sent by express, and from great distances. Hence the representations occur like angels' visits, few and far between; they are reserved for the chief festivals of the church and crown, for the unfeigned devotion of the faithful on the holy days of local saints, and the Virgin; they are also given at the marriages and coronations of the sovereign, and thence are called *Fiestas reales,* Royal festivals—the ceremonial being then deprived of its religious character, although it is much increased in worldly and imposing importance. The sight is indeed one of surpassing pomp, etiquette, and magnificence, and has succeeded to the auto-da-fé, in offering to the most Catholic Queen and her subjects the greatest possible means of tasting rapture, that the limited powers of mortal enjoyment can experience in this world of shadows and sorrows.

They are only given at Madrid, and then are conducted entirely after the ancient Spanish and Moorish customs, of which such splendid descriptions remain in the ballad romances. They take place in the great square of the capital, which is then converted into an arena. The windows of the quaint and lofty houses are arranged as boxes, and hung with velvets and silks. The royal family is seated under a canopy of state in the balcony of the central mansion. There we beheld Ferdinand VII presiding at the solemn swearing of allegiance to his daughter. He was then seated where Charles I. had sat two centuries before; he was guarded by the unchanged halberdiers, and was witnessing the unchanged spectacle. On these royal occasions the bulls are assailed by gentlemen, dressed and armed as in good old Spanish times, before the fatal Bourbon accession obliterated Castilian costume, customs and nationality. The champions, clad in the fashions of the Philips, and mounted on beauteous barbs, the minions of their race, attack the fierce animal with only a short spear, the immemorial weapon of the Iberian. The combatants must be gentlemen by birth, and have each for a padrino, or god-father, a first-rate grandee of Spain, who passes before royalty in a splendid equipage and six, and is attended by bands of running footmen, who are arrayed either as Greeks, Romans, Moors, or fancy characters. It is not easy to obtain these *caballeros en plaza,* or poor knights, who are willing to expose their lives to the imminent dangers, albeit during the fight they have the benefit of experienced *toreros* to advise their actions and cover their retreats.

A gentle dame, without the privity of her lord and husband, inscribed his name as one of the champion volunteers. In procuring him this agreeable surprise, she, so it was said in Madrid, argued thus: "Either my husband will be killed—in that case I shall get a new husband; or he will survive, in which event he will get a pension." She failed in both of these admirable calculations—such is the uncertainty of human events. The terror of this poor *héros malgré lui,* on whom chivalry had been thrust, was absolutely ludicrous when exposed by his well-intentioned better-half, to the horns of this dilemma and bull. Any other horns, my dearest, but these! He was wounded at the first rush, did survive, and did not get a pension; for Ferdinand died soon after, and few pensions have been paid in the Peninsula, since the land has been blessed with a charter, constitution, liberty, and a representative government.

One anecdote, where another lady is in the case, may be new to our fair readers. We quote from an ancient authentic chronicler:—"It will not be amiss here to mention what fell out in the presence of Charles the First of Blessed Memory, who, while Prince of Wales, repaired to the court of Spain, whether to be married to the Infanta, or upon what other design, I cannot well determine: however, all comedies, plays, and festivals (this of the bulls at Madrid being included), were appointed to be as decently and magnificently gone about as possible, for the more sumptuous and stately entertainment of such a splendid prince. Therefore, after three bulls had been killed, and the fourth a-coming forth, there appeared four gentlemen in good equipage; not long after, a brisk lady, in most gorgeous apparel, attended with persons of quality, and some three or four grooms, walked all along the square a-foot. Astonishment seized upon the beholders, that one of the female sex could assume the unheard boldness of exposing herself to the violence of the most furious beast yet seen, which had overcome, yea almost killed, two men of great strength, courage, and dexterity. Incontinently the bull rushed towards the corner where the lady and her attendants stood; she (after all had fled) drew forth her dagger very unconcernedly, and thrust it most dexterously into the bull's neck, having catched hold of his horn; by which stroak, without any more trouble, her design was brought to perfection; after which, turning about towards the king's balcony, she made her obeysance, and withdrew herself in suitable state and gravity."

At the jura of 1833 ninety-nine bulls were massacred; had one more been added the hecatomb would have been complete. These wholesale slaughterings have this year been repeated at the marriage of the same "innocent" Isabel, the critical events of whose life are death-warrants to quadrupeds. Bulls, however, represent in Spain the coronation banquets of England. In that hungry, ascetic land, bulls have always been killed, but no beef eaten; a remarkable fact, which did not escape the learned Justin in his remarks on the no-dinner-giving crowned heads of old Iberia.

These genuine ancient bull-fights were perilous and fatal in the extreme, yet knights were never wanting—valour being the point of honour—who readily exposed their lives in sight of their cruel mistresses. To kill the monster if not killed by him, was, before the time of Hudibras, the sure road to women's love, who very properly admire those qualities the best, in which they feel themselves to be the most deficient:—

> "The ladies' hearts began to melt,
> Subdued by blows their lovers felt;
> So Spanish heroes, with their lances,
> At once wound bulls and ladies' fancies."

The final conquest of the Moors, and the subsequent cessation of the border chivalrous habits of Spaniards, occasioned these love-pastimes to fall into comparative disuse. The gentle Isabella was so shocked at the bull-fights which she saw at Medina del Campo, that she did her utmost to put them down; but she strove in vain, for the game and monarchy were destined to fall together. The accession of Philip V deluged the Peninsula with Frenchmen. The puppies of Paris pronounced the Spaniards and their bulls to be barbarous and brutal, as their artistes to this day prefer the *boeuf gras* of the Boulevards to whole flocks of Iberian lean kine. The spectacle which had withstood her influence, and had beat the bulls of Popes, bowed before the despotism of fashion. The periwigged courtiers deserted the arena, on which the royal Bourbon eye looked coldly, while the sturdy people, foes—then as now—to Frenchmen and innovations, clung closer to the sports of their forefathers. Yet a fatal blow was dealt to the combat: the art, once practised by knights, degenerated into the vulgar butchery of mercenary bull-fighters, who contended not for honour, but base lucre; thus, by becoming the game of the mob, it was soon stripped of every gentlemanlike prestige. So the tournament challenges of our chivalrous ancestors have sunk down to the vulgar boxings of ruffian pugilists.

Baiting a bull in any shape is irresistible to the lower orders of Spain, who disregard injuries to the bodies, and, what is worse, to their cloaks. The hostility to the horned beast is instinctive, and grows with their growth, until it becomes, as men are but children of a larger growth, a second nature. The young urchins in the streets play at *"toro,"* as ours do at leapfrog; they go through the whole mimic spectacle amongst each other, observing every law and rule, as our schoolboys do when they fight. Few adult Spaniards, when journeying through the country, ever pass a herd of cows without this dormant propensity breaking out; they provoke the animals to fight by waving their cloaks or *capas,* a challenge hence called *el capeo.* The villagers, who cannot afford the expense of a regular bullfight, amuse themselves with baiting *novillos,* or bull-youngsters—calves of one year old; and *embolados,* or bulls whose horns are guarded with tips and buttons. These innocent pastimes are despised by the regular *afición,* the "fancy"; because, as neither man nor beast are exposed to be killed, the whole affair is based in fiction, and impotent in conclusion. They cry out for *Toros de muerte*— bulls of death. Nothing short of the reality of blood can allay their excitement. They despise the makeshift spectacle, as much as a true gastronome does mock-turtle, or an old campaigner a sham fight.

In the wilder districts of Andalucía few cattle are ever brought into towns for slaughter, unless led by long ropes, and partially baited by those whose poverty prevents their indulgence in the luxury of real bullfights and beef. The governor of Tarifa was wont on certain days to let a bull loose into the streets, when the delight of the inhabitants was to shut their doors, and behold from their grated windows the perplexities of the unwary or strangers, pursued by him in the narrow lanes without means of escape. Although many lives were lost, a governor in our time, named Dalmau, otherwise a public benefactor to the place, lost all his popularity in the vain attempt to put the custom down. When the Bourbon Philip V first visited the *plaça* at Madrid, all the populace roared, Bulls! give us bulls, my lord! They cared little for the ruin of the monarchy; so when the intrusive Joseph Buonaparte arrived at the same place, the only and absorbing topic of public talk was whether he would grant or suppress the bullfight. And now, as always, the cry of the capital is—*"Pan y toros;* bread and bulls:" these constitute the loaves and fishes of the "only modern court," as Panes et Circenses did of ancient Rome. The national scowl and frown which welcomed Montpensier at his marriage, was relaxed for one moment, when Spaniards beheld his well-put-on admiration for the tauromachian spectacle. Nothing, since the recent vast improvements in Spain, has more progressed than the bull-fight—convents have come down, churches have been levelled, but new amphitheatres have arisen. The diffusion of useful and entertaining knowledge, as the means of promoting the greatest happiness of the greatest number, has thus obtained the best consideration of those patriots and statesmen who preside over the destinies of Spain; the bull is master of his ground. This last remnant and representative of Spanish nationality defies the foreigner and his civilization; he is a fait accompli, and tramples *la charte* under his feet, although the honest Roi citoyen swears that it is *désormais une vérité.*

In Spain there is no mistaking the day and time that the bull-fight takes place, which is generally on Saint Monday, and in the afternoon, when the mid-day heats are past.

The arena, or Plaza, is most unlike a London Place, those enclosures of stunted smoke-blacked shrubs, fenced in with iron *palisadas* to protect aristocratic nurserymaids from the mob. It is at once more classical and amusing. The amphitheatre of Madrid is very spacious, being about 1100 feet in circumference, and will hold 12,000 spectators. In an architectural point of view this ring of the model court, is shabbier than many of those in provincial towns: there is no attempt at orders, pilasters, and Vitruvian columns; there is no adaptation of the Coliseum of Rome: the exterior is bald and plain, as if done so on purpose, while the interior is fitted up with wooden benches, and is scarcely better than a shambles; but for that it was designed, and there is a businesslike, murderous intention about it, which marks the inaesthetic Gotho-Spaniard, who looked for a sport of blood and death, and not to a display of artistical skill. He has no need of extraneous stimulants; the *réalité atroce,* as a tender-hearted foreigner observes, "is all-sufficing, because it is the recreation of the savage, and the sublime of common souls." The locality, however, is admirably calculated for seeing; and this combat is a spectacle entirely for the eyes. The open space is full of the light of heaven, and here the sun is brighter than gas or wax-candles. The interior is as unadorned as the exterior, and looks positively "mesquin" when empty; around the sanded centre rise rows of wooden seats for the humbler classes, and above them a tier of boxes for the fine ladies and gentlemen; but no sooner is the theatre filled than all this meanness is concealed, and the general appearance becomes superb.

On entering the ring when thus full, the stranger finds his watch put back at once eighteen hundred years; he is transported to Rome under the Caesars; and in truth the sight is glorious, of the assembled thousands in their Spanish costume, the novelty of the spectacle, associated with our earliest classical studies, are enhanced by the blue expanse of the heavens, spread above as a canopy. There is something in these out-of-door entertainments, *à l'antique,* which peculiarly affects the shivering denizens of the catch-cold north, where climate contributes so little to the happiness of man. All first-rate connoisseurs go into the pit and place themselves among the mob, in order to be closer to the bulls and combatants. The real thing is to sit near one of the openings, which enables the fancy-man to exhibit his embroidered gaiters and neat leg. It is here that the character of the bull, the nice traits and the behaviour of the bullfighter are scientifically criticised. The ring has a dialect peculiar to itself, which is unintelligible to most Spaniards themselves, while to the sporting-men of Andalucía it expresses their drolleries with idiomatic raciness, and is exactly analogous to the slang and technicalities of our pugilistic craft. The newspapers next day generally give a detailed report of the fight, in which every round is scientifically described in a style that defies translation, but which being drawn up by some Spanish Boz, is most delectable to all who can understand it; the nomenclature of praise and blame is defined with the most accurate precision of language, and the delicate shades of character are distinguished with the nicety of phrenological subdivision. The foundation of this lingo is gipsy Romany, metaphor, and double entendre; to master it is no easy matter; indeed, a distinguished diplomat and tauromachian philologist, whom we are proud to call our friend, was often unable to comprehend the full pregnancy of the meaning of certain terms, without a reference to the late Duke of San Lorenzo, who sustained the character of Spanish ambassador in London and of bullfighter in Madrid with equal dignity; His Grace was a living lexicon of slang. Yet let no student be deterred by any difficulty, since he will eventually be repaid, when he can fully relish the Andalusian wit, or *sal andaluza,* the salt, with which the reports are flavoured: that it is seldom Attic must, however, be confessed. Nor let time or pains be grudged; there is no royal road to Euclid, and life, say the Spanish fancy, is too short to learn bullfighting. This possibly may seem strange, but English squires and country gentlemen assert as much in regard to fox-hunting.

The day appointed for a bull-feast is announced by placards of all colours; the important particulars decorate every wall. The first thing is to secure a good place beforehand, by sending for a *boletín de sombra,* a shade-ticket; and as the great object is to avoid glare and heat, the best places are on the northern side, which are in the shade. The transit of the sun over the Plaza, the zodiacal progress into Taurus, is decidedly the best calculated astronomical observation in Spain; the line of shadow defined on the arena is marked by a gradation of prices. The different seats and prices are everywhere detailed in the bills of the play, with the names of the combatants and the colours of the different breeds of bulls.

The day before the fight, the bulls destined for the spectacle are driven towards the town, and pastured in a meadow reserved for their reception;

then the fine amateurs never fail to ride out to see what the cattle is like, just as the knowing in horseflesh go to Tattersall's of a Sunday afternoon, instead of attending evening service in their parish churches. According to Pepe Illo, who was a very practical man, and the first author on the modern system of the arena, of which he was the brightest ornament, and on which he died in the arms of victory, the "love of bulls is inherent in man, especially in the Spaniard, among which glorious people there have been bullfights ever since there were bulls, because the Spanish men are as much more brave than all other men, as the Spanish bull is more fierce and valiant than all other bulls." Certainly, from having been bred at large, in roomy unenclosed plains, they are more active than the animals raised by John Bull, but as regards form and power they would be scouted in an English cattle-show; a real British bull, with his broad neck and short horns, would make quick work with the men and horses of Spain; his "spears" would be no less effective than the bayonets of our soldiers, which no foreigner faces twice, or the picks of our Navvies, three and three-eighths of whom are calculated by railway economists to eat more beef and do more work than five and five-eighths of corresponding foreign material. By the way, the correct Castilian word for the bull's horns is *astas,* the Latin *hastas,* spears. *Cuernos* must never be used in good Spanish society, since, from its secondary meaning, it might give offence to present company: allusions to common calamities are never made to ears polite, however frequent among the vulgar, who call things by their improper names—nay, roar them out, as in the time of Horace: *"Magnâ compellens voce cucullum."*

Not every bull will do for the Plaza, and none but the fiercest are selected, who undergo trials from the earliest youth; the most celebrated animals come from Utrera near Seville, and from the same pastures where that eminent breeder of old Geryon, raised those wonderful oxen, which all but burst with fat in fifty days, and were "lifted" by the invincible Hercules. Señor Cabrera, the modern Geryon, was so pleased with Joseph Buonaparte, or so afraid, that he offered to him a hundred bulls, as a hecatomb for the rations of his troops, who, braver and hungrier than Hercules, would otherwise have infallibly followed the demigod's example. The Manchegan bull, small, very powerful, and active, is considered to be the original stock of Spain; of this breed was "Manchangito," the pet of the Visconde de Miranda, a tauromachian noble of Córdova, and who used to come into the dining-room, but, having one day killed a guest, he was destroyed after violent resistance on the part of the Viscount, and only in obedience to the peremptory mandate of the Prince of the Peace.

The capital is supplied with animals bred in the valleys of the Jarama near Aranjuez, which have been immemorially celebrated. From hence came that Harpado, the magnificent beast of the magnificent Moorish ballad of Gazul, which was evidently written by a practical *torero,* and on the spot: the verses sparkle with daylight and local colour like a Velazquez, and are as minutely correct as a Paul Potter, while Byron's "Bull-fight" is the invention of a foreign poet, and full of slight inaccuracies.

The *encierro,* or the driving the bulls to the arena, is a service of danger; they are enticed by tame oxen, into a road which is barricaded on each side, and then driven full speed by the mounted and spear-bearing peasants into the Plaza. It is an exciting, peculiar, and picturesque spectacle; and the poor who cannot afford to go to the bullfight, risk their lives and cloaks in order to get the front places, and best chance of a stray poke en passant.

The next afternoon all the world crowds to the Plaza de toros. You need not ask the way; just launch into the tide, which in these Spanish affairs will assuredly carry you away. Nothing can exceed the gaiety and sparkle of a Spanish public going, eager and full-dressed, to the fight. They could not move faster were they running away from a real one. All the streets or open spaces near the outside of the arena present of themselves a spectacle to the stranger, and genuine Spain is far better to be seen and studied in the streets, than in the saloon. Now indeed a traveller from Belgravia feels that he is out of town, in a new world and no mistake; all around him is a perfect saturnalia, all ranks are fused in one stream of living beings, one bloody thought beats in every heart, one heart beats in ten thousand bosoms; every other business is at an end, the lover leaves his mistress unless she will go with him,—the doctor and lawyer renounce patients, briefs, and fees; the city of sleepers is awakened, and all is life, noise, and movement, where to-morrow will be the stillness and silence of death; now the bending line of the Calle de Alcalá, which on other days is broad and dull as Portland Place, becomes the aorta of Madrid, and is scarcely wide enough for the increased circulation; now it is filled with a dense mass coloured as the rainbow, which winds along like a spotted snake to its prey. Oh the din and dust! The merry mob is everything, and, like the Greek chorus, is always on the scene. How national and Spanish are the dresses of the lower classes—for their betters alone appear like Boulevard quizzes, or tigers cut out from our East end tailors' pattern-book of the last new fashion; what *manolas,* what reds and yellows, what fringes and flounces, what swarms of picturesque vagabonds, cluster, or alas, clustered, around *calesas,* whose wild drivers run on foot, whipping, screaming, swearing; the type of these vehicles in form and colour was Neapolitan; they alas! are also soon destined to be sacrificed to civilization to the 'bus and commonplace cab, or vile fly.

The plaza is the focus of a fire, which blood alone can extinguish; what public meetings and dinners are to Britons, reviews and razzias to Gauls, mass or music to Italians, is this one and absorbing bull-fight to Spaniards of all ranks, sexes, ages, for their happiness is quite catching; and yet a thorn peeps amid these rosebuds; when the dazzling glare and fierce African sun calcining the heavens and earth, fires up man and beast to madness, a raging thirst for blood is seen in flashing eyes and the irritable ready knife, then the passion of the Arab triumphs over the coldness of the Goth: the excitement would be terrific were it not on pleasure bent; indeed there is no sacrifice, even of chastity, no denial, even of dinner, which they will not undergo to save money for the bullfight. It is the birdlime with which the devil catches many a female and male soul. The men go in all their best costume and majo-finery; the distinguished ladies wear on these occasions white lace mantillas, and when heated, look, as the Andaluz wag Adrian said, like sausages wrapped up in white paper; a fan, *abanico,* is quite as necessary to all as it was among the Romans. The article is sold outside for a trifle, and is made of rude paper, stuck into a handle of common cane or stick, and the gift of one to his nutbrown *querida* is thought a delicate attention to her complexion from her swarthy swain; at the same time the lower Salamander classes stand fire much better on these occasions than in action, and would rather be roasted fanless alive a la auto-da-fé than miss these hot engagements.

The place of slaughter, like the Abattoirs on the Continent, is erected outside the towns, in order to obtain space, and because horned animals when overdriven in crowded streets are apt to be ill-mannered, as may be seen every Smithfield market-day in the City, as the Lord Mayor well knows.

The seats occupied by the mob are filled more rapidly than our shilling galleries, and the "gods" are equally noisy and impatient. The anxiety of the immortals, wishes to annihilate time and space and make bull-fanciers happy. Now his majesty the many reigns triumphantly, and this—church excepted—is the only public meeting allowed; but even here, as on the Continent, the odious bayonet sparkles, and the soldier picket announces that innocent amusements are not free; treason and stratagem are suspected by coward despots, when one sole thought of pleasure engrosses every one else. All ranks are now fused into one mass of homogeneous humanity; their good humour is contagious; all leave their cares and sorrows at home, and enter with a gaiety of heart and a determination to be amused, which defies wrinkled care; many and not overdelicate are the quips and quirks bandied to and fro, with an eloquence more energetic than unadorned; things and persons are mentioned to the horror of periphrastic euphuists; the liberty of speech is perfect, and as it is all done quite in a parliamentary way, none take offence. Those only who cannot get in are sad; these rejected ones remain outside grinding their teeth, like the unhappy ghosts on the wrong side of the Styx, and listen anxiously to the joyous shouts of the thrice blessed within.

At Seville a choice box in the shade and to the right of the president is allotted as the seat of honour to the canons of the cathedral, who attend in their clerical costume; and such days are fixed upon for the bullfight as will not by a long church service prevent their coming. The clergy of Spain have always been the most uncompromising enemies of the stage, where they never go; yet neither the cruelty nor profligacy of the amphitheatre has ever roused the zeal of their most elect or most fanatic: our puritans at least assailed the bear-bait, which induced the Cavalier Hudibras to defend them; so our Methodists denounced the bull-bait, which was therefore patronised by the Right Hon. W. Windham, in the memorable debate May 24, 1802, on Mr. Dog Dent. The Spanish clergy pay due deference to bulls, both papal and quadruped; they dislike being touched on this subject, and generally reply *"Es costumbre*—it is the custom—*siempre se ha praticado asi*—it has always been done so, or *son cosas de España,* they are things of Spain"—the usual answer given as to everything which appears incomprehensible to strangers, and which they either can't account for, or do not choose. In vain did St. Isidore write a chapter against the amphitheatre—his chapter minds him not; in vain did Alphonso the Wise forbid their attendance. The sacrifice of the bull has always been mixed up with the religion of old Rome and old and modern Spain, where they are classed among acts of charity, since they support the sick and wounded; therefore all the sable countrymen of Loyola hold to the Jesuitical doctrine that the end justifies the means.

When the appointed much-wished-for hour is come, the Queen or the Corregidor takes the seat of honour in a central and splendid box, the mob having been previously expelled from the open arena; this operation is called the *despejo,* and is an amusing one, from the reluctance with which the great unwashed submit to be cleaned out. The proceedings open at a given signal with a procession of the combatants, who advance preceded by *alguaciles,* or officers of police, who are dressed in the ancient Spanish costume, and are always at hand to arrest any one who infringes the severe laws against interruptions of the games. Then follow the *picadores,* or mounted horsemen, with their spears. Their original broad-brimmed Spanish hats are decorated with ribbons; their upper man is clad in a gay silken jacket, whose lightness contrasts with the heavy iron and leather protections of the legs, which give the clumsy look of a French jackbooted postilion. These defences are necessary when the horned animal charges home. Next follow the *chulos,* or combatants on foot, who are arrayed like Figaro at the opera, and have, moreover, silken cloaks of gay colours. The *matadores,* or killers, come behind them; and, last of all, a gaily-caparisoned team of mules, which is destined to drag the slaughtered bulls from the arena. As for the men, those who are killed on the spot are denied the burial-rites if they die without confession. Springing from the dregs of the people, they are eminently superstitious, and cover their breasts with relics, amulets, and papal charms. A clergyman, however, is in attendance with the sacramental wafer, in case *su majestad* may be wanted for a mortally-wounded combatant.

Having made their obeisances to the chief authority, all retire, and the fatal trumpet sounds; then the president throws the key of the gate by which the bull is to enter, to one of the *alguaciles,* who ought to catch it in his hat. When the door is opened, this worthy gallops away as fast as he

A British artist's conception of the bullfight in 1852. This is one of a series by William Lake Price, illustrating Richard Ford's text

can, amid the hoots and hisses of the mob, not because he rides like a constable, but from the instinctive enmity which his majesty the many bear to the finisher of the law, just as little birds love to mob a hawk; now more than a thousand kind wishes are offered up that the bull may catch and toss him. The brilliant army of combatants in the meanwhile separates like a bursting shell, and take up their respective places as regularly as our fielders do at a cricket-match.

The play, which consists of three acts, then begins in earnest; the drawing up of the curtain is a spirit-stirring moment; all eyes are riveted at the first appearance of the bull on this stage, as no one can tell how he may behave. Let loose from his dark cell, at first he seems amazed at the novelty of his position; torn from his pastures, imprisoned and exposed, stunned by the noise, he gazes an instant around at the crowd, the glare, and waving handkerchiefs, ignorant of the fate which inevitably awaits him. He bears on his neck a ribbon, *"la devisa,"* which designates his breeder. The *picador* endeavours to snatch this off, to lay the trophy at his true love's heart. The bull is condemned without reprieve; however gallant his conduct, or desperate his resistance, his death is the catastrophe; the whole tragedy tends and hastens to this event, which, although it is darkly shadowed out beforehand, as in a Greek play, does not diminish the interest, since all the intermediate changes and chances are uncertain; hence the sustained excitement, for the action may pass in an instant from the sublime to the ridiculous, from tragedy to farce.

The bull no sooner recovers his senses, than his splendid Achillean rage fires every limb, and with closing eyes and lowered horns he rushes at the first of the three picadors, who are drawn up to the left, close to the *tablas,* or wooden barrier which walls round the ring. The horseman sits on his trembling Rosinante, with his pointed lance under his right arm, as stiff and valiant as Don Quixote. If the animal be only of second-rate power and courage, the sharp point arrests the charge, for he well remembers this *garrocha,* or goad, by which herdsmen enforce discipline and inculcate instruction; during this momentary pause a quick *picador* turns his horse to the left and gets free. The bulls, although irrational brutes, are not slow on their part in discovering when their antagonists are bold and dexterous, and particularly dislike fighting against the pricks. If they fly and will not face the *picador,* they are hooted at as despicable malefactors, who wish to defraud the public of their day's sport, they are execrated as "goats," "cows," which is no compliment to bulls; these culprits, moreover, are soundly beaten as they pass near the barrier by forests of sticks, with which the mob is provided for the nonce; that of the elegant *majo,* when going to the bull-fight, is very peculiar, and is called la chivata; it is between four and five feet long, is tapered, and terminates in a lump or knob, while the top is forked, into which the thumb is inserted; it is also peeled or painted in alternate rings, black and white, or red and yellow. The lower classes content themselves with a common shillelah; one with a knob at the end is preferred, as administering a more impressive whack; their instrument is called *porra,* because heavy and lumbering.

Nor is this *bastinado* uncalled for, since courage, address, and energy, are the qualities which ennoble tauromachia; and when they are wanting, the butchery, with its many disgusting incidents, becomes revolting to the stranger, but to him alone; for the gentler emotions of pity and mercy, which rarely soften any transactions of hard Iberia, are here banished altogether from the hearts of the natives; they now only have eyes for exhibitions of skill and valour, and scarcely observe those cruel incidents which engross and horrify the foreigner, who again on his part is equally blind to those redeeming excellencies, on which alone the attention of the rest of the spectators is fixed; the tables are now turned against the stranger, whose aesthetic mind's eye can see the poetry and beauty of the picturesque rags and tumbledown hamlets of Spaniards, and yet is blind to the poverty, misery, and want of civilization, to which alone the vision of the higher classed native is directed, on whose exalted soul the coming comforts of cotton are gleaming.

When the bull is turned by the spear of the first *picador,* he passes on to the two other horsemen, who receive him with similar cordiality. If the animal be baffled by their skill and valour, stunning are the shouts of applause which celebrate the victory of the men: should he on the contrary charge home and overwhelm horses and riders, then—for the balances of praise and blame are held with perfect fairness—the fierce lord of the arena is encouraged with roars of compliments, *Bravo toro, Viva toro,* Well done, bull! even a long life is wished to him by thousands who know that he must be dead in twenty minutes.

A bold beast is not to be deterred by a trifling inch-deep wound, but presses on, goring the horse in the flank, and then gaining confidence and courage by victory, and "baptized in blood," à la Française, advances in a career of honour, gore, and glory. The *picador* is seldom well mounted, for the horses are provided, at the lowest possible price, by a contractor, who runs the risk whether many or few are killed; they indeed are the only things economised in this costly spectacle, and are sorry, broken-down hacks, fit only for the dog-kennel of an English squire, or carriage of a foreign pair. This increases the danger to his rider; in the ancient combats, the finest and most spirited horses were used; quick as lightning, and turning to the touch, they escaped the deadly rush. The eyes of those poor horses which see and will not face death, are often bound over with a handkerchief, like criminals about to be executed; thus they await blindfold the fatal horn thrust which is to end their life of misery.

The *picadors* are subject to most severe falls; the bull often tosses horse and rider in one ruin, and when his victims fall with a crash on the ground exhausts his fury upon his prostrate foes. The *picador* manages (if he can) to fall off on the opposite side, in order that his horse may form a barrier and rampart between him and the bull. When these deadly struggles take place, when life hangs on a thread, the amphitheatre is peopled with heads; every feeling of anxiety, eagerness, fear, horror, and delight is stamped on their expressive countenances; if happiness is to be estimated by quality, intensity, and concentration, rather than duration (and it is), these are moments of excitement more precious to them, than ages of placid, insipid, uniform stagnation. . . .

A horse, if killed, is dragged out, leaving a bloody furrow on the sand, as the river-beds of the arid plains of Barbary are marked by the crimson fringe of the flowering oleanders. A universal sympathy is shown for the horseman in these awful moments; the men rise, the women scream, but all this soon subsides; the picador, if wounded, is carried out and forgotten —*"los muertos y idos no tienen amigos"*—a new combatant fills up his gap, the battle rages—wounds and death are the order of the day—he is not missed; and as new incidents arise, no pause is left for regret or reflection. We remember seeing at Granada a *matador* cruelly gored by a bull: he was carried away as dead, and his place immediately taken by his son, as coolly as a viscount succeeds to an earl's estate and title. Carnerero, the musician, died while fiddling at a ball at Madrid, in 1838; neither the band nor the dancers stopped one moment. The boldness of the *picadors* is great. Francisco Sevilla, when thrown from his horse and lying under the dying animal, seized the bull, as he rushed at him, by his ears, turned round to the people, and laughed; but, in fact, the long horns of the bull make it difficult for him to gore a man on the ground; he generally bruises them with his nose: nor does he remain long busied with his victim, since he is lured to fresh attacks by the glittering cloaks of the *chulos* who come instantly to the rescue. At the same time we are free to confess, that few *picadors,* although men of bronze, can be said to have a sound rib in their body. When one is carried off apparently dead, but returns immediately mounted on a fresh horse, the applauding voice of the people outbellows a thousand bulls. If the wounded man should chance not to come back, *n'importe,* however courted outside the Plaza, now he is ranked, like the gladiator was by the Romans, no higher than a beast—or about the same as a slave under the perfect equality and man rights of the model republic.

The poor horse is valued at even less, and he, of all the actors, is the one in which Englishmen, true lovers and breeders of the noble animal, take the liveliest interest; nor can any bullfighting habit ever reconcile them to his sufferings and ill-treatment. The hearts of the *picadors* are as devoid of feeling as their iron-cased legs; they only think of themselves, and have a nice tact in knowing when a wound is fatal or not. Accordingly, if the horn-thrust has touched a vital part, no sooner has the enemy passed on to a new victim, than an experienced *picador* quietly dismounts, takes off the saddle and bridle, and hobbles off like Richard, calling out for another horse—a horse! The poor animal, when stripped of these accoutrements, has a most rippish look, as it staggers to and fro, like a drunken man, until again attacked by the bull and prostrated; then it lies dying unnoticed in the sand, or, if observed, merely rouses the jeers of the mob; as its tail quivers in the last agony of death, your attention is called to the fun; *Mira, mira, que cola!* The words and sight yet haunt us, for they were those that first caught our inexperienced ears and eyes at the first rush of the first bull of our first bullfight. While gazing on the scene in a total abstraction from the world, we felt our coat-tails tugged at, as by a greedily-biting pike; we had caught, or, rather, were caught by a venerable harridan, whose quick perception had discovered a novice, whom her kindness prompted to instruct, for e'en in the ashes live the wonted fires; a bright, fierce eye gleamed alive in a dead and shrivelled face, which evil passions had furrowed like the lava-seared sides of an extinct volcano, and dried up, like a cat starved behind a wainscot, into a thing of fur and bones, in which gender was obliterated—let her pass. . . .

The bull is the hero of the scene; yet, like Satan in the *Paradise Lost*, he is foredoomed. Nothing can save him from a certain fate, which awaits all, whether brave or cowardly. The poor creatures sometimes endeavour in vain to escape, and have favourite retreats, to which they fly; or they leap over the barrier, among the spectators, creating a vast hubbub and fun, upsetting water-carriers and fancy men, putting sentinels and old women to flight, and affording infinite delight to all who are safe in the boxes; for, as Bacon remarks, "It is pleasant to see a battle from a distant hill." Bulls which exhibit this cowardlike activity are insulted: cries of *"fuego"* and *"perros,"* fire and dogs, resound, and he is condemned to be baited. As the Spanish dogs have by no means the pluck of the English assailants of bulls, they are longer at the work, and many are made minced-meat of:

> "Up to the stars the growling mastiffs fly
> And add new monsters to the frighted sky."

When at length the poor brute is pulled down, he is stabbed in the spine, as if he were only fit for the shambles, being a civilian ox, not a soldierlike bull. All these processes are considered as deadly insults; and when more than one bull exhibits these craven propensities to baulk nobler expectancies, then is raised the cry of *"Cabestros al circo!"* tame oxen to the circus. This is a mortal affront to the *empresa,* or management, as it implies that it has furnished animals fitter for the plough than for the arena. The indignation of the mob is terrible; for, if disappointed in the blood of bulls, it will lap that of men.

The bull is sometimes teased with stuffed figures, men of straw with leaded feet, which rise up again as soon as he knocks them down. An old author relates that in the time of Philip IV "a despicable peasant was occasionally set upon a lean horse, and exposed to death." At other times, to amuse the populace, a monkey is tied to a pole in the arena. This art of ingeniously tormenting is considered as unjustifiable homicide by certain lively philosimious foreigners; and, indeed, all these episodes are despised as irregular hors d'oeuvres, by the real and businesslike amateur.

After a due time the first act terminates: its length is uncertain. Sometimes it is most brilliant, since one bull has been known to kill a dozen horses, and clear the plaza. Then he is adored; and as he roams, snorting about, lord of all he surveys, he becomes the sole object of worship to ten thousand devotees; at the signal of the president, and sound of a trumpet, the second act commences with the performances of the *chulo,* a word which signifies, in the Arabic, a lad, a merryman, as at our fairs. The duty of this light division, these skirmishers, is to draw off the bull from the *picador* when endangered, which they do with their coloured cloaks; their address and agility are surprising, they skim over the sand like glittering humming-birds, scarcely touching the earth. They are dressed in short breeches, and without gaiters, just as Figaro is in the opera of the "Barbiere de Seviglia." Their hair is tied into a knot behind, and enclosed in the once universal silk net, the *redecilla*—the identical reticulum—of which so many instances are seen on ancient Etruscan vases. No bull-fighters ever arrive at the top of their profession without first excelling in this apprenticeship; then, they are taught how to entice the bull to them, and learn his mode of attack, and how to parry it. The most dangerous moment is when these *chulos* venture out into the middle of the plaza, and are followed by the bull to the barrier. There is a small ledge, on which they place their foot, and vault over, and a narrow slit in the boarding, through which they slip. Their escapes are marvellous, and they win by a neck; they seem really sometimes, so close is the run, to be helped over the fence by the bull's horns. The *chulos,* in the second act, are the sole performers; their part is to place small barbed darts, on each side of the neck of the bull, which are called *banderillas,* and are ornamented with cut paper of different colours—gay decorations under which cruelty is concealed. The *banderilleros* go right up to him, holding the arrows at the shaft, and pointing the barbs at the bull; just when the animal stoops to toss his foes, they jerk them into his neck and slip aside. The service appears to be more dangerous than it is, but it requires a quick eye, a light hand and foot. The barbs should be placed to correspond with each other exactly on both sides. Such pretty pairs are termed *buenos pares* by the Spaniards, and the feat is called *coiffer le taureau* by the French, who undoubtedly are first-rate perruquiers. Very often these arrows are provided with crackers, which, by means of a detonating powder, explode the moment they are affixed in the neck; thence they are called *banderillas de fuego.* The agony of the scorched and tortured animal makes him plunge and bound like a sportive lamb, to the intense joy of the populace, while the fire, the smell of singed hair and roasted flesh, which our gastronome neighbours would call a *bifstec à l'Espagnole,* faintly recall to many a dark scowling priest the superior attractions of his former amphitheatre, the auto-da-fé.

The last trumpet now sounds, the arena is cleared, and the *matador,* the executioner, the man of death, stands before his victim alone; on entering, he addresses the president, and throws his cap to the ground. In his right hand he holds a long straight Toledan blade; in his left he waves the *muleta,* the red flag, or the *engaño,* the lure, which ought not (so Romero laid down in our hearing) to be so large as the standard of a religious brotherhood, nor so small as a lady's pocket-handkerchief, but about a yard square. The colour is always red, because that best irritates the bull and conceals blood. There is always a spare slayer at hand in case of accidents, which may happen in the best regulated bullfights.

The *matador,* from being alone, concentrates in himself all the interest as regards the human species, which was before frittered away among the many other combatants, as was the case in the ancient gladiatorial shows of Rome. He advances to the bull, in order to entice him towards him, or, in nice technical idiom, *citarlo a la jurisdicción del engaño,* to cite him into the jurisdiction of the trick; in plain English, to subpoena him, or, as our ring would say, get his head into chancery. And this trial is nearly as awful, as the *matador* stands confronted with his foe, in the presence of inexorable witnesses, the bar and judges, who would rather see the bull kill him twice over, than that he should kill the bull contrary to the rules and practice of the court and tauromachian precedent. In these brief but trying moments the *matador* generally looks pale and anxious, as well he may, for life hangs on the edge of a razor, but he presents a fine picture of fixed purpose and concentration of moral energy. And Seneca said truly that the world had seen as many examples of courage in gladiators, as in the Catos and Scipios.

The *matador* endeavours rapidly to discover the character of the animal, and examines with eye keener than Spurzheim, his bumps of combativeness, destructiveness, and other amiable organs; nor has he many moments to lose, where mistake is fatal, as one must die, and both may. Here, as Falstaff says, there is no scoring, except on the pate. Often even the brute bull seems to feel that the last moment is come, and pauses, when face to face in the deadly duel with his single opponent. Be that as it may, the contrast is very striking. The slayer is arrayed in a ball costume, with no buckler but skill, and as if it were a pastime: he is all coolness, the beast all rage; and time it is to be collected, for now indeed knowledge is power, and could the beast reason, the man would have small chance. Meanwhile the spectators are wound up to a greater pitch of madness than the poor bull, who has undergone a long torture, besides continued excitement: he at this instant becomes a study for a Paul Potter; his eyes flash fire—his inflated nostrils snort fury; his body is covered with sweat and foam, or crimsoned with a glaze of gore streaming from gaping wounds. *"Mira! que bello cuerpo de sangre!*—look! what a beauteous body of blood!" exclaimed the worthy old lady, who, as we before mentioned, was kind enough to point out to our inexperience the tit bits of the treat, the pearls of greatest price.

There are several sorts of *toros,* whose characters vary no less than those of men: some are brave and dashing, others are slow and heavy, others sly and cowardly. The *matador* foils and plays with the bull until he has discovered his disposition. The fundamental principle consists in the animal's mode of attack, the stooping his head and shutting his eyes, before he butts; the secret of mastering him lies in distinguishing whether he acts on the offensive or defensive. Those which are fearless, and rush boldly on at once, closing their eyes, are the most easy to kill; those which are cunning—which seldom go straight when they charge, but stop, dodge, and run at the man, not the flag, are the most dangerous. The interest of the spectators increases in proportion as the peril is great.

Although fatal accidents do not often occur (and we ourselves have never seen a man killed, yet we have beheld some hundred bulls despatched), such events are always possible. At Tudela, a bull having killed seventeen horses, a *picador* named Blanco, and a *banderillero,* then leapt over the barriers, where he gored to death a peasant, and wounded many others. The newspapers simply headed the statement, "Accidents have happened." Pepe Illo, who had received thirty-eight wounds in the wars, died, like Nelson, the hero's death. He was killed on the 11th of May, 1801. He had a presentiment of his death, but said that he must do his duty.

Every *matador* must be quick and decided. He must not let the bull run at the flag above two or three times; the moral tension of the multitudes is too strained to endure a longer suspense; they vent their impatience in jeers, noises, and endeavour by every possible manner to irritate him, and make him lose his temper, and perhaps life. Under such circumstances, Manuel Romero, who had murdered a man, was always saluted with cries of *"A la Plaza de Cebada*—to Tyburn." The populace absolutely loathe those who show the smallest white feather, or do not brave death cheerfully.

There are many ways of killing the bull: the principal is when the *matador* receives him on his sword when charging; then the weapon, which is held still and never thrust forward, enters just between the left shoulder and the blade-bone; a firm hand, eye, and nerve, are essential, since in nothing is the real fancy so fastidious as in the exact nicety of the placing this death-wound. The bull very often is not killed at the first effort; if not true, the sword strikes a bone, and then it is ejected high in air by the rising neck. When the blow is true, death is instantaneous, and the bull, vomiting forth blood, drops at the feet of his conqueror. It is indeed the triumph of knowledge over brute force; all that was fire, fury, passion, and life, falls in an instant, still for ever. The gay team of mules now enter, glittering with flags, and tinkling with bells; the dead bull is carried off at a rapid gallop, which always delights the populace. The *matador* then wipes the hot blood from his sword, and bows to the spectators with admirable sang froid, who fling their hats into the arena, a compliment which he returns by throwing them back again (they are generally "shocking bad" ones); when Spain was rich, a golden, or at least a silver shower was rained down—*ces beaux jours là sont passés;* thanks to her kind neighbour. The poverty-stricken Spaniard, however, gives all he can, and lets the bullfighter dream the rest. As hats in Spain represent grandeeship, so these beavers, part and parcel of themselves, are given as symbols of their generous hearts and souls; and none but a huckster would go into minute details of value or condition. . . .

Such is a single bullfight; each of which is repeated eight times with succeeding bulls, the excitement of the multitude rising with each indulgence; after a short collapse new desires are roused by fresh objects, the fierce sport is renewed, which night alone can extinguish; nay, often when royalty is present, a ninth bull is clamoured for, which is always graciously granted by the nominal monarch's welcome sign, the pulling his royal ear; in truth here the mob is autocrat, and his majesty the many will take no denial; the bullfight terminates when the day dies like a dolphin, and the curtain of heaven hung over the bloody show, is incarnadined and crimsoned; this glorious finish is seen in full perfection at Seville, where the plaza from being unfinished is open toward the cathedral, which furnishes a Moorish distance to the picturesque foreground. On particular occasions this side is decorated with flags. When the blazing sun setting on the red Giralda tower, lights up its fair proportions like a pillar of fire, the refreshing evening breeze springs up, and the flagging banners wave in triumph over the concluding spectacle; then when all is come to an end, as all things human must, the congregation depart, with rather less decorum than if quitting a church; all hasten to sacrifice the rest of the night to Bacchus and Venus, with a passing homage to the knife, should critics differ too hotly on the merits of some particular thrust of the bullfight.

To conclude; the minds of men, like the House of Commons in 1802, are divided on the merits of the bullfight; the Wilberforces assert (especially foreigners, who, notwithstanding, seldom fail to sanction the arena by their presence) that all the best feelings are blunted—that idleness, extravagance, cruelty, and ferocity are promoted at a vast expense of human and animal life by these pastimes; the Windhams contend that loyalty, courage, presence of mind, endurance of pain, and contempt of death, are inculcated—that, while the theatre is all illusion, the opera all effeminacy, these manly, national games are all truth, and in the words of a native eulogist "elevate the soul to those grandiose actions of valour and heroism which have long proved the Spaniards to be the best and bravest of all nations. . . ."

The Spaniards invariably bring forward our boxing-matches in self-justification, as if a *tu quoque* could be so; but it must always be remembered in our excuse that these are discountenanced by the good and respectable, and legally stigmatised as breaches of the peace; although disgraced by beastly drunkenness, brutal vulgarity, ruinous gambling and betting, from which the Spanish arena is exempt, as no bull yet has been backed to kill so many horses or not; our matches, however, are based on a spirit of fair play which forms no principle of the Punic politics, warfare, or bullfighting of Spain. The Plaza there is patronised by church and state, to whom, in justice, the responsibility of evil consequences must be referred. The show is conducted with great ceremonial, combining many elements of poetry, the beautiful and sublime; insomuch that a Spanish author proudly says: "When the countless assembly is honoured by the presence of our august monarchs, the world is lost in admiration at the majestic spectacle afforded by the happiest people in the world, enjoying with rapture an exhibition peculiarly their own, and offering to their idolised sovereigns the due homage of the truest and most refined loyalty;" and it is impossible to deny the magnificent *coup d'oeil* of the assembled thousands. Under such conflicting circumstances, we turn away our eyes during moments of painful detail which are lost in the poetical ferocity of the whole, for the interest of the tragedy of real death is undeniable, irresistible, and all absorbing.

The Spaniards seem almost unconscious of the cruelty of those details which are most offensive to a stranger. They are reconciled by habit, as we are to the bleeding butchers' shops which disfigure our gay streets, and which if seen for the first time would be inexpressibly disgusting. The feeling of the chase, that remnant of the savage, rules in the arena, and mankind has never been nice or tender-hearted in regard to the sufferings of animals, when influenced by the destructive propensities. In England no sympathy is shown for game,—fish, flesh, or fowl; nor for vermin—stoats, kites, or poachers. The end of the sport is—death; the amusement is the playing, the fine run, as the prolongation of animal suffering is termed in the tender vocabulary of the Nimrods; the pang of mortal sufferance is not regulated by the size of the victim; the bull moreover is always put at once out of his misery, and never exposed to the thousand lingering deaths of the poor wounded hare; therefore we must not see a *toro* in Spanish eyes and wink at the fox in our own, nor

> "Compound for vices we're inclined to
> By damning those we have no mind to."

It is not clear that animal suffering on the whole predominates over animal happiness. The bull roams in ample pastures, through a youth and manhood free from toil, and when killed in the plaza only anticipates by a few months the certain fate of the imprisoned, over-laboured, mutilated ox.

In Spain, where capital is scanty, person and property insecure (evils not quite corrected since the late democratic reforms), no one would adventure on the speculation of breeding cattle on a large scale, where the return is so distant, without the certain demand and sale created by the amphitheatre; and as a small proportion only of the produce possess the requisite qualifications, the surplus and females go to the plough and market, and can be sold cheaper from the profit made on the bulls. Spanish political economists proved that many valuable animals were wasted in the arena—but their theories vanished before the fact, that the supply of cattle was rapidly diminished when bullfights were suppressed. Similar results take place as regards the breed of horses, though in a minor degree; those, moreover, which are sold to the Plaza would never be bought by any one else. With respect to the loss of human life, in no land is a man worth so little as in Spain; and more English aldermen are killed indirectly by turtles, than Andalusian *picadors* directly by bulls; while, as to time, these exhibitions always take place on holidays, which even industrious Britons horse away occasionally in pothouses, and idle Spaniards invariably smoke out in sunshiny *dolce far niente*. The attendance, again, of idle spectators prevents idleness in the numerous classes employed directly and indirectly in getting up and carrying out this expensive spectacle.

It is poor and illogical philosophy to judge of foreign customs by our own habits, prejudices, and conventional opinions; a cold, unprepared, calculating stranger comes without the freemasonry of early associations, and criticises minutiae which are lost on the natives in their enthusiasm and feeling for the whole. He is horrified by details to which the Spaniards have become as accustomed as hospital nurses, whose finer sympathetic emotions of pity are deadened by repetition.

A most difficult thing it is to change long-established usages and customs with which we are familiar from our early days, and which have come down to us connected with many fond remembrances. We are slow to suspect any evil or harm in such practices; we dislike to look the evidence of facts in the face, and shrink from a conclusion which would require the abandonment of a recreation, which we have long regarded as innocent, and in which we, as well as our parents before us, have not scrupled to indulge. Children, *l'age sans pitié,* do not speculate on cruelty, whether in bull-baiting or bird's-nesting, and Spaniards are brought up to the bullfight from their infancy, when they are too simple to speculate on abstract questions, but associate with the Plaza all their ideas of reward for good conduct, of finery and holiday; in a land where amusements are few—they catch the contagion of pleasure, and in their young bias of imitation approve of what is approved of by their parents. They return to their homes unchanged—playful, timid, or serious, as before; their kindly, social feelings are uninjured: and where is the filial or parental bond more affectionately cherished than in Spain—where are the noble courtesies of life, the kind, considerate, self-respecting demeanour so exemplified as in Spanish society?

The successive feelings experienced by most foreigners are admiration, compassion, and weariness of the flesh. The first will be readily understood, as it will that the horses' sufferings cannot be beheld by novices without compassion: "In troth it was more a pittie than a delight," wrote the herald of Lord Nottingham. This feeling, however, regards the animals who are forced into wounds and death; the men scarcely excite much of it, since they willingly court the danger, and have therefore no right to complain. These heroes of low life are applauded, well paid, and their risk is more apparent than real; our British feelings of fair play make us side rather with the poor bull who is overmatched; we respect the gallantry of his unequal defence. Such must always be the effect produced on those not bred and brought up to such scenes. So Livy relates that, when the gladiatorial shows were first introduced by the Romans into Asia, the natives were more frightened than pleased, but by leading them on from sham-fights to real, they became as fond of them as the Romans. The predominant sensation experienced by ourselves was bore, the same thing over and over again, and too much of it. But that is the case with everything in Spain, where processions and professions are interminable. The younger Pliny, who was no amateur, complained of the eternal sameness of seeing what to have seen once, was enough; just as Dr. Johnson, when he witnessed a horse race, observed that he had not met with such a proof of the paucity of human pleasures as in the popularity of such a spectacle. But the life of Spaniards is uniform, and their sensations, not being blunted by satiety, are intense. Their bullfight to them is always new and exciting, since the more the toresque intellect is cultivated the greater the capacity for enjoyment; they see a thousand minute beauties in the character and conduct of the combatants, which escape the superficial unlearned glance of the uninitiated.

Spanish ladies, against whom every puny scribbler shoots his petty barbed arrow, are relieved from the infliction of ennui, by the never-flagging, ever-sustained interest, in being admired. They have no abstract nor Pasiphaic predilections; they were taken to the bullfight before they knew their alphabet, or what love was. Nor have we heard that it has even rendered them particularly cruel, save and except some of the elderly and tougher lower-classed females. The younger and more tender scream and are dreadfully affected in all real moments of danger, in spite of their long familiarity. Their grand object, after all, is not to see the bull, but to let themselves and their dresses be seen. The better classes generally interpose their fans at the most painful incidents, and certainly show no want of sensibility. The lower order of females, as a body, behave quite as respectably as those of other countries do at executions, or other dreadful scenes, where they crowd with their babies. The case with English ladies is far different. They have heard the bullfight not praised from their childhood, but condemned; they see it for the first time when grown up; curiosity is perhaps their leading feature in sharing an amusement, of which they have an indistinct idea that pleasure will be mixed with pain. The first sight delights them; a flushed, excited cheek, betrays a feeling that they are almost ashamed to avow; but as the bloody tragedy proceeds, they get frightened, disgusted, and disappointed. Few are able to sit out more than one course, and fewer ever re-enter the amphitheatre:

"The heart that is soonest awake to the flower
Is always the first to be touched by the thorn."

Probably a Spanish woman, if she could be placed in precisely the same condition, would not act very differently, and something of a similar test would be to bring her, for the first time, to an English boxing match. . . .

Montes, the Matador

by FRANK HARRIS

Frank Harris, 1856–1931, was a naturalized American of Irish birth who was a highly controversial writer and editor in the early era of this century. He lived for years in Europe, writing rather scabrously about the celebrities of his time, including himself. But he was a versatile fellow, and produced some interesting fiction, volumes of short stories and novels. His short story, "Montes, the Matador," is well known in Spain.

"Yes! I'm better, and the doctor tells me I've escaped once more—as if I cared! . . . And all through the fever you came every day to see me, so my niece says, and brought me the cool drink that drove the heat away and gave me sleep. You thought, I suppose, like the doctor, that I'd escape you, too. Ha! ha! And that you'd never hear old Montes tell what he knows of bullfighting and you don't. . . . Or perhaps it was kindness; though, why you, a foreigner and a heretic, should be kind to me, God knows. . . . The doctor says I've not got much more life in me, and you're going to leave Spain within the week—within the week, you said, didn't you? . . . Well, then, I don't mind telling you the story.

"Thirty years ago I wanted to tell it often enough, but I knew no one I could trust. After that fit passed, I said to myself I'd never tell it; but as you're going away, I'll tell it to you, if you swear by the Virgin you'll never tell it to any one, at least until I'm dead. You'll swear, will you? easily enough! they all will; but as you're going away, it's much the same. Besides, you can do nothing now; no one can do anything; they never could have done anything. Why, they wouldn't believe you if you told it to them, the fools! . . . My story will teach you more about bullfighting than "Frascuelo" or Mazzantini, or—yes, "Lagartijo" knows. Weren't there Frascuelos and Mazzantinis in my day? Dozens of them. You could pick one Frascuelo out of every thousand labourers if you gave him the training and the practice, and could keep him away from wine and women. But a Montes is not to be found every day, if you searched all Spain for one. . . . What's the good of bragging? I never bragged when I was at work: the deed talks— louder than any words. Yet I think, no one has ever done the things I used to do; for I read in a paper once an account of a thing I often did, and the writer said 'twas incredible. Ha, ha! incredible to the "Frascuelos" and Mazzantinis and the rest who can kill bulls and are called *espadas*. Oh, yes! bulls so tired out they can't lift their heads. You didn't guess when you were telling me about "Frascuelo" and Mazzantini that I knew them. I knew all about both of them before you told me. I know their work, though I've not been within sight of a ring for more than thirty years. . . . Well, I'll tell you my story: I'll tell you my story—if I can."

The old man said the last words as if to himself in a low voice, then sank back in the armchair, and for a time was silent.

Let me say a word or two about myself and the circumstances which led me to seek out Montes.

I had been in Spain off and on a good deal, and from the first had taken a great liking to the people and country; and no one can love Spain and the Spaniards without becoming interested in the bullring—the sport is so characteristic of the people, and in itself so enthralling. I set myself to study it in earnest, and when I came to know the best bullfighters, "Frascuelo," Mazzantini and "Lagartijo," and heard them talk of their trade, I began to understand what skill and courage, what qualities of eye and hand and heart, this game demands. Through my love of the sport, I came to hear of Montes. He had left so great a name that thirty years after he had disappeared from the scene of his triumphs, he was still spoken of not infrequently. He would perhaps have been better remembered, had the feats attributed to him been less astounding. It was "Frascuelo" who told me that Montes was still alive:

"Montes," he cried out in answer to me, "I can tell you about Montes. You mean the old *espada* who, they say, used to kill the bull in its first rush into the ring—as if any one could do that! I can tell you about him. He must have been clever; for an old aficionado I know, swears no one of us is fit to be in his *cuadrilla*. Those old fellows are all like that, and I don't believe half they tell about Montes. I dare say he was good enough in his day, but there are just as good men now as ever there were. When I was in Ronda, four years ago, I went to see Montes. He lives out of the town in a nice little house all alone, with one woman to attend to him, a niece of his, they say. You know he was born in Ronda; but he would not talk to me; he only looked at me and laughed—the little, lame, conceited one!"

"You don't believe then, in spite of what they say, that he was better than "Lagartijo" or Mazzantini?" I asked.

"No, I don't," "Frascuelo" replied. "Of course, he may have known more than they do; that wouldn't be difficult, for neither of them knows much. Mazzantini is a good *matador* because he's very tall and strong—that's his advantage. For that, too, the women like him, and when he makes a mistake and has to try again, he gets forgiven. It wasn't so when I began. There were aficionados then, and if you made a mistake they began to jeer, and you were soon pelted out of the ring. Now the crowd knows nothing and is no longer content to follow those who do know. "Lagartijo?" Oh! he's very quick and daring, and the women and boys like that, too. But he's ignorant: he knows nothing about a bull. Why, he's been wounded oftener in his five years than I in my twenty. And that's a pretty good test. Montes must have been clever; for he's very small and I shouldn't think he was ever very strong, and then he was lame almost from the beginning, I've heard. I've no doubt he could teach the business to Mazzantini or 'Lagartijo,' but that's not saying much. . . . He must have made a lot of money, too, to be able to live on it ever since. And they didn't pay as high then or even when I began as they do now."

So much I knew about Montes when, in the spring of 188–, I rode from Seville to Ronda, fell in love with the place at first sight, and resolved to stop at Polos' inn for some time. Ronda is built, so to speak, upon an island tableland high above the sea-level, and is ringed about by still higher mountain ranges. It is one of the most peculiar and picturesque places in the world. A river runs almost all round it; and the sheer cliffs fall in many places three or four hundred feet, from the tableland to the water, like a wall. No wonder that the Moors held Ronda after they had lost every other foot of ground in Spain. Taking Ronda as my headquarters I made almost daily excursions, chiefly on foot, into the surrounding mountains. On one of these I heard again of Montes. A peasant with whom I had been talking and who was showing me a short cut back to the town, suddenly stopped and said, pointing to a little hut perched on the mountain-shoulder in front of us, "From that house you can see Ronda. That's the house where Montes, the great *matador*, was born," he added, evidently with some pride. Then and there the conversation with "Frascuelo" came back to my memory, and I made up my mind to find Montes out and have a talk with him. I went to his house, which lay just outside the town, next day with the alcalde, who introduced me to him and then left us. The first sight of the man interested me. He was short—about five feet three or four, I should think—of well-knit, muscular frame. He seemed to me to have Moorish blood in him. His complexion was very dark and tanned; the features clean-cut; the nose sharp and inquisitive; the nostrils astonishingly mobile; the chin and jaws square, boney—resolute. His hair and thick moustache were snow white, and this, together with the deep wrinkles on the forehead and round the eyes and mouth, gave him an appearance of great age. He seemed to move, too, with extreme difficulty, his lameness, as he afterwards told me, being complicated with rheumatism. But when one looked at his eyes, the appearance of age vanished. They were large and brown, usually inexpressive, or rather impenetrable, brooding wells of unknown depths. But when anything excited him, the eyes would suddenly flash to life and become intensely luminous. The effect was startling. It seemed as if all the vast vitality of the man had been transmuted into those wonderful gleaming orbs: they radiated courage, energy, intellect. Then as his mood changed, the light would die out of the eyes, and the old, wizened, wrinkled face would settle down into its ordinary, ill-tempered, wearied expression. There was evidently so much in the man—courage, melancholy, keen intelligence —that in spite of an anything but flattering reception I returned again and again to the house. One day his niece told me that Montes was in bed, and from her description I inferred that he was suffering from an attack of malarial fever. The doctor who attended him, and whom I knew, confirmed this. Naturally enough I did what I could for the sufferer, and so it came about that after his recovery he received me with kindness, and at last made up his mind to tell me the story of his life.

"I may as well begin at the beginning," Montes went on. "I was born near here about sixty years ago. You thought I was older. Don't deny it. I saw the surprise in your face. But it's true: in fact, I am not yet, I think, quite sixty. My father was a peasant with a few acres of land of his own and a cottage."

"I know it," I said. "I saw it the other day."

"Then you may have seen on the further side of the hill the pasture-ground for cattle which was my father's chief possession. It was good pasture; very good. . . . My mother was of a better class than my father; she was the daughter of the chemist in Ronda; she could read and write, and she did read, I remember, whenever she could get the chance, which wasn't often, with her four children to take care of—three girls and a boy—and the house to look after. We all loved her, she was so gentle; besides, she told us wonderful stories; but I think I was her favourite. You see I was the youngest and a boy, and women are like that. My father was hard—at least, I thought him so, and feared rather than loved him; but the girls got on better with him. He never talked to me as he did to them. My mother wanted me to go to school and become a priest; she had taught me to read and write by the time I was six. But my father would not hear of it. 'If you had had three boys and one girl,' I remember him saying to her once, 'you could have done what you liked with this one. But as there is only one boy, he must work and help me.' So by the time I was nine I used to go off down to the pasture and watch the bulls all day long. For though the herd was a small one—only about twenty head—it required to be constantly watched. The cows were attended to in an enclosure close to the house. It was my task to mind the bulls in the lower pasture. Of course I had a pony, for such bulls in Spain are seldom approached, and cannot be driven by a man on foot. I see you don't understand. But it's simple enough. My father's bulls were of good stock, savage and strong; they were always taken for the ring, and he got high prices for them. He generally managed to sell three *novillos* and two bulls of four years old each year. And there was no bargaining, no trouble; the money was always ready for that class of animal. All day long I sat on my pony, or stood near it, minding the bulls. If any of them strayed too far, I had to go and get him back again. But in the heat of the day they never moved about much, and that time I turned to use by learning the lessons my mother gave me. So a couple of years passed. Of course in that time I got to know our bulls pretty well; but it was a remark of my father which first taught me that each bull had an individual character and first set me to watch them closely. I must have been then about twelve years old; and in that summer I learned more than in the two previous years. My father, though he said nothing to me, must have noticed that I had gained confidence in dealing with the bulls; for one night, when I was in bed, I heard him say to my mother—'The little fellow is as good as a man now.' I was proud of his praise, and from that time on, I set to work to learn everything I could about the bulls.

"By degrees I came to know every one of them—better far than I ever got to know men or women later. Bulls, I found, were just like men, only simpler and kinder; some were good-tempered and honest, others were sulky and cunning. There was a black one which was wild and hot-tempered, but at bottom good, while there was one almost as black, with light horns and flanks, which I never trusted. The other bulls didn't like him. I could see they didn't; they were all afraid of him. He was cunning and suspicious, and never made friends with any of them; he would always eat by himself far away from the others—but he had courage, too; I knew that as well as they did. He was sold that very summer with the black one for the ring in Ronda. One Sunday night, when my father and eldest sister (my mother would never go to *los toros*) came back from seeing the game in Ronda, they were wild with excitement, and began to tell the mother how one of our bulls had caught the *matador* and tossed him, and how the *chulos* could scarcely get the *matador* away. Then I cried out—'I know; 'twas Judas' (so I had christened him), and as I saw my father's look of surprise I went on confusedly, 'the bull with the white horns I mean. Juan, the black one, wouldn't have been clever enough.' My father only said, 'The boy's right'; but my mother drew me to her and kissed me, as if she were afraid. . . . Poor mother! I think even then she knew or divined something of what came to pass later. . . .

"It was the next summer, I think, that my father first found out how much I knew about the bulls. It happened in this way. There hadn't been much rain in the spring, the pasture, therefore, was thin, and that, of course, made the bulls restless. In the summer the weather was unsettled—spells of heat and then thunderstorms—till the animals became very excitable. One day, there was thunder in the air I remember, they gave me a great deal of trouble and that annoyed me, for I wanted to read. I had got to a very interesting tale in the story-book my mother had given me on the day our bulls were sold. The story was about Cervantes—ah, you know who I mean, the great writer. Well, he was a great man, too. The story told how he escaped from the prison over there in Algiers and got back to Cádiz, and how a widow came to him to find out if he knew her son, who was also a slave of the Moors. And when she heard that Cervantes had seen her son working in chains, she bemoaned her wretchedness and ill-fortune, till the heart of the great man melted with pity, and he said to her, 'Come, mother, be hopeful, in one month your son shall be here with you.' And then the book told how Cervantes went back to slavery, and how glad the Bey was to get him again, for he was very clever; and how he asked the Bey, as he had returned of his free will, to send the widow's son home in his stead; and the Bey consented. That Cervantes was a man! . . . Well, I was reading the story, and I believed every word of it, as I do still, for no ordinary person could invent that sort of tale; and I grew very much excited and wanted to know all about Cervantes. But as I could only read slowly and with difficulty, I was afraid the sun would go down before I could get to the end. While I was reading as hard as ever I could, my father came down on foot and caught me. He hated to see me reading—I don't know why; and he was angry and struck at me. As I avoided the blow and got away from him, he pulled up the picket line, and got on my pony to drive one of the bulls back to the herd. I have thought since, he must have been very much annoyed before he came down and caught me. For though he knew a good deal about bulls, he didn't show it then. My pony was too weak to carry him easily, yet he acted as if he had been well mounted. For as I said, the bulls were hungry and excited, and my father should have seen this and driven the bull back quietly and with great patience. But no; he wouldn't let him feed even for a moment. At last the bull turned on him. My father held the goad fairly against his neck, but the bull came on just the same, and the pony could scarcely get out of the way in time. In a moment the bull turned and prepared to rush at him again. My father sat still on the little pony and held the goad; but I knew that was no use; he knew it too; but he was angry and wouldn't give in. At once I ran in between him and the bull, and then called to the bull, and went slowly up to him where he was shaking his head and pawing the ground. He was very angry, but he knew the difference between us quite well, and he let me come close to him without rushing at me, and then just shook his head to show me he was still angry, and soon began to feed quietly. In a moment or two I left him and went back to my father. He had got off the pony and was white and trembling, and he said,

"'Are you hurt?'

"And I said laughing, 'No: he didn't want to hurt me. He was only showing off his temper.'

"And my father said, 'There's not a man in all Spain that could have done that! You know more than I do—more than anybody.'

"After that he let me do as I liked, and the next two years were very happy ones. First came the marriage of my second sister; then the eldest one was married, and they were both good matches. And the bulls sold well, and my father had less to do, as I could attend to the whole herd by myself. Those were two good years. My mother seemed to love me more and more every day, or I suppose I noticed it more, and she praised me for doing the lessons she gave me; and I had more and more time to study as the herd got to know me better and better.

"My only trouble was that I had never seen the bulls in the ring. But when I found my father was willing to take me, and 'twas mother who wanted me not to go, I put up with that, too, and said nothing, for I loved her greatly. Then of a sudden came the sorrow. It was in the late winter, just before my fifteenth birthday. I was born in March, I think. In January my mother caught cold, and as she grew worse my father fetched the doctor, and then her father and mother came to see her, but nothing did any good. In April she died. I wanted to die too.

"After her death my father took to grumbling about the food and house and everything. Nothing my sister could do was right. I believe she only married in the summer because she couldn't stand his constant blame. At any rate she married badly, a good-for-nothing who had twice her years, and who ill-treated her continually. A month or two later my father, who must have been fifty, married again, a young woman, a labourer's daughter without a *duro*. He told me he was going to do it, for the house needed a woman. I suppose he was right. But I was too young then to take such things into consideration, and I had loved my mother. When I saw his new wife I did not like her, and we did not get on well together.

"Before this, however, early in the summer that followed the death of my mother, I went for the first time to see a bullfight. My father wanted me to go, and my sister, too; so I went. I shall never forget that day. The *chulos* made me laugh, they skipped about so and took such extra-good care of themselves; but the *banderilleros* interested me. Their work required skill and courage, that I saw at once; but after they had planted the *banderillas* twice, I knew how it was done, and felt I could do it just as well or better. For the third or fourth *banderillero* made a mistake! He didn't even know with which horn the bull was going to strike; so he got frightened, and did not plant the *banderillas* fairly—in fact, one was on the side of the shoulder and the other didn't even stick in. As for the *picadors,* they didn't interest me at all. There was no skill or knowledge in their work. It was for the crowd, who like to see blood and who understand nothing. Then came the turn of the *espada.* Ah! that seemed splendid to me. He knew his work I thought at first, and his work evidently required knowledge, skill, courage, strength—everything. I was intensely excited, and when the bull, struck to the heart, fell prone on his knees, and the blood gushed from his nose and mouth, I cheered and cheered till I was hoarse. But before the games were over, that very first day, I saw more than one *matador* make a mistake. At first I thought I must be wrong, but soon the event showed I was right. For the *matador* hadn't even got the bull to stand square when he tried his stroke and failed. You don't know what that means—'to stand square.' "

"I do partly," I replied, "but I don't see the reason of it. Will you explain?"

"It's very simple," Montes answered. "So long as the bull's standing with one hoof in front of the other, his shoulder-blades almost meet, just as when you throw your arms back and your chest out; they don't meet, of course, but the space between them is not as regular, and, therefore, not as large as it is when their front hooves are square. The space between the shoulder-blades is none too large at any time, for you have to strike with force to drive the sword through the inch-thick hide, and through a foot of muscle, sinew, and flesh besides to the heart. Nor is the stroke a straight one. Then, too, there's always the backbone to avoid. And the space between the backbone and the nearest thick gristle of the shoulder-blade is never more than an inch and a half. So if you narrow this space by even half an inch you increase your difficulty immensely. And that's not your object. Well, all this I've been telling you, I divined at once. Therefore, when I saw the bull wasn't standing quite square, I knew the *matador* was either a bungler or else very clever and strong indeed. In a moment he proved himself to be a bungler, for his sword turned on the shoulder-blade, and the bull, throwing up his head, almost caught him on his horns. Then I hissed and cried, 'Shame!' And the people stared at me. That butcher tried five times before he killed the bull, and at last even the most ignorant of the spectators knew I had been right in hissing him. He was one of your Mazzantinis, I suppose."

"Oh, no!" I replied, "I've seen Mazzantini try twice, but never five times. That's too much!"

"Well," Montes continued quietly, "the man who tries once and fails ought never to be allowed in a ring again. But to go on. That first day taught me I could be an *espada*. The only doubt in my mind was in regard to the nature of the bulls. Should I be able to understand new bulls— bulls, too, from different herds and of different race, as well as I understood our bulls? Going home that evening I tried to talk to my father, but he thought the sport had been very good, and when I wanted to show him the mistakes the *matadors* had made, he laughed at me, and, taking hold of my arm, he said, 'Here's where you need the gristle before you could kill a bull with a sword, even if he were tied for you.' My father was very proud of his size and strength, but what he said had reason in it, and made me doubt myself. Then he talked about the gains of the *matadors*. A fortune, he said, was given for a single day's work. Even the pay of the *chulos* seemed to me to be extravagant, and a *banderillero* got enough to make one rich for life. That night I thought over all I had seen and heard, and fell asleep and dreamt I was an *espada*, the best in Spain, and rich, and married to a lovely girl with golden hair—as boys do dream.

"Next day I set myself to practice with our bulls. First I teased one till he grew angry and rushed at me; then, as a *chulo,* I stepped aside. And after I had practised this several times, I began to try to move aside as late as possible and only just as far as was needful; for I soon found out the play of horn of every bull we had. The older the bull the heavier his neck and shoulders become, and, therefore, the sweep of horns in an old bull is much smaller than a young one's. Before the first morning's sport was over I knew that with our bulls at any rate I could beat any *chulo* I had seen the day before. Then I set myself to quiet the bulls, which was a little difficult, and after I had succeeded I went back to my pony to read and dream. Next day I played at being a *banderillero,* and found out at once that my knowledge of the animal was all important. For I knew always on which side to move to avoid the bull's rush. I knew how he meant to strike by the way he put his head down. To plant the *banderillas* perfectly would have been child's play to me, at least with our bulls. The *matador's* work was harder to practise. I had no sword; besides, the bull I wished to pretend to kill, was not tired and wouldn't keep quiet. Yet I went on trying. The game had a fascination for me. A few days later, provided with a makeshift red *capa,* I got a bull far away from the others. Then I played with him till he was tired out. First I played as a *chulo,* and avoided his rushes by an inch or two only; then, as *banderillero,* I escaped his stroke, and, as I did so, struck his neck with two sticks. When he was tired I approached him with the *capa* and found I could make him do what I pleased, stand crooked or square in a moment, just as I liked. For I learned at once that as a rule the bull rushes at the *capa* and not at the man who holds it. Some bulls, however, are clever enough to charge the man. For weeks I kept up this game, till one day my father expressed his surprise at the thin and wretched appearance of the bulls. No wonder! The pasture ground had been a ring to them and me for many a week.

"After this I had to play *matador*—the only part which had any interest for me—without first tiring them. Then came a long series of new experiences, which in time made me what I was, a real *espada,* but which I can scarcely describe to you.

"For power over wild animals come to a man, as it were, by leaps and bounds. Of a sudden one finds he can make a bull do something which the day before he could not make him do. It is all a matter of intimate knowledge of the nature of the animal. Just as the shepherd, as I've been told, knows the face of each sheep in a flock of a thousand, though I can see no difference between the faces of sheep, which are all alike stupid to me, so I came to know bulls, with a complete understanding of the nature and temper of each one. It's just because I can't tell you how I acquired this part of my knowledge that I was so long-winded in explaining to you my first steps. What I knew more than I have told you, will appear as I go on with my story, and that you must believe or disbelieve as you think best."

"Oh," I cried, "you've explained everything so clearly, and thrown light on so many things I didn't understand, that I shall believe whatever you tell me."

Old Montes went on as if he hadn't heard my protestation:

"The next three years were intolerable to me: my stepmother repaid my dislike with interest and found a hundred ways of making me uncomfortable, without doing anything I could complain of and get altered. In the spring of my nineteenth year I told my father I intended to go to Madrid and become an *espada*. When he found he couldn't induce me to stay, he said I might go. We parted, and I walked to Seville; there I did odd jobs for a few weeks in connection with the bull ring, such as feeding the bulls, helping to separate them, and so forth; and there I made an acquaintance who was afterwards a friend. Juan Valdera was one of the *cuadrilla* of Girvalda, a *matador* of the ordinary type. Juan was from Estramadura, and we could scarcely understand each other at first; but he was kindly and careless and I took a great liking to him. He was a fine man; tall, strong and handsome, with short, dark, wavy hair and dark moustache, and great black eyes. He liked me, I suppose, because I admired him and because I never wearied of hearing him tell of his conquests among women and even great ladies. Of course I told him I wished to enter the ring, and he promised to help me to get a place in Madrid where he knew many of the officials. 'You may do well with the *capa*,' I remember he said condescendingly, 'or even as a *banderillero*, but you'll never go further. You see, to be an *espada*, as I intend to be, you must have height and strength,' and he stretched his fine figure as he spoke. I acquiesced humbly enough. I felt that perhaps he and my father were right, and I didn't know whether I should ever have strength enough for the task of an *espada*. To be brief, I saved a little money, and managed to get to Madrid late in the year, too late for the bull ring. Thinking over the matter I resolved to get work in a blacksmith's shop, and at length succeeded. As I had thought, the labour strengthened me greatly, and in the spring of my twentieth year, by Juan's help, I got employed on trial one Sunday as a *chulo*.

"I suppose," Montes went on, after a pause, "I ought to have been excited and nervous on that first Sunday—but I wasn't; I was only eager to do well in order to get engaged for the season. The blacksmith, Antonio, whom I had worked with, had advanced me the money for my costume, and Juan had taken me to a tailor and got the things made, and what I owed Antonio and the tailor weighed on me. Well, on that Sunday I was a failure at first. I went in the procession with the rest, then with the others I fluttered my *capa;* but when the bull rushed at me, instead of running away, like the rest, I wrapped my *capa* about me and, just as his horns were touching me, I moved aside—not half a pace. The spectators cheered me, it is true, and I thought I had done very well, until Juan came over to me, and said:

" 'You mustn't show off like that. First of all, you'll get killed if you play that game; and then you fellows with the *capa* are there to make the bull run about, to tire him out so that we *matadors* may kill him.'

"That was my first lesson in professional jealousy. After that I ran about like the rest, but without much heart in the sport. It seemed to me stupid. Besides, from Juan's anger and contempt, I felt sure I shouldn't get a permanent engagement. Bit by bit, however, my spirits rose again with the exercise, and when the fifth or sixth bull came in, I resolved to make him run. It was a good, honest bull; I saw that at once; he stood in the middle of the ring, excited, but not angry, in spite of the waving of the *capas* all round him. As soon as my turn came, I ran forward, nearer to him than the others had considered safe, and waved the challenge with my *capa*. At once he rushed at it, and I gave him a long run, half round the circle, and ended it by stopping and letting him toss the *capa* which I held not quite at arm's length from my body. As I did this I didn't turn round to face him. I knew he'd toss the *capa* and not me, but the crowd rose and cheered as if the thing were extraordinary. Then I felt sure I should be engaged, and I was perfectly happy. Only Juan said to me a few minutes later:

" 'You'll be killed, my boy, one of these fine days if you try those games. Your life will be a short one if you begin by trusting a bull.'

"But I didn't mind what he said. I thought he meant it as a friendly warning, and I was anxious only to get permanently engaged. And sure enough, as soon as the games were over, I was sent for by the director. He was kind to me, and asked me where I had played before. I told him that was my first trial.

" 'Ah!' he said, turning to a gentleman who was with him, 'I knew it, Señor Duque; such courage always comes from—want of experience, let me call it.'

" 'No,' replied the gentleman, whom I afterwards knew as the Duke of Medinaceli, the best aficionado, and one of the noblest men in Spain; 'I'm not so sure of that. Why,' he went on, speaking now to me, 'did you keep your back turned to the bull?'

" 'Señor,' I answered, ' 'twas an honest bull, and not angry, and I knew he'd toss the *capa* without paying any attention to me.'

" 'Well,' said the Duke, "if you know that much, and aren't afraid to risk your life on your knowledge, you'll go far. I must have a talk with you some day, when I've more time; you can come and see me. Send in your name; I shall remember.' And as he said this, he nodded to me and waved his hand to the director, and went away.

"Then and there the director made me sign an engagement for the season, and gave me one hundred *duros* as earnest money in advance of my pay. What an evening we had after that! Juan, the tailor, Antonio the blacksmith, and I. How glad and proud I was to be able to pay my debts and still have sixty *duros* in my pocket after entertaining my friends. If Juan had not hurt me every now and then by the way he talked of my foolhardiness,

I should have told them all I knew; but I didn't. I only said I was engaged at a salary of a hundred *duros* a month.

" 'What!' said Juan. 'Come, tell the truth; make it fifty.'

" 'No,' I said; 'it was a hundred,' and I pulled out the money.

" 'Well,' he said, 'that only shows what it is to be small and young and foolhardy! Here am I, after six years' experience, second, too, in the *cuadrilla* of Girvalda, and I'm not getting much more than that.'

"Still, in spite of such little drawbacks, in spite, too, of the fact that Juan had to go away early, to meet 'a lovely creature,' as he said, that evening was one of the happiest I ever spent.

"All that summer through I worked every Sunday, and grew in favour with the *madrileños,* and with the *madrileñas,* though not with these in Juan's way. I was timid and young; besides, I had a picture of a woman in my mind, and I saw no one like it. So I went on studying the bulls, learning all I could about the different breeds, and watching them in the ring. Then I sent money to my sister and to my father, and was happy.

"In the winter I was a good deal with Antonio; every day I did a spell of work in his shop to strengthen myself, and he, I think, got to know that I intended to become an *espada.* At any rate, after my first performance with the *capa,* he believed I could do whatever I wished. He used often to say God had given him strength and me brains, and he only wished he could exchange some of his muscle for some of my wits. Antonio was not very bright, but he was good-tempered, kind and hard-working, the only friend I ever had. May Our Lady give his soul rest!

"Next spring when the director sent for me, I said that I wanted to work as a *banderillero.* He seemed to be surprised, told me I was a favorite with the *capa,* and had better stick to that for another season at least. But I was firm. Then he asked me whether I had ever used the *banderillas* and where? The director always believed I had been employed in some other ring before I came to Madrid. I told him I was confident I could do the work. 'Besides,' I added, 'I want more pay,' which was an untruth; but the argument seemed to him decisive, and he engaged me at two hundred *duros* a month, under the condition that, if the spectators wished it, I should work now and then with the *capa* as well. It didn't take me long to show the aficionados in Madrid that I was as good with the *banderillas* as I was with the *capa.* I could plant them when and where I liked. For in this season I found I could make the bull do almost anything. You know how the *banderillero* has to excite the bull to charge him before he can plant the darts. He does that to make the bull lower his head well, and he runs towards the bull partly so that the bull may not know when to toss his head up, partly because he can throw himself aside more easily when he's running fairly fast. Well, again and again I made the bull lower his head and then walked to him, planted the *banderillas,* and as he struck upwards swayed aside just enough to avoid the blow. That was an infinitely more difficult feat than anything I had ever done with the *capa,* and it gave me reputation among the aficionados and also with the *espadas;* but the ignorant herd of spectators preferred my trick with the *capa.* So the season came and went. I had many a carouse with Juan, and gave him money from time to time, because women always made him spend more than he got. From that time, too, I gave my sister fifty *duros* a month, and my father fifty. For before the season was half over my pay was raised to four hundred *duros* a month, and my name was always put on the bills. In fact I was rich and a favorite of the public.

"So time went on, and my third season in Madrid began, and with it came the beginning of the end. Never was any one more absolutely content than I when we were told *los toros* would begin in a fortnight. On the first Sunday I was walking carelessly in the procession beside Juan, though I could have been next to the *espadas,* had I wished, when he suddenly nudged me, saying:

" 'Look up! there on the second tier; there's a face for you.'

"I looked up, and saw a girl with the face of my dreams, only much more beautiful. I suppose I must have stopped, for Juan pulled me by the arm crying: 'You're moonstruck, man; come on!' and on I went—love-struck in heart and brain and body. What a face it was! The golden hair framed it like a picture, but the great eyes were hazel, and the lips scarlet, and she wore the mantilla like a queen. I moved forward like a man in a dream, conscious of nothing that went on round me, till I heard Juan say:

" 'She's looking at us. She knows we've noticed her. All right, pretty one! we'll make friends afterwards.'

" 'But how?' I asked, stupidly.

" 'How!' he replied, mockingly. 'I'll just send some one to find out who she is, and then you can send her a box for next Sunday, and pray for her acquaintance, and the thing's done. I suppose that's her mother sitting behind her,' he went on. 'I wonder if the other girl next to her is the sister. She's as good-looking as the fair-haired one, and easier to win, I'd bet. Strange how all the timid ones take to me.' And again he looked up.

"I said nothing; nor did I look up at the place where she was sitting; but I worked that day as I had never worked before. Then, for the first time, I did something that has never been done since by any one. The first bull was honest and kindly: I knew the sort. So, when the people began to call for El Pequeño (the little fellow)—that was the nickname they had given me—I took up a *capa,* and, when the bull chased me, I stopped suddenly, faced him, and threw the *capa* round me. He was within ten paces of me before he saw I had stopped, and he began to stop; but before he came to a standstill his horns were within a foot of me. He tossed his head once or twice as if he would strike me, and then went off. The people cheered and cheered as if they would never cease. Then I looked up at her. She must have been watching me, for she took the red rose from her hair and threw it into the ring towards me, crying, *'Bien! Muy bien! El Pequeño!'*

"As I picked up the rose, pressed it to my lips, and hid it in my breast,

I realized all that life holds of triumphant joy! . . . Then I made up my mind to show what I could do, and everything I did that day seemed to delight the public. At last, as I planted the *banderillas,* standing in front of the bull, and he tried twice in quick succession to strike me and failed, the crowd cheered and cheered and cheered, so that, even when I went away, after bowing and stood among my fellows, ten minutes passed before they would let the game go on. I didn't look up again. No! I wanted to keep the memory of what she looked like when she threw me the rose.

"After the games were over, I met her, that same evening. Juan had brought it about, and he talked easily enough to the mother and daughter and niece, while I listened. We all went, I remember, to a restaurant in the Puerta del Sol, and ate and drank together. I said little or nothing the whole evening. The mother told us they had just come from the north: Alvareda was the family name; her daughter was Clemencia, the niece, Liberata. I heard everything in a sort of fever of hot pulses and cold fits of humility, while Juan told them all about himself, and what he meant to do and to be. While Clemencia listened to him, I took my fill of gazing at her. At last Juan invited them all to *los toros* on the following Sunday, and promised them the best *palco* in the ring. He found out, too, where they lived, in a little street running parallel to the Alcalá, and assured them of our visit within the week. Then they left, and as they went out of the door Liberata looked at Juan, while Clemencia chatted with him and teased him.

" 'That's all right,' said Juan, turning to me when they were gone, 'and I don't know which is the more taking, the niece or Clemencia. Perhaps the niece; she looks at one so appealingly; and those who talk so with their eyes are always the best. I wonder have they any money. One might do worse than either with a good portion.'

" 'Is that your real opinion?' I asked hesitatingly.

" 'Yes,' he answered; 'why?'

"Because, in that case leave Clemencia to me. Of course you could win her if you wanted to. But it makes no difference to you, and to me all the difference. If I cannot marry her, I shall never marry.'

" 'Gesu!' he cried, 'how fast you go, but I'd do more than that for you, Montes; and besides, the niece really pleases me better.'

"So the matter was settled between us.

"Now, if I could tell you all that happened, I would. But much escaped me at the time that I afterwards remembered, and many things that then seemed to me to be as sure as a straight stroke, have since grown confused. I only know that Juan and I met them often, and that Juan paid court to the niece, while I from time to time talked timidly to Clemencia.

"One Sunday after another came and went, and we grew to know each other well. Clemencia did not chatter like other women: I liked her the better for it, and when I came to know she was very proud, I liked that, too. She charmed me; why? I can scarcely tell. I saw her faults gradually, but even her faults appeared to me fascinating. Her pride was insensate. I remember one Sunday afternoon after the games, I happened to go into a restaurant, and found her sitting there with her mother. I was in costume and carried in my hand a great nosegay of roses that a lady had thrown me in the ring. Of course as soon as I saw Clemencia I went over to her and—you know it is the privilege of the *matadors* in Spain, even if they do not know the lady—taking a rose from the bunch I presented it to her as the fairest of the fair. Coming from the cold North, she didn't know the custom and scarcely seemed pleased. When I explained it to her, she exclaimed that it was monstrous; she'd never allow a mere *matador* to take such a liberty unless she knew and liked him. Juan expostulated with her laughingly; I said nothing; I knew what qualities our work required, and didn't think it needed any defence. I believe in that first season, I came to see that her name Clemencia wasn't very appropriate. At any rate she had courage and pride, that was certain. Very early in our friendship she wanted to know why I didn't become an *espada*.

" 'A man without ambition,' she said, 'was like a woman without beauty.'

"I laughed at this and told her my ambition was to do my work well, and advancement was sure to follow in due course. Love of her seemed to have killed ambition in me. But no. She wouldn't rest content in spite of Juan's telling her my position already was more brilliant than that of most of the *espadas*.

" 'He does things with the *capa* and the *banderillas* which no *espada* in all Spain would care to imitate. And that's position enough. Besides, to be an *espada* requires height and strength.'

"As he said this she seemed to be convinced, but it annoyed me a little, and afterwards as we walked together, I said to her,

" 'If you want to see me work as an *espada*, you shall.'

" 'Oh, no!' she answered half carelessly; 'if you can't do it, as Juan says, why should you try? To fail is worse than to lack ambition.'

" 'Well,' I answered, 'you shall see.'

"And then I took my courage in both hands and went on:

" 'If you cared for me I should be the first *espada* in the world next season.'

"She turned and looked at me curiously and said,

" 'Of course I'd wish it if you could do it.'

"And I said, 'See, I love you as the priest loves the Virgin; tell me to be an *espada* and I shall be one for the sake of your love.'

" 'That's what all men say, but love doesn't make a man tall and strong.'

" 'No; nor do size and strength take the place of heart and head. Do you love me? That's the question.'

" 'I like you, yes. But love—love, they say, comes after marriage.'

" 'Will you marry me?'

" 'Become an *espada* and then ask me again,' she answered coquettishly.

"The very next day I went to see the Duke of Medinaceli; the servants would scarcely let me pass till they heard my name and that the Duke had asked me to come. He received me kindly. I told him what I wanted.

" 'Have you ever used the sword?' he asked in surprise. 'Can you do it? You see we don't want to lose the best man with *capa* and *banderillas* ever known, to get another second-class *espada*.'

"And I answered him,

" 'Señor Duque, I have done better with the *banderillas* than I could with the *capa*. I shall do better with the *espada* than with the *banderillas*.'

" 'You little fiend!' he laughed, 'I believe you will, though it is unheard of to become an *espada* without training; but now for the means. All the *espadas* are engaged; it'll be difficult. Let me see. . . . The Queen has asked me to superintend the sports early in July, and then I shall give you your chance. Will that do? In the meantime, astonish us all with *capa* and *banderillas,* so that men may not think me mad when I put your name first on the bill.'

"I thanked him from my heart, as was his due, and after a little more talk I went away to tell Clemencia the news. She only said:

" 'I'm glad. Now you'll get Juan to help you.'

"I stared at her.

" 'Yes!' she went on, a little impatiently; 'he has been taught the work; he's sure to be able to show you a great deal.'

"I said not a word. She was sincere, I saw, but then she came from the North and knew nothing. I said to myself, 'That's how women are!'

"She continued, 'Of course you're clever with the *capa* and *banderillas,* and now you must do more than ever, as the Duke said, to deserve your chance.' And then she asked carelessly, 'Couldn't you bring the Duke and introduce him to us some time or other? I should like to thank him.'

"And I, thinking it meant our betrothal, was glad, and promised. And I remember I did bring him once to the box and he was kind in a way, but not cordial as he always was when alone with me, and he told Clemencia that I'd go very far, and that any woman would be lucky to get me for a husband, and so on. And after a little while he went away. But Clemencia was angry with him and said he put on airs, and, indeed, I had never seen him so cold and reserved; I could say little or nothing in his defence.

"Well, all that May I worked as I had never done. The Director told me he knew I was to use the *espada* on the first Sunday in July, and he seemed to be glad; and one or two of the best *espadas* came to me and said they'd heard the news and should be glad to welcome me among them. All this excited me, and I did better and better. I used to pick out the old prints of Goya, the great painter—you know his works are in the Prado—and do everything the old *matadors* did, and invent new things. But nothing 'took' like my trick with the *capa*. One Sunday, I remember, I had done it with six bulls, one after the other, and the people cheered and cheered. But the seventh was a bad bull, and, of course, I didn't do it. And afterwards Clemencia asked me why I didn't, and I told her. For you see I didn't know then that women rate high what they don't understand. Mystery is everything to them. As if the explanation of such a thing makes it any easier. A man wins great battles by seizing the right moment and using it—the explanation is simple. One must be great in order to know the moment, that's all. But women don't see that it is only small men who exaggerate the difficulties of their work. Great men find their work easy and say so, and, therefore, you'll find that women underrate great men and overpraise small ones. Clemencia really thought I ought to learn the *espada's* work from Juan. Ah! women are strange creatures. . . . Well, after that Sunday she was always bothering me to do the *capa* trick with every bull.

" 'If you don't,' she used to say, 'you won't get the chance of being an *espada*.' And when she saw I laughed and paid no attention to her talk, she became more and more obstinate.

" 'If the people get to know you can only do it with some bulls, they won't think much of you. Do it with every bull, then they can't say anything.'

"And I said 'No! and I shouldn't be able to say anything either.'

" 'If you love me you will do as I say!'

"And when I didn't do as she wished,—it was madness—she grew cold to me, and sneered at me, and then urged me again, till I half yielded. Really, by that time I hardly knew what I couldn't do, for each day I seemed to get greater power over the bulls. At length a Sunday came, the first, I think in June, or the last in May. Clemencia sat with her mother and cousin in the best *palco;* I had got it from the Director, who now refused me nothing. I had done my *capa* trick with three bulls, one after the other, then the fourth came in. As soon as I saw him, I knew he was bad, cunning I mean, and with black rage in the heart of him. The other men stood aside to let me do the trick, but I wouldn't. I ran away like the rest, and let him toss the *capa*. The people liked me, and so they cheered just the same, thinking I was tired; but suddenly Clemencia called out: 'The *capa* round the shoulders; the *capa* trick!' and I looked up at her; and she leaned over the front of the *palco*, and called out the words again.

"Then rage came into me, rage at her folly and cold heart; I took off my cap to her, and turned and challenged the bull with the *capa*, and, as he put down his head and rushed, I threw the *capa* round me and stood still. I did not even look at him. I knew it was no use. He struck me here on the thigh, and I went up into the air. The shock took away my senses. As I came to myself they were carrying me out of the ring, and the people were all standing up; but, as I looked towards the *palco*, I saw she wasn't standing up: she had a handkerchief before her face. At first I thought she was crying, and I felt well, and longed to say to her, 'It doesn't matter, I'm content;' then she put down the handkerchief and I saw she wasn't crying;

there wasn't a tear in her eyes. She seemed surprised merely and shocked. I suppose she thought I could work miracles, or rather she didn't care much whether I was hurt or not. That turned me faint again. I came to myself in my bed, where I spent the next month. The doctor told the Duke of Medinaceli—he had come to see me the same afternoon—that the shock hadn't injured me, but I should be lame always, as the bull's horn had torn the muscles of my thigh from the bone. 'How he didn't bleed to death,' he said, 'is a wonder; now he'll pull through, but no more play with the bulls for him.' I knew better than the doctor, but I said nothing to him, only to the Duke I said:

"'Señor, a promise is a promise; I shall use the *espada* in your show in July.'

"And he said, 'Yes, my poor boy, if you wish it, and are able to; but how came you to make such a mistake?'

"'I made no mistake, Señor.'

"'You knew you'd be struck?'

"I nodded. He looked at me for a moment, and then held out his hand. He understood everything I'm sure; but he said nothing to me then.

"Juan came to see me in the evening, and next day Clemencia and her mother. Clemencia was sorry, that I could see, and wanted me to forgive her. As if I had anything to forgive when she stood there so lithe and straight, with her flower-like face and the appealing eyes. Then came days of pain while the doctors forced the muscles back into their places. Soon I was able to get up, with a crutch, and limp about. As I grew better, Clemencia came seldomer, and when she came, her mother never left the room. I knew what that meant. She had told her mother not to go away; for, though the mother thought no one good enough for her daughter, yet she pitied me, and would have left us alone—sometimes. She had a woman's heart. But no, not once. Then I set myself to get well soon. I would show them all, I said to myself, that a lame Montes was worth more than other men. And I got better, so the doctor said, with surprising speed. . . . One day, towards the end of June, I said to the servant of the Duke—he sent a servant every day to me with fruit and flowers—that I wished greatly to see his master. And the Duke came to see me, the very same day.

"I thanked him first for all his kindness to me, and then asked:

"'Señor, have you put my name on the bills as *espada?*'

"'No,' he replied; 'you must get well first, and, indeed, if I were in your place, I should not try anything more till next season.'

"And I said, 'Señor Duque, it presses. Believe me, weak as I am, I can use the sword.'

"And he answered my very thought: 'Ah! She thinks you can't. And you want to prove the contrary. I shouldn't take the trouble, if I were you; but there! Don't deceive yourself or me; there is time yet for three or four days: I'll come again to see you, and if you wish to have your chance you shall. I give you my word.' As he left the room I had tears in my eyes; but

I was glad, too, and confident: I'd teach the false friends a lesson. Save Antonio, the blacksmith, and some strangers, and the Duke's servant, no one had come near me for more than a week. Three days afterwards I wrote to the Duke asking him to fulfil his promise, and the very next day Juan, Clemencia, and her mother all came to see me together. They all wanted to know what it meant. My name as *espada* for the next Sunday, they said, was first on the bills placarded all over Madrid, and the Duke had put underneath it—'By special request of H.M. the Queen.' I said nothing but that I was going to work; and I noticed that Clemencia wouldn't meet my eyes.

"What a day that was! That Sunday I mean. The Queen was in her box with the Duke beside her as our procession saluted them, and the great ring was crowded tier on tier, and she was in the best box I could get. But I tried not to think about her. My heart seemed to be frozen. Still I know now that I worked for her even then. When the first bull came in and the *capa* men played him, the people began to shout for me—'El Pequeño! El Pequeño! El Pequeño!'—and wouldn't let the games go on. So I limped forward in my *espada's* dress and took a *capa* from a man and challenged the bull, and he rushed at me—the honest one; I caught his look and knew it was all right, so I threw the *capa* round me and turned my back upon him. In one flash I saw the people rise in their places, and the Duke lean over the front of the *palco;* then, as the bull hesitated and stopped, and they began to cheer, I handed back the *capa,* and, after bowing, went again among the *espadas.* Then the people christened me afresh—'El Cojo!' (The Cripple!)— and I had to come forward and bow again and again, and the Queen threw me a gold cigarette case. I have it still. There it is. . . . I never looked up at Clemencia, though I could see her always. She threw no rose to me that day. . . . Then the time came when I should kill the bull. I took the *muleta* in my left hand and went towards him with the sword uncovered in my right. I needed no trick. I held him with my will, and he looked up at me. 'Poor brute,' I thought, 'you are happier than I am.' And he bowed his head with the great, wondering, kindly eyes, and I struck straight through to the heart. On his knees he fell at my feet, and rolled over dead, almost without a quiver. As I hid my sword in the *muleta* and turned away, the people found their voices, 'Well done, The Cripple! Well done!' When I left the ring that day I left it as the first *espada* in Spain. So the Duke said, and he knew—none better. After one more Sunday the sports were over for the year, but that second Sunday I did better than the first, and I was engaged for the next season as first *espada,* with fifty thousand *duros* salary. Forty thousand I invested as the Duke advised—I have lived on the interest ever since—the other ten thousand I kept by me.

"I had resolved never to go near Clemencia again, and I kept my resolve for weeks. One day Juan came and told me Clemencia was suffering because of my absence. He said:

"'She's proud, you know, proud as the devil, and she won't come and see you or send to you, but she loves you. There's no doubt of that: she loves you. I know them, and I never saw a girl so gone on a man. Besides they're poor now, she and her mother; they've eaten up nearly all they had, and you're rich and could help them.'

"That made me think. I felt sure she didn't love me. That was plain enough. She hadn't even a good heart, or she would have come and cheered me up when I lay wounded—because of her obstinate folly. No! It wasn't worth while suffering any more on her account. That was clear. But if she needed me, if she were really poor? Oh, that I couldn't stand. I'd go to her. 'Are you sure?' I asked Juan, and when he said he was, I said:

"'Then I'll visit them to-morrow.'

"And on the next day I went. Clemencia received me as usual: she was too proud to notice my long absence, but the mother wanted to know why I had kept away from them so long. From that time on the mother seemed to like me greatly. I told her I was still sore—which was the truth —and I had had much to do.

"'Some lady fallen in love with you, I suppose,' said Clemencia half scoffingly—so that I could hardly believe she had wanted to see me.

"'No,' I answered, looking at her, 'one doesn't get love without seeking for it, sometimes not even then—when one's small and lame as I am.'

"Gradually the old relations established themselves again. But I had grown wiser, and watched her now with keen eyes as I had never done formerly. I found she had changed—in some subtle way had become different. She seemed kinder to me, but at the same time her character appeared to be even stronger than it had been. I remember noticing one peculiarity in her I had not remarked before. Her admiration of the physique of men was now keen and outspoken. When we went to the theatre (as we often did) I saw that the better-looking and more finely-formed actors had a great attraction for her. I had never noticed this in her before. In fact she had seemed to me to know nothing about virile beauty, beyond a girl's vague liking for men who were tall and strong. But now she looked at men critically. She had changed; that was certain. What was the cause? . . . I could not divine. Poor fool that I was! I didn't know then that good women seldom or never care much for mere bodily qualities in a man; the women who do are generally worthless. Now, too, she spoke well of the men of Southern Spain; when I first met her she professed to admire the women of the South, but to think little of the men. Now she admired the men, too; they were warmer-hearted, she said; had more love and passion in them, and were gentler with women than those of the North. Somehow I hoped that she referred to me, that her heart was beginning to plead for me, and I was very glad and proud, though it all seemed too good to be true.

"One day in October, when I called with Juan, we found them packing their things. They had to leave, they said, and take cheaper lodgings.

Juan looked at me, and some way or other I got him to take Clemencia into another room. Then I spoke to the mother: Clemencia, I hoped, would soon be my wife; in any case I couldn't allow her to want for anything; I would bring a thousand *duros* the next day, and they must not think of leaving their comfortable apartments. The mother cried and said, I was good: 'God makes few such men,' and so forth. The next day I gave her the money, and it was arranged between us without saying anything to Clemencia. I remember about this time, in the early winter of that year, I began to see her faults more clearly, and I noticed that she had altered in many ways. Her temper had changed. It used to be equable though passionate. It had become uncertain and irritable. She had changed greatly. For now, she would let me kiss her without remonstrance, and sometimes almost as if she didn't notice the kiss, whereas before it used always to be a matter of importance. And when I asked her when she would marry me she would answer half-carelessly, 'Some time, I suppose,' as she used to do, but her manner was quite different. She even sighed once as she spoke. Certainly she had changed. What was the cause? I couldn't make it out, therefore I watched, not suspiciously, but she had grown a little strange to me—a sort of puzzle, since she had been so unkind when I lay wounded. And partly from this feeling, partly from my great love for her, I noticed everything. Still I urged her to marry me. I thought as soon as we were married, and she had a child to take care of and to love, it would be all right with both of us. Fool that I was!

"In April, which was fine, I remember, that year in Madrid—you know how cold it is away up there, and how keen the wind is; as the madrileños say, ' 'twon't blow out a candle, but it'll kill a man'—Clemencia began to grow pale and nervous. I couldn't make her out; and so, more than ever, pity strengthening love in me, I urged her to tell me when she would marry me; and one day she turned to me, and I saw she was quite white as she said:

" 'After the season, perhaps.'

"Then I was happy, and ceased to press her. Early in May the games began—my golden time. I had grown quite strong again, and was surer of myself than ever. Besides, I wanted to do something to deserve my great happiness. Therefore, on one of the first days when the Queen and the Duke and Clemencia were looking on, I killed the bull with the sword immediately after he entered the ring, and before he had been tired at all. From that day on the people seemed crazy about me. I couldn't walk in the streets without being cheered; a crowd followed me wherever I went; great nobles asked me to their houses, and their ladies made much of me. But I didn't care, for all the time Clemencia was kind, and so I was happy.

"One day suddenly she asked me why I didn't make Juan an *espada*. I told her I had offered him the first place in my *cuadrilla;* but he wouldn't accept it. She declared that it was natural of him to refuse when I had passed him in the race; but why didn't I go to the Duke and get him made an *espada?* I replied laughingly that the Duke didn't make men *espadas,* but God or their parents. Then her brows drew down, and she said she hadn't thought to find such mean jealousy in me. So I answered her seriously that I didn't believe Juan would succeed as an *espada,* or else I should do what I could to get him appointed. At once she came and put her arms on my shoulders, and said 'twas like me, and she would tell Juan; and after that I could do nothing but kiss her. A little later I asked Juan about it, and he told me he thought he could do the work at least as well as Girvalda, and if I got him the place, he would never forget my kindness. So I went to the Director and told him what I wished. At first he refused, saying Juan had no talent, he would only get killed. When I pressed him he said all the *espadas* were engaged, and made other such excuses. So at last I said I'd work no more unless he gave Juan a chance. Then he yielded after grumbling a great deal.

"Two Sundays later Juan entered the ring for the first time as an *espada.* He looked the part to perfection. Never was there a more splendid figure of a man, and he was radiant in silver and blue. His mother was in the box that day with Clemencia and her mother. Just before we all parted as the sports were about to begin, Clemencia drew me on one side, and said, 'You'll see that he succeeds, won't you?' And I replied, 'Yes, of course, I will. Trust me; it'll be all right.' And it was, though I don't think it would have been, if she hadn't spoken. I remembered my promise to her, and when I saw that the bull which Juan ought to kill was vicious, I told another *espada* to kill him, and so got Juan an easy bull, which I took care to have tired out before I told him the moment had come. Juan wasn't a coward—no! but he hadn't the peculiar nerve needed for the business. The *matador's* spirit should rise to the danger, and Juan's didn't rise. He was white, but determined to do his best. That I could see. So I said to him, 'Go on, man! Don't lose time, or he'll get his wind again. You're all right; I shall be near you as one of your *cuadrilla.*' And so I was, and if I hadn't been, Juan would have come to grief. Yes, he'd have come to grief that very first day.

Naturally enough we spent the evening together. It was a real *tertulia,* Señora Alvareda said; but Clemencia sat silent with the great, dark eyes turned in upon her thoughts, and the niece and myself were nearly as quiet, while Juan talked for every one, not forgetting himself. As he had been depressed before the trial so now he was unduly exultant, forgetting altogether, as it seemed to me, not only his nervousness but also that it had taken him two strokes to kill the bull. His first attempt was a failure, and the second one, though it brought the bull to his knees, never reached his heart. But Juan was delighted and seemed never to weary of describing the bull and how he had struck him, his mother listening to him the while adoringly. It was past midnight when we parted from our friends; and Juan, as we returned to my rooms, would talk of nothing but the salary he expected to get. I was out of sorts; he had bragged so incessantly I had scarcely got a word with Clemencia, who could hardly find time to tell me she had a bad headache. Juan would come up with me; he wanted to know whether I'd go on the morrow to the Director to get him a permanent engagement. I got rid of him, at last, by saying I was tired to death, and it would look better to let the Director come and ask for his services. So at length we parted. After he left me I sat for some time wondering at Clemencia's paleness. She was growing thin too! And what thoughts had induced that rapt expression of face?

"Next morning I awoke late and had so much to do that I resolved to put off my visit to Clemencia till the afternoon, but in the meantime the Director spoke to me of Juan as rather a bungler, and when I defended him, agreed at last to engage him for the next four Sundays. This was a better result than I had expected, so as soon as I was free I made off to tell Juan the good news. I met his mother at the street door where she was talking with some women; she followed me into the patio saying Juan was not at home.

"'Never mind,' I replied carelessly, 'I have good news for him, so I'll go upstairs to his room and wait.'

"'Oh!' she said, 'you can't do that; you mustn't; Juan wouldn't like it.'

"Then I laughed outright. Juan wouldn't like it—oh no! It was amusing to say that when we had lived together like brothers for years, and had had no secrets from one another. But she persisted and grew strangely hot and excited. Then I thought to myself—there you are again; these women understand nothing. So I went away, telling her to send Juan to me as soon as he came in. At this she seemed hugely relieved and became voluble in excuses. In fact her manner altered so entirely that before I had gone fifty yards down the street, it forced me to wonder. Suddenly my wonder changed to suspicion. Juan wasn't out! Who was with him I mustn't see?

"As I stopped involuntarily, I saw a man on the other side of the street who bowed to me. I went across and said:

"'Friend, I am Montes, the *matador*. Do you own this house?'

"He answered that he did, and that every one in Madrid knew me.

"So I said, 'Lend me a room on your first-floor for an hour; *cosa de mujer;* (A lady's in the case.) you understand.'

"At once he led me up-stairs and showed me a room from the windows of which I could see the entrance to Juan's lodging. I thanked him, and when he left me I stood near the window and smoked and thought. What could it all mean? . . . Had Clemencia anything to do with Juan? She made me get him his trial as *espada;* charged me to take care of him. He was from the South, too, and she had grown to like Southern men: 'they were passionate and gentle with women.' Curses on her! Her paleness occurred to me, her fits of abstraction. As I thought, every memory fitted into its place, and what had been mysterious grew plain to me; but

I wouldn't accept the evidence of reason. No! I'd wait and see. Then I'd
—at once I grew quiet. But again the thoughts came—like the flies that
plague the cattle in summer time—and again I brushed them aside, and
again they returned.

"Suddenly I saw Juan's mother come into the street wearing altogether
too careless an expression. She looked about at haphazard as if she expected
someone. After a moment or two of this she slipped back into the patio
with mystery in her sudden decision and haste. Then out came a form I
knew well, and, with stately, even step, looking neither to the right hand
nor the left, walked down the street. It was Clemencia, as my heart had
told me it would be. I should have known her anywhere even had she not
—just below the window where I was watching—put back her mantilla
with a certain proud grace of movement which I had admired a hundred
times. As she moved her head to feel that the mantilla draped her properly I saw her face; it was drawn and set like one fighting against pain. That
made me smile with pleasure.

"Five minutes later Juan swung out of the doorway in the full costume
of an *espada*—he seemed to sleep in it now—with a cigarette between his
teeth. Then I grew sad and pitiful. We had been such friends. I had meant
only good to him always. And he was such a fool! I understood it all now;
knew, as if I had been told, that the intimacy between them dated from
the time when I lay suffering in bed. Thinking me useless and never having had any real affection for me, Clemencia had then followed her inclination and tried to win Juan. She had succeeded easily enough, no doubt,
but not in getting him to marry her. Later, she induced me to make Juan
an *espada,* hoping against hope that he'd marry her when his new position
had made him rich. On the other hand he had set himself to cheat me because of the money I had given her mother, which relieved him from the
necessity of helping them, and secondly, because it was only through my
influence that he could hope to become an *espada*. Ignoble beasts! And then
jealousy seized me as I thought of her admiration of handsome men, and
at once I saw her in his arms. Forthwith pity, and sadness, and anger left
me, and, as I thought of him swaggering past the window, I laughed aloud.
Poor weak fools! I, too, could cheat.

"He had passed out of the street. I went downstairs and thanked the
landlord for his kindness to me. 'For your good-nature,' I said, "you must
come and see me work from a box next Sunday. Ask for me, I won't forget.' And he thanked me with many words and said he had never missed
a Sunday since he had first seen me play with the *capa* three years before.
I laughed and nodded to him and went my way homewards, whither I
knew Juan had gone before me.

"As I entered my room, he rose to meet me with a shadow as of doubt
or fear upon him. But I laughed cheerfully, gaily enough to deceive even
so finished an actor as he was, and told him the good news. 'Engaged,' I
cried, slapping him on the shoulder. 'The Director engages you for four

Sundays certain.' And that word 'certain' made me laugh louder still—jubilantly. Then afraid of overdoing my part, I sat quietly for some time and listened to his expressions of fatuous self-satisfaction. As he left me to go and trumpet the news from café to café, I had to choke down my contempt for him by recalling that picture, by forcing myself to see them in each other's arms. Then I grew quiet again and went to call upon my betrothed.

"She was at home and received me as usual, but with more kindness than was her wont. 'She feels a little remorse at deceiving me,' I said to myself, reading her now as if her soul were an open book. I told her of Juan's engagement and she let slip 'I wish I had known that sooner!' But I did not appear to notice anything. It amused me now to see how shallow she was and how blind I had been. And then I played with her as she had often, doubtless, played with me. 'He will go far, will Juan,' I said, 'now that he has begun—very far, in a short time.' And within me I laughed at the double meaning as she turned startled eyes upon me. And then, 'His old loves will mourn for the distance which must soon separate him from them. Oh, yes, Juan will go far and leave them behind.' I saw a shade come upon her face, and, therefore, added: 'But no one will grudge him his success. He's so good-looking and good-tempered, and kind and true.' And then she burst into tears, and I went to her and asked as if suspiciously, 'Why, what's the matter? Clemencia!' Amid her sobs, she told me she didn't know, but she felt upset, out of sorts, nervous; she had a headache. 'Heartache,' I laughed to myself, and bade her go and lie down; rest would do her good; I'd come again on the morrow. As I turned to leave the room she called me back and put her arms round my neck and asked me to be patient with her; she was foolish, but she'd make it up to me. . . . And I comforted her, the poor, shallow fool, and went away.

"In some such fashion as this the days passed; each hour—now my eyes were opened—bringing me some fresh entertainment; for, in spite of their acting, I saw that none of them were happy. I knew everything. I guessed that Juan, loving his liberty, was advising Clemencia to make up to me, and I saw how badly she played her part. And all this had escaped me a few days before; I laughed at myself more contemptuously than at them. It interested me, too, to see that Liberata had grown suspicious. She no longer trusted Juan's protestations implicitly. Every now and then, with feminine bitterness, she thrust the knife of her own doubt and fear into Clemencia's wound. 'Don't you think, Montes, Clemencia is getting pale and thin?' she'd ask; 'it is for love of you, you know. She should marry soon.' And all the while she cursed me in her heart for a fool, while I laughed to myself. The comedy was infinitely amusing to me, for now I held the cords in my hand, and knew I could drop the curtain and cut short the acting just when I liked. Clemencia's mother, too, would sometimes set to work to amuse me as she went about with eyes troubled, as if anxious for the future, and yet stomach-satisfied with the comforts of the present. She, too, thought it worth while, now and then, to befool me, when fear came upon her—between meals. That did not please me! When she tried to play with me, the inconceivable stupidity of my former blind trust became a torture to me. Juan's mother I saw but little of; yet I liked her. She was honest at least, and deceit was difficult to her. Juan was her idol; all he did was right in her eyes; it was not her fault that she couldn't see he was like a poisoned well. All these days Juan was friendly to me as usual, with scarcely a shade of the old condescension in his manner. He no longer showed envy by remarking upon my luck. Since he himself had been tested, he seemed to give me as much respect as his self-love could spare. Nor did he now boast, as he used to do, of his height and strength. Once, however, on the Friday evening, I think it was, he congratulated Clemencia on my love for her, and joked about our marriage. The time had come to drop the curtain and make an end.

"On the Saturday I went to the ring and ordered my *palco* to be filled with flowers. From there I went to the Duke of Medinaceli. He received me as always, with kindness, thought I looked ill, and asked me whether I felt the old wound still. 'No,' I replied, 'no Señor Duque, and if I come to you now it is only to thank you once more for all your goodness to me.'

"And he said after a pause—I remember each word; for he meant well:

"'Montes, there's something very wrong.' And then, 'Montes, one should never adore a woman; they all want a master. My hairs have grown grey in learning that. . . . A woman, you see, may look well and yet be cold-hearted and—not good. But a man would be a fool to refuse nuts because one that looked all right was hollow.'

"'You are wise,' I said, 'Señor Duque! and I have been foolish. I hope it may be well with you always; but wisdom and folly come to the same end at last.'

"After I left him I went to Antonio and thanked him, and gave him a letter to be opened in a week. There were three enclosures in it—one for himself, one for the mother of Juan, and one for the mother of Clemencia, and each held three thousand *duros*. As they had cheated me for money, money they should have—with my contempt. Then I went back to the ring, and as I looked up to my *palco* and saw that the front of it was one bed of white and scarlet blossoms, I smiled. 'White for purity,' I said, 'and scarlet for blood, a fit show!' And I went home and slept like a child.

"Next day in the ring I killed two bulls, one on his first rush, and the other after the usual play. Then another *espada* worked, and then came the turn of Juan. As the bull stood panting I looked up at the palco. There they all were, Clemencia with hands clasped on the flowers and fixed, dilated eyes, her mother half asleep behind her. Next to Clemencia, the niece with flushed cheeks, and leaning on her shoulder his mother. Juan was much more nervous than he had been on the previous Sunday. As his bull came into the ring he asked me hurriedly: 'Do you think it's an easy one?'

I told him carelessly that all bulls were easy and he seemed to grow more and more nervous. When the bull was ready for him he turned to me, passing his tongue feverishly over his dry lips.

" 'You'll stand by me, won't you, Montes?'

"And I asked with a smile:

" 'Shall I stand by you as you've stood by me?'

" 'Yes, of course, we've always been friends.'

" 'I shall be as true to you as you have been to me!' I said. And I moved to his right hand and looked at the bull. It was a good one; I couldn't have picked a better. In his eyes I saw courage that would never yield and hate that would strike in the death-throe, and I exulted and held his eyes with mine, and promised him revenge. While he bowed his horns to the *muleta,* he still looked at me and I at him; and as I felt that Juan had levelled his sword, and was on the point of striking, I raised my head with a sweep to the side, as if I had been the bull; and as I swung, so the brave bull swung too. And then—then all the ring swam round with me, and yet I had heard the shouting and seen the spectators spring to their feet. . . .

"I was in the street close to the Alvaredas'. The mother met me at the door; she was crying and the tears were running down her fat, greasy cheeks. She told me Clemencia had fainted and had been carried home, and Juan was dead—ripped open—and his mother distracted, and 'twas a pity, for he was so handsome and kind and good-natured, and her best dress was ruined, and *los toros* shouldn't be allowed, and—as I brushed past her in disgust—that Clemencia was in her room crying.

"I went upstairs and entered the room. There she sat with her elbows on the table and her hair all round her face and down her back, and her fixed eyes stared at me. As I closed the door and folded my arms and looked at her, she rose, and her stare grew wild with surprise and horror, and then, almost without moving her lips, she said:

" 'Holy Virgin! You did it! I see it in your face!'

"And my heart jumped against my arms for joy, and I said in the same slow whisper, imitating her:

" 'Yes; I did it.'

"As I spoke she sprang forward with hate in her face, and poured out a stream of loathing and contempt on me. She vomited abuse as from her very soul: I was low and base and cowardly; I was—God knows what all. And he was handsome and kind, with a face like a king. . . . And I had thought she could love me, me, the ugly, little, lame cur while he was there. And she laughed. She'd never have let my lips touch her if it hadn't been that her mother liked me and to please him. And now I had killed him, the best friend I had. Oh, 'twas horrible! Then she struck her head with her fists and asked how God, God, God could allow me to kill a man whose finger was worth a thousand lives such as mine!

"Then I laughed and said:

" 'You mistake. You killed him. You made him an *espada*—you!'

"As I spoke her eyes grew fixed and her mouth opened, and she seemed to struggle to speak, but she only groaned—and fell face forwards on the floor.

"I turned and left the room as her mother entered it." After a long pause Montes went on:

"I heard afterwards that she died next morning in premature childbirth. I left Madrid that night and came here, where I have lived ever since, if this can be called living. . . . Yet at times now fairly content, save for one thing—'Remorse?' Yes!"—And the old man rose to his feet, while his great eyes blazing with passion held me—"Remorse! That I let the bull kill him.

"I should have torn his throat out with my own hands."

Excerpt from
Spain and the Spaniards

by EDMUNDO DE AMICIS

Edmundo De Amicis, 1846–1908, was an Italian novelist and essayist who had great popularity, as well, for his travel writings. His *Cuore,* a schoolboy's journal, was one of the most widely read of Italian books. De Amicis had an enthusiastic, colorful style. His travel book, *Spain and the Spaniards,* sold ten editions in Italy and was translated into English for Henry T. Coates & Co., Philadelphia, 1895. This excerpt is one of the most interesting commentaries by an Italian on the Spanish festival.

The thirty-first of March inaugurates the spectacle of the bullfights. Let us discuss them at leisure, for they form a worthy subject.

He who has read Baretti's description may consider that he has read nothing. Baretti saw only the bullfights of Lisbon, which are mere child's play beside those of Madrid. Madrid is the home of the art: here are the great artists, here the stupendous spectacles, here the skilled spectators, here the judges who distribute the honors. The circus of Madrid is the Theatre della Scala of the art of bullfighting.

The inauguration of the bullfights at Madrid is even more important than a change of the ministry. A month beforehand the news spreads throughout all Spain: from Cádiz to Barcelona, from Bilbao to Almería, in the palaces of the grandees and the cabins of the poor, they talk only of the artists and the breed of bulls; they arrange fights for pleasure between the provinces and the capital; he who is short of money begins to save so as to get a good place in the circus on that great day; fathers and mothers promise their children to take them if they will study well; lovers make similar promises to their sweethearts; the papers assure you that it will be a good season; the famous *toreros,* who already begin to appear in Madrid, are pointed out with the finger; rumors are afloat that the bulls have arrived, and some have seen them or have arranged to do so.

There are bulls from the pastures of the Duke of Veragua, the Marquis de Merced, and of Her Excellency the dowager of Villaseca, prodigious and terrible. The office is opened to receive subscriptions; the dilettanti crowd around, together with the servants of the noble families, the brokers, and friends commissioned by the absent. The first day the manager has received fifty thousand francs, on the second thirty thousand, and a hundred thousand in a week. "Frascuelo," the famous *matador,* has arrived; Cuco has arrived; Calderón has arrived, and all the others three days before the time. Thousands of people can talk of nothing else; ladies dream of the circus; ministers have no thought for other affairs; old dilettanti can hardly contain themselves; soon laboring-men stop buying their cigarettes to have a few pennies on the day of the spectacle. Finally, on Saturday morning, before dawn, they commence to sell tickets in a room on the street Alcalá. A crowd collects before the doors are opened, yelling, pushing, and knocking each other about; twenty policemen with revolvers in their belts are scarcely able to keep decent order; there is a continuous stream of people until night.

The long-expected day has arrived. The spectacle commences at three o'clock; at noon the people start from all directions toward the circus, which stands at the edge of the suburb of Salamanca, beyond the Prado, outside of the gate of Alcalá; all the streets which lead there are crowded with a procession of people. The circus looks like a great anthill; troops of soldiers and Volunteers of Liberty arrive, headed by bands of music; a crowd of water-carriers and orange-sellers fill the air with their cries; ticket-sellers run here and there, hailed by a thousand voices. Woe for him who has not yet bought his ticket! He will pay double, treble, quadruple! But what cares he if a ticket costs even fifty or eighty francs? They are looking for the king; they say the queen is coming too. The chariots of the great guns begin to arrive; the Duke of Fernan Núñe, the Duke d'Abrantes, the Marquis de la Vega de Armijo, a crowd of the grandees of Spain, the goddesses of the aristocracy, the ministers, generals, and ambassadors—all that is beautiful, splendid, and powerful in the great city. One may enter the circus by many doors, but before entering one is deafened by the noise.

I entered. The circus is immense. The outside is in no way remarkable; it is a low circular yellow building without windows, but on entering one feels the liveliest surprise. It is a circus for a people, where ten thousand spectators can be seated and in which a regiment of cavalry might drill. The arena is circular, and so vast that it could hold ten of our equestrian circuses. It is encircled by a wooden barrier about even with a man's shoulders, provided on the inside with a narrow ledge a little way from the ground, on which the *toreros* place their feet to jump over when the bull chases them. Beyond this barrier there is another higher one, for the bull often leaps over the first; between the two a narrow course, a little more than a metre in width, runs all the way round the arena; here the *toreros* stroll before the combat, and here stand the attendants of the circus—the carpenters ready to repair the gaps which the bull has made, the guards, the orange-venders, the dilettanti who enjoy the friendship of the manager, and the great guns who are allowed to transgress the rules. Beyond the second barrier rises a tier of stone seats, and beyond this are the boxes; below the boxes runs a gallery containing three rows of seats. The boxes are each large enough to hold three or four families; the king's box is a great drawing-room; next to it is that of the city officials, in which sits the mayor or whoever presides at the spectacle. Then there is the box for the ministers, for the governors, and for the ambassadors; every noble family has one; the young bon tons, as Giusti would say, have a box to themselves; then there are boxes to let which cost a fortune.

Every seat in the tiers is numbered, every person has a ticket; so the entrance is made without the least disorder. The circus is divided into two parts—one in the shade, the other in the sunshine; in the first one pays more; in the second sit the common people. The arena has four doors at equal distances from each other—the door through which the *toreros* enter, the door for the bulls, another for the horses, and a fourth, under the king's box, for the heralds of the spectacle. Over the door through which the bulls enter rises a sort of sloping platform which is called the *toril*, and well for him who can find a place there! Upon this platform, in a little box, stand the men who at a sign from the mayor's box sound the trumpet and drum to announce the entrance of the bull. Facing the *toril* on the opposite side of the arena along the stone balcony is the band of music. The whole balcony is divided into compartments, each of which has its own door.

Before the show begins the people are allowed to enter the arena and to walk through all the passages of the building. They go to see the horses enclosed in a courtyard, and most of them destined to be killed, more's the pity! They go to see the dark chambers where are confined the bulls, which are driven from one enclosure to another until they reach a corridor and dash into the arena; they go to see the infirmary where the wounded *toreros* are borne; once there was a chapel to visit in which mass was celebrated during the combat, and there the *toreros* went to pray before confronting the angry brutes; then they go to the principal entrance, where are exhibited the *banderillas* that are to be inserted in the bulls' necks, and where one sees a group of old *toreros*—one lame, another without an arm, a third on crutches—and the young *toreros* who have not yet been admitted to the honors of the circus of Madrid. One buys a copy of the *Bulletin of the Bulls*, which promises miracles for the doings of the day. Then one gets from the guard the programme of the spectacle and a printed leaflet divided into columns for noting the strokes of the spear, the thrusts, the falls, and the wounds. One climbs along endless corridors and interminable stairways in the midst of a crowd which comes and goes, ascends and descends, crying and shouting, so that the whole building trembles, and finally one returns to one's seat.

The circus is crowded full, and presents a spectacle of which it is impossible to form an idea unless one has seen it: it is a sea of heads, hats, fans, and hands waving in the air; on the side where sit the better classes in the shade all is dark; on the other side, in the sun,where the common people sit, a thousand brilliant colors of vesture, parasols, and paper fans— an immense masquerade.

There is not room enough for another child; the crowd is as compact as a phalanx; no one can go out, and it is difficult even to move one's arms. It is not a buzzing like the noise of other theatres; it is different: it is an agitation, a life altogether peculiar to the circus; everybody is shouting, gesticulating, and saluting each other with frantic joy; the women and children scream; the gravest men frolic like boys; the young men, in groups of twenty and thirty, shout in chorus and beat with their canes against the stone balustrade as a sign to the mayor that the hour has arrived. In the boxes there is an overflow of spirits, like that in the galleries of the regular theatres; the discordant cries of the crowd are augmented by the howls of a hundred hawkers, who are throwing oranges in every direction; the band plays, the bulls bellow, the crowd outside roars; it is a spectacle which makes one dizzy, and before the struggle commences one is exhausted, intoxicated, and stupefied.

Suddenly there is a cry, "The king!" The king has arrived; he is come in a chariot drawn by white horses, with mounted grooms in picturesque Andalusian costumes; the glass doors of the royal box swing back, and the king enters with a stately crowd of ministers, generals, and major-domos. The queen is not there: one foresaw that; every one knows that she has a horror of this spectacle. Oh! but the king would not miss it; he has always come. They say he is mad over it. The hour has come, the spectacle begins. I shall remember to my dying day the chill which passed over me at that moment.

A blare of trumpets; four guards of the circus on horseback, with cap and plume à la Henri IV, with black mantles, tight-fitting jackets, jackboots, and swords, enter by the gate under the king's box and slowly make the circuit of the arena. The people separate; every one goes to his seat; the arena is deserted. The four cavaliers take their places, two by two, in front of the door opposite the royal box, which is still closed.

Ten thousand spectators fix their eyes on that spot; there is a universal silence. For through it will come the *cuadrilla*, with all the *toreros* in gala

Excerpt from "Spain and the Spaniards"   201

dress to present themselves to the king and the people. The band plays, the door springs open, there is a burst of applause; the *toreros* advance. First come the three *espadas,* "Frascuelo," "Lagartijo," and "Cayetano," the three famous ones, dressed in the costume of Figaro in the "Barber of Seville," in satin, silk, and velvet, orange, scarlet, and blue, covered with embroidery, fringe, lace, filigree, tinsel, spangles of gold and silver which almost conceal their dress; enveloped in full capes of yellow and red, with white stockings, silken girdles, a bunch of tassels on the neck, and a fur cap. Next come the *banderilleros* and the *capeadors,* a troop covered like the others with gold and silver; then the *picadors,* on horseback, two by two, each with a great battle-lance, a low-crowned gray hat, an embroidered jacket, breeches of yellow buffalo skin, padded and lined inside with strips of iron; then the *chulos,* or servants, dressed in their holiday best; and altogether they walk majestically across the arena toward the box of the king. One cannot imagine anything more picturesque than this spectacle: there are all the colors of a garden, all the splendors of a royal court, all the gayety of a rout of maskers, all the grandeur of a band of warriors; on closing one's eyes one sees only a gleaming of gold and silver. They are very handsome men—the *picadors* tall, stout of limb like athletes; the others slight and nimble, with chiseled forms, swarthy faces, and great fierce eyes—figures like the ancient gladiators, clothed with the magnificence of Asiatic princes.

The entire *cuadrilla* stops in front of the royal box and salutes; the mayor makes a sign that they may begin; the key of the *toril,* where the bulls are confined, is tossed from the box into the arena; a guard of the circus picks it up and gives it to the custodian, who places himself before the door ready to open it. The band of *toreros* separates, the *espadas* leap over the barrier, the *capeadors* scatter through the arena, waving their red and yellow *capas;* the *picadors* retire to await their turn; the rest spur their horses and take their positions to the left of the *toril* at a distance of twenty paces apart, with their backs to the barrier and their lances in rest.

It is a moment of keen excitement, of unexpressible anxiety; all eyes are fixed on the door by which the bull will enter; all hearts are beating high; a profound silence broods over the whole circus; one hears only the bellowing of the bull as he advances from cell to cell in the darkness of his vast prison; one can almost hear him crying, "Blood! blood!" The horses tremble, the *picadors* grow pale: another instant a blare of trumpets, the door is thrown wide open, and the terrible bull dashes into the arena saluted by a terrific shout, which bursts at that moment from ten thousand throats.

Ah! it is a good thing to have strong nerves: at that moment one turns as white as a corpse. . . .

How many shocks, how many tremors, how many chills at the heart and rushes of blood to the head does one feel during that spectacle! how many sudden pallors! But you, stranger, you alone are pale; the boy beside you is laughing, the girl in front of you is wild with delight, the lady whom you see in the next box says she has never enjoyed herself so much. What shouting! what exclamations! That is the place to learn the language! As the bull appears he is judged by a thousand voices: "What a fine head! what eyes! he will draw blood! he is worth a fortune!" They break out into words of love. He has killed a horse. *"Bueno!* see how much has fallen from the belly!" A *picador* misses his stroke and wounds the bull badly or is afraid to confront him; then there is a deluge of insulting names: "Poltroon! imposter! assassin! go hide yourself! go and be hanged!" They all rise, point with their fingers, shake their fists, throw orange-peel and cigar-stumps in his face, and threaten him with their canes. When the *espada* kills the bull with one stroke, then follow the delirious words of lovers and extravagant gestures: "Come here, angel! God bless thee, 'Frascuelo!' " They throw him kisses, call to him, and stretch out their hands as if to embrace him. What a profusion of epithets, witticisms, and proverbs! What fire! what life!

In the entire *corrida* a thousand accidents occur. In that same day a bull thrust his head under a horse's belly, raised the horse and horseman, and, carrying them in triumph across the arena, threw them both to the ground like a bundle of rags. Another bull killed four horses in a few minutes; a third attacked a *picador* so violently that he fell, struck his head against the barrier, fainted, and was carried out. But not for this nor for a graver wound, nor even for the death of a *torero*, is the spectacle interrupted—it is so stated in the programme; if one is killed, another is ready.

In the crowd, a thousand incidents occur during the spectacle. Suddenly two spectators fall to fighting. The people are so closely packed that some one of the neighbors receives a blow from a cane; then they seize their canes and join the fray. The circle of the combatants grows wider; the row extends through entire compartments in the gallery; in a few moments there are hats flying through the air, torn cravats, bloody faces, a din which rises to heaven; all the spectators are on their feet; the guards run about; the *toreros* cease to be actors and become spectators. At other times a group of lively young fellows turn in one direction and shout all together, "There he is!" "Who?" No one, but meanwhile the persons next to them get up, and those at a distance stand on the seats; the ladies lean from the boxes, and in a moment the whole circus is topsy-turvy. Then the group of young men give a loud laugh; their neighbors, so as not to appear ridiculous, do the same; the laugh spreads to the boxes and through the galleries till ten thousand people are laughing. At other times it is a foreigner, seeing his first bullfight, who faints; the news spreads in a trice; they all get up, stare, shout, and make a pandemonium that baffles description. Again, it is a good-humored man who hails his friend away on the other side of the theatre in a voice which sounds like a clap of thunder. That great crowd is stirred in a few moments with a thousand contrary emotions, passes with incessant change from terror to enthusiasm, from enthusiasm to pity, from pity to anger, from anger to delight, admiration, and unbridled enjoyment.

The final impression which this spectacle makes upon the mind is indescribable; it is a mingling of sensations, among which it is impossible to recollect anything clearly or to know one's thoughts. At one moment you turn in horror to flee from the circus, and swear you will never come back; a moment later, astonished, enraptured, and almost intoxicated, you hope the spectacle will never end; now you are almost sickened; now you, too, like your neighbors, shout, laugh, and applaud; the blood makes you shudder, but the marvellous courage of the men exalts you; the danger clutches at your heart, but you are reassured by the victory; little by little the fever which works in the crowd steals into your veins; you do not know yourself, you are another person; you too are stirred by anger, ferocity, and enthusiasm; you feel bold and valiant; the struggle fires your blood; the gleaming of the sword enrages you; and then the thousands of faces, the clamor, the music, the bellowing, the blood, the profound silences and tumultuous bursts of applause, the vastness, the light, the colors, the indescribable grandeur, courage, cruelty, and magnificence, dazzle, amaze and bewilder you.

It is a fine sight to see the people go out; there are ten torrents which pour from ten gates and flood in a few moments the suburb of Salamanca, the Prado, the avenues of the Recoletos, and the street Alcalá; a thousand carriages wait at the exits of the circus; for an hour, wherever one turns, one sees only a swarm of human ants as far as the eye can reach; and all is silent; their passions have exhausted them all; one hears only the roar of passing feet; it seems as if the crowd wishes to steal away secretly; a sort of sadness succeeds their clamorous joy. I, for my part, as I came from the circus for the first time, had scarcely strength to stand on my feet; my head was spinning like a top; my ears buzzed, and everywhere I saw the horns of bulls, eyes swimming in blood, dead horses, and flashing swords. I took the shortest way home, and as soon as I arrived there tumbled into bed and fell into a heavy sleep.

On the following morning the landlady came in great haste to ask me, "Well, how did it strike you? Did it amuse you? Are you going again? What do you say?"

"I do not know," I replied; "it seems like a dream. I will tell you later; I must think it over."

Saturday came, the day before the second bullfight. "Are you going?" asked the landlady. "No," I replied, thinking of something else. I went out, turned into the street Alcalá, and found myself accidentally in front of the shop where tickets are sold; there was a crowd of people. "Shall I go?" I asked myself. "Yes or no?"

"Do you want a ticket?" a boy demanded: "a shady seat, No. 6, near the barrier—fifteen reales?" "Done!" I replied.

But to clearly comprehend the nature of this spectacle it is necessary to know its history. . . . All through the Middle Ages this was the favorite spectacle of the court—the chosen exercise of warriors, not only among the Spaniards, but among the Moors as well; and they both waged war in the circus as well as on the battlefield. Isabella the Catholic wished to prohibit the bullfights, because she had been horrified on once seeing them, but the numerous and powerful patrons of the spectacle dissuaded her from putting her purpose into effect. After Isabella the circus received great encouragement. Charles V with his own hand killed a bull in the great square of Valladolid; Ferdinand Pizarro, the celebrated conqueror of Peru, was a valiant *torero;* King Sebastian of Portugal won many laurels in the arena; Philip III adorned the circus of Madrid; Philip IV fought in it; Charles II fostered the art; in the reign of Philip V a number of circuses were built by order of the government, but the honor of fighting belonged exclusively to the nobility; they fought only on horseback, splendidly mounted, and yet the only blood shed was that of the bull.

It was not until the middle of the last century that the art became popular, and *toreros,* properly called artists of the profession, who fought on foot and on horseback, came into existence. The famous Francisco Romero perfected the art of fighting on foot, introduced the custom of killing the bull face to face with the sword and *muleta,* and established the practice. Thereupon the spectacle became national and the people welcomed it with enthusiasm. Charles III forbade it, but his prohibition only served to increase the popular enthusiasm into a complete epidemic, as a Spanish chronicler puts it. King Ferdinand VII, who was passionately fond of bulls, instituted a school of bullfighting at Seville. Isabella II was more enthusiastic than Ferdinand VII; Amadeus I, it is said, was not a whit behind Isabella II. And now bullfighting flourishes more than ever before in Spain; there are more than a hundred great proprietors who raise bulls for the spectacles; Madrid, Seville, Barcelona, Cádiz, Valencia, Jerez, and Puerto de Santa María have circuses of the first order; there are no less than fifty small circuses, with a capacity of from three to nine thousand spectators; in all the villages where there is no circus they hold the *corridas* in the square.

At various times they have bullfights with lions and with tigers; it is only a few years since one of these combats was held in the circus of Madrid. It was that celebrated event which the count-duke de Olivares commanded in honor of the birthday, if my memory does not fail me, of Don Baltasar Carlos of Asturia, prince of the Asturias. The bull fought with a lion, a tiger, and a leopard, and succeeded in conquering them all. Also in a combat a few years ago the tiger and the lion got the worst of it; they both jumped impetuously upon the back of the bull, but before they were able to fasten their teeth in his neck they fell to the ground in a pool of blood, pierced by the terrible horns. Only the elephant—a huge elephant which still lives in the gardens of Buen Retiro—carried the day; the bull attacked him, and he simply placed his head on the bull's back and pressed, and the pressure was so delicate that his reckless assailant was crushed as flat as a pancake.

But it is not easy to imagine what skill, what courage, and what imperturbable tranquillity of mind must be possessed by a man who with his sword faces an animal that kills lions, attacks elephants, and tears in pieces, crushes, and covers with blood everything that he touches. And there are men who face them every day

The *toreros* are by no means artists, as one would suppose, to be placed in the same category with mountebanks and those for whom the people feel no other sentiment than that of admiration. The *torero* is respected even outside of the circus; he enjoys the protection of the young aristocrats, has his box in the theatre, frequents the best cafés in Madrid, and is saluted in the street with a low bow by persons of refinement. Famous *espadas* like "Frascuelo," "Lagartijo," and "Cayetano" receive the nice little sum of about ten thousand francs a year; they own houses and villas, live in sumptuous apartments, dress with elegance, spend heaps of money on their costumes embroidered with gold and silver, travel like nabobs, and smoke Havana cigars. Their dress out of the circus is very curious: an Orsini hat of black velvet; a jacket fitting closely around the waist, unbuttoned and reaching barely to the trousers; a waistcoat opened almost to the waist, which allows a white shirt of very fine texture to be seen; no cravat; a sash of red or blue silk about the loins; a pair of breeches fitting the limb like the tights of a ballet-dancer; a pair of low shoes, of morocco leather, ornamented with embroidery; a little periwig falling down the back; and then gold studs, chains, diamonds, rings, and trinkets; in short, an entire jewelry-shop on their persons. Many keep their saddle-horse and some their carriages, and when they are not killing bulls they are always walking in the Prado, at the Puerta del Sol, or in the gardens of Recoletos with their wives and their sweethearts, splendidly dressed and proudly affectionate. Their names, their faces, and their deeds are even better known to the people than the deeds, faces, and names of their commanders and statesman. *Toreros* in comedies, *toreros* in song, *toreros* in pictures, *toreros* in the windows of the print shops, statues of *toreros,* fans painted with *toreros,* handkerchiefs with figures of *toreros*—these one sees again and again, on every occasion and in every place.

The business of the *torero* is the most lucrative and the most honorable to which a courageous son of the people my aspire: very many, in fact, devote themselves to it, but very few become proficient; most of them remain mediocre *capeadores,* a few become *banderilleros* of note, still fewer famous *picadors;* only the few chosen ones of nature and fortune become brave *espadas;* it is necessary to come into the world with that bump developed; one is born an *espada* as one is born a poet. Those killed by the bulls are very few, and one may count them on one's fingers for a long period of time; but the crippled, the maimed, those who are rendered unfit for the combat, are innumerable. One sees them in the city with canes and crutches, some without an arm, others without a leg. The famous "Tato," the first of the *toreros* of modern time, lost a leg; in the few months which I spent in Spain a *banderillero* was half killed at Seville, a *picador* was seriously wounded at Madrid, "Lagartijo" was injured, and three amateur *capeadores* were killed at a village. There is scarcely a *torero* who has not bled in the arena.

Before leaving Madrid I wished to talk to the celebrated "Frascuelo," the prince of *espadas,* the idol of the people of Madrid, the glory of the art. A Genoese captain who knew him took it upon himself to present me: we fixed the day and met at the Imperial Café at the Puerta del Sol. It makes me laugh when I think of my emotions on seeing him in the distance and watching him come toward us. He was very richly dressed, loaded with jewelry, and resplendent as a general in full uniform; as he crossed the café a thousand heads were turned and a thousand eyes fixed upon him, my companion, and myself: I felt myself growing pale. "This is Signor Salvador Sánchez," said the captain ("Frascuelo" is a nickname). And then, presenting me to "Frascuelo," "This is Signor So-and-So, his admirer." The illustrious *matador* bowed, I bowed more profoundly; we sat down and commenced to talk. What a strange man! To hear him talk one would say that he had not the heart to stick a fly with a pin. He was a young man, about twenty-five years old, of medium stature, quick, dark, and handsome, with a firm glance and the smile of an absent-minded man. I asked him a thousand questions about his art and his life; he answered in monosyllables; I was obliged to draw the words from his mouth, one by one, by a storm of questions. He replied to my compliments by looking modestly at the tips of his shoes. I asked him if he had ever been wounded: he touched his knee, thigh, shoulder, and breast, and said, "Here, and here, and here, and here too," with the simplicity of a child. He obligingly wrote out the address of his house for me, asked me to come and see him, gave me a cigar, and went away. Three days later, at the bullfight, I had a seat near the barrier, and as he paused near me to gather up the cigars which the spectators threw him, I tossed him one of those Milan cigars which are covered with straw; he picked it up, examined it, smiled, and tried to discover who had thrown it: I made a sign, he saw me and exclaimed, "Ah! the Italian!" I seem to see him yet; he was dressed in gray embroidered with gold, and one hand was stained with blood.

But, in conclusion, a final judgment on the bullfights! Are they or are they not a barbarous sport, unworthy of a civilized people? Are they or are they not a spectacle which corrupts the heart? Now for a frank opinion! A frank opinion? I do not wish to answer in one way and to draw upon myself a flood of invective, nor to answer otherwise and put my foot in a trap, so I must confess that I went to the circus every Sunday. I have told about it and described it: the reader knows as much as I do; let him judge for himself and allow me to keep my own counsel.

Excerpt from
Gran Diccionario Taurómaco

by JOSÉ SÁNCHEZ DE NEIRA

The famous historian and essayist, José Sánchez de Neira takes his readers by the hand in 1896 to a couple of cafés after a *corrida* to show the reactions of the aficionados. And they had a few, too, as you will plainly read.

At the Door of the Royal Café

"Look, Manolo, if I had had the *banderillas* in that first bull, I certainly would not have done what Pinilla——not by any stretch of imagination—— no, siree."

"But what did Pinilla do? What would you have done?"

"Nothing, man, no, indeed; with an uncertain bull that prowled around like that——and this fellow going right up to his horns exposing himself to a sudden death. Why, man, why?"

"Ah, go on, getting in there close he planted a fine pair of *banderillas.*"

"Pure luck. And what if he had been caught? I am twenty years a *banderillero* and I have never been foolish enough to fool around like that, posing and exposing my body in the face of the bulls. Why? Because sooner or later you get it. And, I want you to know I am first and the public next. What if they don't applaud me? What do I do? I get me my money and let them talk to themselves."

"You got a point. It's better to do your job and leave the fancy work to the big shots; and take no chances under no circumstances."

"Boy, right is right. My job don't pay much and I'm just a member of the team, but I put up with a lot. And about money: what my gal Paca earns and the dozen *corridas* I pick up a season, I got a dollar and I live okay. When the day comes I haven't got it some friend will let me have it: Right, Pareja?"

"You got another point there. You know, they tell me too that it's your fault, Señor Pareja, that you are not with a *matador* who has a lot of fights. Why don't you press your luck? I tell them to shut up. If I am in such a situation, Lord forbid, I'd have to be on my toes every day. And my toes get tired."

A bystander interrupted. "And what did you think of the fight today? I'd like an expert opinion."

"Nothing special. Some good things, some bad things. More or less routine."

"And what happened to Butoldo? He got a terrible bump, and I thought he was finished. He looked dead when they carried him out."

"Nothing to speak of. I understand he had a broken arm and three cracked ribs. Nothing else."

"By golly, and you call that nothing?"

"Nothing much. Talking about a goring: one I got in Palua ten years ago, I thought I had lost twenty ribs on the left side alone, and another twenty on the right, maybe. I was unconscious over two hours, and woke up at home. That was some wound!"

"And, finally, how many ribs came loose? Were you laid up long?"

"It was nothing, my boy, nothing. But everybody agreed with me, it looked like I was a goner."

Now this is the talk of the fighters who did not have a good word to say about the fight. They are the hacks who don't know what they are talking about anyway. They are hangers-on. But inside a café are various people of different social classes, to judge by appearances.

In the Café de la Costa

"Okay. Granted what you say. But people don't understand the fiesta any more. In your opinion, which *matador* was best today?"

The question was addressed by a large, fat gentleman, but not too fat, with bushy side burns and a wide grave face, to a tall dry, brown young man, with light marks on his neck which his watchman's uniform usually covered.

"I tell you, Don Eusebio. You know, I am very impartial. I think I liked 'The Bug' best. He is very tough but not as ugly as the others. And furthermore, when I came here three years ago, the daughter of the seamstress who sews in the shop of a friend of the brother of the lady who owns the house where I work—she assured me, on her honor, that he was the best *matador* of the past, present or future. And I believed her! I sure am glad I did," he concluded, running his finger around his neck where the collar had rubbed it tender, and twisting his face into a wise frown.

"You're right as right. You got a lot of sense, and very smart to understand all the angles of the fight, after only three years! That's really something!"

"Well, you see I buy all the bullfight periodicals. And I read them inside out. It's true they don't all agree, but there is always somebody who says sometimes, 'The Bug knows a lot,' or 'The Bug is a master.' And that's the paper I like best at the time."

"Certainly, you talk right down my street: The critic who thinks like I do, I understand. Good, my friend, good. You had reason to say you are impartial. Keep it up and you will get somewhere."

"Listen, Don Eusebio, what Pacheco says. That if 'Liberator' had been fighting the fourth bull he would have killed by receiving it on the point of his sword."

"Yes, sir, I agree, and will repeat it a hundred times."

"Well, pardon me, but, if I may say so, you would have been wrong. If 'Liberator' had tried that stunt he would have pulled a bad one. Didn't you observe that that bull had defective eyes, in the more or less second degree?"

"B-but the bull responded to the bullfighter's maneuvers, and a bull that responds . . . ."

"Heavenly days! He responded from a distance, because he was far-sighted. He couldn't see close to his nose. 'The Bug' did all right calling him from where he was, and taking advantage of the weak eyes."

"I don't agree," grumbled Pacheco as he left the group. "What an intelligence. He reads the press and applauds 'The Bug.' "

"Well, what about the 'Herdsman'? Those passes, have you ever seen Montes or 'Cayetano' do better?"

"My good friend, Sol, the passes were fine. But did you note that he abused his dexterity. He wore out the bull, and made it impossible for a decent kill. They were all low passes and the bull got tired lifting its head. Why didn't he mix in some high passes? Because the bull had nearly collapsed he could not go in for the kill; the animal's nose was on the ground. That was very bad, and all his fault. This 'Herdsman' is very cold although somewhat elegant. And I think he sometimes lacks dash and courage."

"Don't say that, Mr. López. That he's not brave. That's for people who don't know. You can't call the man timid. After the horn wound he got in Sierra, he rose right up and killed the bull dead with one stroke of the sword."

"Ah, if he weren't so uncertain now. This hesitation will cost him some day."

" 'Little Beak' was worse the first time he fought after being caught by a horn in Colmenar."

"Stop right there. Let's don't make comparisons. I am one of those people who think it is hateful to criticize the spectacle where a man risks his life."

"You talk sense. Let's go back to the fight, and see if we can't agree. Fair to middling bulls, not very big and not very noble. Ordinary *picadors,* specially Alacrán, who stayed outside looking toward the inside and not getting close to the bull at the barrier. So-so the *banderilleros,* except for a couple of pairs. The *matadors,* nothing to shout about."

"Looks like everything was lousy, according to you. What about the lance of 'Pliers' in the first bull? And the *banderillas* of 'Combat' in the third?

The passes of 'Herdsman' with the same bull? The way 'The Bug' killed the fifth?"

"Nevertheless, it was lousy."

"No, sir."

"Wait a minute before you pop off. Those *banderillas* of 'Combat.' Had or had not the bull's horns passed him before 'Combat' stuck in the barbs?"

"No, sir."

"Pardon me, but a lot of people saw it. And about those 'Herdsman' passes, you heard me say they were very good but not according to the book."

" 'The Bug's' kill, I have nothing to say except he was running on a bias when he shoved in the sword, more like a *banderillero*."

"And so what? The blade went into the right place, all the way up to the hilt. Didn't the bull topple over dead. What better do you want?"

"If you are satisfied when they are crude, okay. But I'm not. Good night, gentlemen."

"Listen to him. He's mad now. Some people think they know everything."

And, one by one, they went away, each firmly convinced that he knows more about fighting bulls than anybody.

The Ethics of a Corrida

by LUCIA PURDY

"The Ethics of a Corrida" is unique because it is the earliest analysis of bullfighting by an American woman writer I have been able to find, and because it is an interesting vignette of a famous fighter. The article was published in *Harper's New Monthly Magazine*, July, 1898.

"A letter which has been awaiting mademoiselle for about ten days; the telegram arrived this morning."

Both were thrust in through the bars of the little cage of an *ascenseur* to where, covered with wraps and surrounded by any amount of small luggage, I was seated in solitary state, patiently waiting to be mounted to the *troisième étage* according to the cautious and altogether mysterious manner of procedure habitual to the French elevator. I managed, with the hand that had least in it, to tear open the blue envelope containing the despatch, and puzzled out the words of the message one by one—for I was left in almost total darkness:

PLACES FOR CORRIDA SECURED. ADVISE COMING FRIDAY TO AVOID CROWD. HAVE ENGAGED YOUR ROOM AT HOTEL MANIVET.

DE BRESSON

Why had my charming acquaintance, Made de Bresson, sent me this most unexpected and incomprehensible summons? Perhaps the letter—yes, it was addressed in her handwriting—would supply the key to the enigma. As it was, the sense and purpose of the telegram seemed hopelessly remote. I hastened to take possession of the room which had been assigned to me, dismissed the voluble *femme de chambre,* and, glancing once more at the despatch to be quite sure of the date—September 23—and to convince myself that I had made no error in thinking it had been sent from Nimes, read the pretty foreign letter with its gracefully turned phrases and suggestive use of Spanish terms. She knew that by this time I must be at the Hotel Tivollier, Toulouse, where I had told her I would rest for a day or two on my return from the mountains. Since she had had the pleasure of that little glimpse of me at Mount Louis, our conversation about the *corrida de toros* had constantly occurred to her—I did not in the least recall it!—and now there was to be a *gran corrida* in the old Roman amphitheatre at Nimes, on the twenty-sixth of September, which she believed I would like to see. They were going, of course. Her husband was such an ardent aficionado, and would not miss being there for worlds. She had quite set her heart on initiating me, and wrote to insist upon my joining them at Nimes. "Guerrita," the most famous "espadeo" in Spain, and "Minuto"—the tiniest of creatures, but possessed of courage and daring which were absolutely marvellous, were to be the *matadors.* Everything and everybody connected with the *corrida* was to come from Spain. It was sure to be fine, and it would be impossible for me to see one under better circumstances, as their friend Monsieur D—— knew "Guerrita," "Minuto," and everybody connected with the management, and through his influence I could meet these interesting *matadors,* and be taken behind the scenes the day before the *corrida* took place. As subscribers they were entitled to the best of seats, and she was sure a good one could be procured for me. It would be very crowded at Nimes. Should she secure a room for me at the little hotel they were accustomed to stay at? Our mutual friend Mademoiselle R—— of Marseilles had hoped to be one of our little party, but she was quite ill, poor child, and would probably have to give up accompanying her father, who was to sit in the president's loge to help preside, and who would always journey any distance to witness a good *corrida.* It was evident, after reading all this, that a great deal of trouble had been taken in my behalf, and although I possessed absolutely no curiosity to see a bullfight, and held the usual ideas concerning its barbarity, I felt that matters had gone too far for me to be able to excuse myself on the plea of scruples as to the immorality of the exhibition. It was a day's journey to Nimes, but at least I would have all the next day in which to recover from my fatigue. A telegram must be sent off at once to say that I would arrive Friday night, September twenty-fourth, and I could only hope that, once there, my distaste for the disagreeable features of the spectacle would not prevent me from meeting all this enthusiasm with some degree of responsiveness.

I had often heard that Spain's national sport had taken the deepest possible root in the land of its adoption, but when one does not come in contact with those who are interested in a special diversion of this kind, it may exist on all sides, thrive and increase, and yet scarcely attract the notice of the uninitiated. I had often travelled through the Midi, knew vaguely that bullfights were extensively patronized by its inhabitants, but had never concerned myself on the subject or dreamed of attending a *corrida*. On the way to Nimes it seemed to me that every one was talking *toros,* and at even the smallest stopping-places along the road gorgeous bill-posters with pictures of the arenas, the *paseo,* and groups of *toreros, picadors, banderilleros,* etc., flaunted their vivid colors in my face. I read them over and over until I fairly knew every name by heart.

Sunday, the 26th of September, 1897, at 3¼ o'clock.

GRAN CORRIDA OF SIX SPANISH BULLS
FROM THE GANADERÍA OF D. JOSE MANUEL
DE LA CAMARA,
TO BE FOUGHT BY THE MATADORES GUERRITA
AND MINUTO,

Accompanied by their Complete Cuadrillas.

And underneath were the names of the members of these *cuadrillas*— their real names, and the still more familiar ones by which they were publicly known in the exercise of their profession:

CUADRILLA DE GUERRITA	CUADRILLA DE MINUTO
MATADOR	**MATADOR**
Rafael Guerra—"Guerrita"	Enrique Vargas—"Minuto"
PICADORES	**PICADORES**
Antonio Bejarano—"Pegote"	Manuel Vargas—"Tornero"
Rafael Moreno—"Beao"	Angel Guerrero—"Grande"
Reserve: Antonio Medina	Reserve: Teodoro Amare
BANDERILLEROS	**BANDERILLEROS**
Juan Molina—"Lagartijo"	Manuel Antolín
Antonio Guerra	José Gonzalo—"Gonzalito"
Francisco Gonzalez—"Patatero"	José Vargas—"Noteveas"
PUNTILLERO	**PUNTILLERO**
Joaqín del Río—"Alones"	Francisco Roig—"Pastoret"

Seeing my interest in one of these *affiches,* a woman selling books and papers at a stand near where it was posted up offered me a little pamphlet with sketches of "Guerrita" and "Minuto." I gained from it a good deal of information that surprised me, for one could not follow the developments in the lives of these men without realizing what I had previously failed to take into consideration—that in order to work up from the ranks to a consummate mastership of the *matador's* art, phenomenal strength of purpose and complete self-control are required. "Minuto's" parents destined him for a profession, but the boy's absorbing desire to be a *torero* evinced itself in childhood, and failing to overcome predilections which seemed inborn, they abandoned their ambitions in favor of his own. His public career began at an extremely early age, and when only sixteen he figured as *matador* in a celebrated *cuadrilla* of Sevillian youths—niños Sevillanos. It seemed strange, handicapped as he was by diminutive proportions, that he should have been able to achieve the long list of triumphs recorded in the notes as to his different successful appearances, but the fact that he had served as alternative with such noted *diestros* as "Lagartijo" and Mazzantini, for example, was proof as to ability. And now, at twenty-seven years of age, he was to appear with the great "Guerrita," his senior by ten years, and far and away the most experienced and finished of all these swordsmen.

"Guerrita" seems to have been surrounded from the moment of his birth by every influence which could serve to make the adoption of such a career as he eventually chose especially legitimate and wise. His father was concierge in an abattoir at Córdova; and one of the most famous *matadors* of that time, José Rodríguez, or "Pequete," as he was called, stood sponsor for the little Rafael when he was christened. "Pequete" met with a tragic death in the arena while the child was still an infant in arms, but from the time that he could think for himself he determined to become as celebrated as this renowned godfather, whose memory was held dear, and whose great deeds were cited for the purpose of firing the imagination of the child and of arousing his ambition.

There was a pretty story* of the way in which "Guerrita," at twelve years of age, killed his first *toros,* arising from his bed in the middle of the night to steal his father's keys, and going forth alone by moonlight to do battle with and conquer the animals which were to have been slaughtered on the following day. It seemed too picturesque an episode to be quite natural, and likely enough was exaggerated. His having killed full-grown *toros* at that age and unassisted was in a high degree improbable. I should certainly ask him if it was true, when I met him—if I really did meet him. I wondered if this would come to pass.

Nimes was crowded when I reached there; but that was nothing to what it would be on the morrow, my friends assured me, according me the warmest of welcomes, and telling me of all the kind plans they had made— by which forethought I was to gain many privileges, it was easy to believe.

*A true one, as I found.

The next morning Monsieur D—— arrived, and at once assured us he was at our disposal and in readiness to take us anywhere, everywhere. Mademoiselle was an American, and unfamiliar with all the details in regard to a *corrida*? He would do his best to enlighten her. He should suggest walking out to the corral, if we did not mind a little exercise, and on the way he would try to tell me about *toros* and *toreros*. He certainly kept his word, and by the time our walk was over I felt that I had begun to grasp the meaning of much which I had hitherto felt puzzled about. It was interesting to hear that there were regular schools for the training of *toreros*. They were made athletic and supple by every conceivable form of exercise, he assured me, and the scientific parts of their art were systematized and developed there in all the perfection of minute detail. A great *torero* was born a *torero*—it was in him to become one. The necessary gifts could not be acquired; only cultivated when possessed.

The ceremony of the giving of the sword was very impressive, and it was a thoroughly solemn moment when a *torero* was created. The sword and *muleta*—the red scarf used by *toreros* to place the bull in position for the death-thrust—were handed to him with the words, *"Toma usted, y quiera Dios que le salga con provecho"* (Take these, and please God you may prove an honor to your country). A still more beautiful ceremony marked the withdrawal of a *matador* from public life. The *coleta*, or long lock of hair (to which the *mona*, or small silken waterfall, was fastened—the badge of a *torero*, and of use in the support of his *capa* during some of the passes executed), was then cut off with a golden scissors.

I asked about the duties of the different members of the *cuadrillas*, and was told in just what ways the clever *picadors* could save their horses; of how adroit *banderilleros* were best able to fulfil their dangerous task of piercing the *toro* with pairs of *banderillas*, or little decorated javelins, and of the *faena*, or particular style of work identified with each *torero*, individually entering into the use of *capa*, *muleta*, or sword, although conventional passes were rigidly adhered to and traditions sustained. Naturally much of the success of a *corrida* depends on the *toros*, and the *ganaderías* where they are raised are therefore a very important feature of the enterprise.

I was curious to know something about the prices paid for the different animals, and was told that six fine *toros* would cost nine thousand francs, and that the horses averaged about two hundred and fifty francs apiece. "And the *matador*, how much does he make," I asked, "for risking his life, as I suppose he does every time he enters the arena?" " 'Guerrita' receives a thousand dollars for each *corrida*." The answer was given in English, so that I should not fail to realize the importance of the sum. "And the less distinguished ones?" "Well, they of course have less. I suppose I may say between four and six hundred dollars, according to the reputations they may have achieved."

We had at last arrived at the corral, and were allowed to pass through the heavily barred doors at sight of our escort, who was evidently a great favorite with the officials, besides being a privileged member of various *toro* clubs. The strictest possible discipline was in force, and admittance was with-held from all save those identified with the management. The men moved about silently and gravely in the fulfilment of their tasks, it being considered important to avoid any disturbance likely to excite the *toros* in the adjoining enclosure.

The stables to the right of the main entrance contained twenty-four horses, ranged in their stalls—a dozen on each side—peacefully disposing of their rations and happily unconscious of their impending doom. Before each *corrida* the *picadors* have a trial of their mounts in the arena, and are thus able to discard such animals as promise to especially imperil their own and their riders' lives through inability to fulfil what is required of them. There was a good deal to be seen in the harness-room, for two of the head men were su-perintending the packing of saddles, gay trappings for the mules, and various accoutrements, all of which were to be transported to the arena during the course of the day. My attention was called to the chain-armor hangings de-pending from the saddles so as to protect the horses from the horns of the *toro*. The stirrups were very cumbersome, and had great iron foot-pieces, the right shoe being completely boxed in. It was from this side that the *pica-dor* was to lunge with his *pica* at the *toro,* therefore it was necessary that his foot should be encased in this massive shield; but one wondered how he could disentangle himself from his horse while thus fastened, in the event of his falling.

With the mayoral, or head keeper, as our guide, we went to the upper story to look down at the bulls in the open. We conferred in whispers, it being against the rule to speak out loud, and took turns in trying to see the animals through small peep-holes made for that purpose in a temporary door which shut off the gallery surrounding the enclosure outside. It was not very satisfactory, and I, for my part, felt anything but content with the mere glimpse I had had of one large black *toro* reposing beneath the shadow of a tree. I had brought my camera, hoping to snatch a photograph of the scene, and my disappointment must have been evident, for our friend the mayoral signed me to follow him, and smuggling me quickly outside, led the way to the extreme end of the enclosure, where favorable conditions as to light and view were to be obtained. A peculiar low whistle, a handful of gravel lightly thrown in their direction, and the clumsy creatures were set in motion, and several pictures secured. A word to my silent guide as we were about to retrace our steps, and with ready acquiescence—as being happy to gratify a lady's passing whim, and with absolute freedom from self-consciousness—the man drew himself up against the wall as simply and as naturally as if he had spent the better part of his life in having his picture taken.

The opposite side of the stables from where the horses were kept was de-voted to the *toros*. It was there that we inspected the simple but effective ap-paratus for transferring them from the cars they came in to box-stalls, and later from these compartments to the covered enclosure annexed to the one we had just come from. The cars were mammoth wooden vehicles, like square boxes on wheels, each one just large enough to hold a *toro*. They were tremendously thick through, unwieldy enough in their empty state, and I could not understand how it was possible to move them about the country when once the bulls were inside of them. But it was in these same cars that the very animals we had been looking at had journeyed from the *ganadería* near Seville. They had been *en route*, and had travelled by land and water. Everything in this section was made massive, bolts, bars, and ropes being suggestively thick and strong, and the mechanical processes of the simplest order. A system of trap-doors worked by ropes and pulleys was adopted whenever the transferences were made, the men being stationed in safety overhead, and the door being raised up to allow of the animal passing out or in.

In the afternoon we visited the arena. First, the places we were to occupy the next day were hunted up, and I was shown how the seats selected were situated directly to the left of the president's box and on the same row —they certainly could not have been better. We watched the carpenters at work on the extra benches erected to meet the unusual demand for additional tickets; saw the decorators drape a few flags here and there, effectively interweaving the Spanish colors with those of France; but the splendid lines of the superb old structure needed very little adornment, and the draperies were neither elaborate nor profuse. Some of the photographers were busy taking views of the interior; an occasional sight-seer would enter—a priest, a woman wearing the costume of an Arlesienne, a soldier in vivid scarlet, would glance curiously at the preparations and then disappear. We climbed to the summit and looked at the centre of the arena. I tried to fancy what it would be like as the scene of a *corrida,* but somehow it was an easier matter to people it with the audiences of the past, and to conjure up a vision of the Roman games. Here and there, blossoming from a handful of earth hidden within the crevices of the rock, were occasional wild flowers, and the sombre gray stones were lighted by many a patch of delicate verdure, tempted into existence by the warmth of the sun and the protection of the neighboring arched walls. Caught up high in one of the apertures and stretching out its branches to the light was a fig-tree. How strangely it had taken root there, and how odd that it should thus flourish with only the capricious elements to give it care!

We lost our way while wandering through some curious cavernous passages, for the points of exit were irregular and somewhat difficult to discover. When we regained the lower part of the building we crossed to the opposite side and sought admittance at the *toril,* entering from the street in company with the president, Monsieur ——, who, like ourselves, was obliged to slip through a half-opened and jealously guarded door; however, recognition and attention were accorded when once we were safely inside. The employes were hard at work unpacking things sent from the corral, and in distributing them through the dressing-rooms and stables. The *toril* is in reality, as its name implies, the place where the bulls are kept, and from which they pass directly into the theatre, and it is also where the *paseo* forms. The six compartments for the *toros* were in single file and reached to the gateway, being divided one from the other by the same sort of trap-doors we had been shown at the corral. The *toros* are installed in these compartments according to precedence. I had noticed a list of the names and colors of the bulls, and of the device of the special *ganadería* they had come from, pinned up against the wall of the corral, and now saw that these compartments were duly labelled with the same names—Capachuelo, Bigoto, Prevenido, Benona, Mojoso, and Sanguijuelo. When the time arrived for the first *toro* to enter the ring, the trap-door would be pulled up from above, and the bull, in running out, would find himself facing his opponents. Bigoto would in turn pass through the compartment his predecessor had vacated, and so on till the six trap-doors had been pulled up one after another, the last *toro*, Sanguijuelo, having to course through five empty compartments before reaching the scene of action.

I had read stories of the cruel way in which *toros* had to be driven to their death, and had believed that they were goaded to a pitch of frenzy behind the scenes in order to cause them to make a brilliant entrance; but certainly these animals could come in contact with no one in passing through these divisions and the connecting gateway which led to the theatre.

I had been so absorbed in studying these interior arrangements that the chief actors had passed completely out of my mind, and a realization of this came while listening to a group of young girls who were standing near the entrance of my hotel while I finally made my way back to it through the crowded avenues. " 'Guerrita' will be here at eight o'clock; it is the latest news," said one of them. "I am going to the station to see him arrive—are you?" I heard afterwards that there were hundreds of people waiting to catch a glimpse of the distinguished *matador* and his *cuadrilla,* and that a little company of eminent gentlemen received and conducted him to his hotel, all such forms being invariably carefully observed, and the desire to do him honor being marked by every possible attention during the period of his stay in the place where a *corrida* is given.

By night-time the town was thronged. Thousands of people poured in from all directions, and the capacities of the different hotels and cafés were taxed to the utmost. Beds were erected in the salons, and even improvised in the offices and halls, every lounge and sofa finding a tenant, and people who had been unable to engage a place to sleep in willingly paid large sums for the privilege of even occupying chairs and of obtaining a roof over their heads.

The morning of the twenty-sixth gave promise that it would be a rarely perfect day. The church-bells had awakened me at an early hour, and I sat at my window watching the multitudes on their way to mass. Later the scenes in the streets were indescribable, and the chimes mingled oddly enough with the babel of sounds in the squares and from the out-of-door cafés, where the voices rose and swelled as would the excited utterances of a mob. The one all-engrossing interest prevailed, but apparently every one went to church—and probably prayed for a good *corrida*.

Wonderful tales of deeds of heroism, of generous actions, and of noble characteristics were recited. The special attributes of this or that favorite *torero* were discussed, and the merits of the different *ganaderías* entered into. Had I ever seen such excitement? I was asked by my group of friends, who came to suggest that we should wander about to see what was going on in the different quarters of the town. I hesitated. No; we knew something of tremendous local enthusiasm as inspired by sport through the college games; and I attempted to describe the value and scientific interest of football, with a desire to paint it in the most glowing and attractive of colors, so as to put the favorite amusement of so many of my fellow-countrymen in the most favorable light. My hearers were certainly not impressed; a visible shudder ran through Monsieur D——'s frame, and he could not help exclaiming: "How horrible! It must be a very brutal game." The difference of our points of view struck me as almost ludicrous. Here was I, secretly treasuring the conviction that no more barbarous sport than a bullfight could exist, and sincerely dreading lest I should not be able to sit through the performance they were looking forward to. To the aficionado such ideas would simply mean that I had allowed myself to be prejudiced by biased statements, usually based on ignorance. Was I not really thinking that Monsieur D——'s intense dislike of what to us were the natural developments of our football game must have grown out of similar prejudices imbibed from foreign criticisms placing the sport in disfavor? It was not at all impossible that an aficionado of the *corrida* would find his aesthetic soul in revolt against the seeming barbarity of the play were he to be suddenly introduced at any one of the certain crucial moments when life and limb were in danger.

I wanted to take a photograph of the beautiful Roman temple the Maison Carree, which was directly opposite the hotel, so I started out with my kodak—my almost inseparable companion in this city where architectural remnants of a great past are to be met with in the course of the shortest of strolls. A dark, handsome man, dressed in the peculiar costume worn by all members of the *cuadrillas,* the straight-brimmed hat and light gray clothes showing his regular features and stalwart frame to no little advantage, crossed over with a pleasant smile of greeting, was cordially welcomed, and presented as Antonio Guerra—the brother of "Guerrita," and one of his *banderilleros.* The fatigue of the preceding day's journey was referred to. "Guerrita" had slept badly; and this morning, when he could have made up for his loss of rest if left in peace, he was actually invaded by the photographers of the London and Parisian illustrated papers, who thrust themselves into his bedroom, and at last had to be ejected by force. They were a perfect torment, and on the morning of a *corrida* one was in no state of mind to be willing to pose for one's portrait. We passed on, and an hour later, turning through a quiet, shady side street which opened off of one of the main avenues where the crowd was dense and the noise overpowering, I caught sight of a form drawn into shadow within a narrow door. It was the last place I would have expected to see him in, and yet, even before my companion darted forward impulsively with an exclamation of the name, I knew that it must be the great *matador* of whom every one was talking and thinking. He came forth immediately from his hiding-place, was introduced, gave me a straight-forward, manly glance and firm pressure of the hand, and stood talking to us for a few moments, affording me the very chance of all others to form an opinion as to what the real man was like, before seeing him in public as the central figure of a great drama. He was utterly different from my preconceived ideas of a *toreador*—as I still felt inclined to call a *torero*—in this way confessing how entirely my knowledge of their type and attributes was limited to the stage caricatures seen in such operas as "Carmen"; for there was no hint of expansiveness of temperament in that peculiarly self-contained, almost impassive bearing, and the physique seemed of the nervous, high-strung order rather than of the vigorous kind indicating a superabundant supply of animal strength. Will power predominated over every other characteristic, and the nature was essentially honest, the character virile. I felt sure that I had grasped a very general idea, but still a clearly defined one, as to the individuality of this Rafael Guerra, and was giving myself up to the more superficial study of his Japanese coloring and picturesque dress, the absence of gesture, and many little details which I could not fail to notice as of marked peculiarity and interest, when I was startled to hear the suggestion, "Mademoiselle would be much gratified to have a photograph of you, Guerra, if you do not mind posing." The words were spoken in Spanish, and remembering all the ordeal of the morning as related to us by the brother, I felt almost sorry the request had been made; but the courteous responsiveness with which "Guerrita" at once placed himself where the few available rays of light penetrated the overhanging foliage reassured me, and the slight smile which brightened his usually severe face was a still further indication that I was not overtaxing his patience too severely. In spite of an industrious morning with my kodak, I had fortunately not exhausted my entire film, and though "Guerrita" stood in partial shadow, I felt sure that the likeness would be good. It was strange indeed that we could stand here in what was, after all, an open street, and that I should be able to take this photograph unobserved, while all around us the world was waiting to see this very man pass on his way to the arena!

At the hotel there was hardly room enough to push one's way through the crowded halls. The restaurant was still thronged, those who had waited in vain for seats at a table munching sandwiches and fruit while standing, and picnic repasts being spread on the very stairs and landings. I followed the general example, seized a roll and a bunch of grapes from a passing waiter, and escaped with them to my room, the time having nearly arrived when we were to start for the arena.

It was exactly three o'clock when we took our places and studied the audience, afterwards estimated as having numbered over nineteen thousand souls. The darkened walls formed a wonderfully effective background for the masses of people, and with brilliant sunshine flooding the amphitheatre, and overhead a clear blue sky, the scene was one to be remembered. Seated as we were to the left of the president's loge, and directly opposite the gates opening from the *toril,* our view of the *paseo* could not but be perfect. A few late arrivals created the usual disturbance, the entrance of two or three eminent persons and of several well-known clubs causing the crowd to break out into occasional rounds of applause; programme-venders ran with the agility of cats along the dangerously narrow ledges of the balconies; the military band thundered martial airs; hundreds of little white balloons were sent floating into space; every one was in a state of suspense and excitement, and the tumult was overpowering.

At last the doors of the *toril* were swung open, two mounted alguazils crossed over to the president, and authority was given to set the procession in motion. It advanced slowly, in a direct line, to our side of the arena, being led by the alguazils, and with the two *matadors,* "Guerrita" and "Minuto," walking abreast at quite a distance apart. They were gorgeously costumed, and carried themselves with great dignity; and the members of their *cuadrillas,* which came next in order, were faultlessly gotten up and beautifully grouped. It was remarkable to notice how even the servants, who with the mules brought up the rear, seemed to have an innate feeling for spectacular effect in that they conducted themselves with natural grace, and so carefully preserved the necessary order and form. When they drew up in front of us, the details of the picturesque garments caught my attention, and I noticed that Guerrita's choice of colors was comparatively subdued, a soft heliotrope predominating, the one vivid note being supplied by the brilliant emerald satin *capa,* or mantle, tightly drawn about the body, and discarded at the close of the *paseo* for the more practical *capa* in use in the arena. It is considered an honor to have these capes which are worn in the parade thrown to one; therefore I was pleased when two of the handsome young *banderilleros* who were passing beneath us lightly tossed theirs in our direction, to be seized and spread out before us by the friend who sat next to us, with the rapidity born of long practice. A moment later the key of the *toril* was thrown down to an alguazil as the president's signal for the opening of the *corrida,* and the distribution of the forces began.

From that time on I was deeply impressed with one fact: the continual sense of responsibility experienced by the *matadors* in regard to the members of their *cuadrillas.* The moment peril threatened a comrade, the ever-watchful superior officer was at hand to ward it off, or to come to the relief of the endangered one. The evident loyalty of the men and the unanimity of their work were also noteworthy features, each one accomplishing his special task with a delicate precision and nice regard for order which spoke volumes for the careful drilling and discipline of the forces. It was a revelation, taken all in all, for one hears absolutely nothing of the scientific side of the sport shown; and the close sense of comradeship, watchfulness for each other's safety, and generosity of feeling were matters of continual surprise, and of which it is a pleasure to speak.

Capachuelo, the first *toro*—an enormous black and white bull, with entire black head and very solidly armed as to horns—burst into the ring like fury, and left the spectators breathless by his furious attack directed against the *picadors*. I confess to confusion as to what happened just here, for, seeing lives in danger, I turned away; but a second later I was fascinated by the extremely clever work of "Guerrita" and "Minuto" in luring the infuriated *toro* from his prey, and creating a furor by the intrepidity and finesse displayed. The banderillas were placed, each pair bringing forth an expression of enthusiastic approval or of satisfaction, according to the success of the effort in planting these barbed sticks; and this second stage of the drama brought to an end, "Guerrita" forward, sword in hand, to deliver his *brindis* to the president. The moment is very dramatic, and of great solemnity, and the peculiar sombre character of the famous *torero's* face, the somewhat harsh and penetrating tones of his voice, and the impressive significance of his gesture accented the meaning of the words uttered: "I dedicate this *toro* to you. I promise to kill him if he does not kill me." The first *toro* is invariably dedicated to the president; and later, if the *matador* desires to especially honor any one prominent individual he dedicates to this person the *toro* he is about to kill in the same public way, pronouncing his *brindis* as he goes forth for the final struggle and death-blow.

With a nonchalance which contrasted with his concentration of manner while delivering the address, "Guerrita" calmly approached the *toro*, and in a surprisingly short time hypnotized the animal—for it is surely little else but that—by the play of his *muleta* (a square of red stuff, it will be remembered, used in making the passes), and gave the *estocada* with a sureness of aim and skill which aroused the people to a wild pitch of enthusiasm.

During the development of the succeeding scenes, in which the remaining *toros* were disposed of, I learned something of the technique of the sport, and grew to see that the *"suerte"* (untranslatable term telling of the work accomplished with *capa*, *muleta*, sword, *banderilla*, and lance) of each man made evident his individual grace, daring, or acute powers of reasoning.

The second *toro's* battle with the *picadors* was immediate and decisive, bringing forward both "Guerrita" and "Minuto" to the rescue, and giving them an opportunity to display a very singular pass (*al alimón*), rarely attempted, I was told. In this pass the *capa* was drawn by the two men underneath the *toro*, was rapidly waved backward and forward, and at the close of this extraordinary exhibition they fearlessly knelt before the bewildered beast and tossed a handful of dust upon his foaming muzzle, an ovation being accorded them, and the uproar proving impossible to repress for some time. When "Minuto's" *brindis* had been pronounced, for it was now his turn to take up his sword, the battle between the two combatants presented fearful odds because of his diminutive stature. There was much to praise in "Minuto's" clever work, and his fearlessness prompted him to take risks which stirred the people's enthusiasm. His limitations sprang from his lack of inches, for owing to this defect it was impossible for him to render effective the concluding thrust of the sword.

It was Prevenido, a black bull, who next came before us. He entered slowly, but as suddenly flung himself upon one of the horses with so ferocious an attack that rider and steed went down together in one awful quivering mass. But "Guerrita" was there, and his wizard play with the *capa* soon liberated the hapless *picador* whose time had seemed so near at hand. This *quite* was rapturously applauded to the echo, and was followed by some clever thrusts from a young *picador* named Zurrito, after which Antonio Guerra and Juan Molina—two of "Guerrita's" *banderilleros*—aroused consideration by their skillful work with the *banderillas*. "Guerrita," imperturbable, calm, never wasting a moment, making each gesture count, and employing very beautiful and wonderful passes—recognized and successively named by my neighbors, whose running comments gave proof that it was really as marvellous an exhibition as I intuitively felt it to be—finished by a quick thrust at close aim, and with inimitable command of the resources of his art, persuaded the animal to follow him, that it might die at his feet, as he seated himself by the barriere and quietly, almost mournfully, regarded it.

Benona, of lustrous black coat and with *oeil de perdrix,* permitted "Minuto" to display his dexterity and to accomplish wonders with his *capa,* but the little *diestro's* most surprising feat was in turning his back on the huge brute while he invited it with his *muleta* to follow him.

The fifth *toro,* Mojoso, a large red and white bull, was really the *toro* of the day. The impetuous anger and savage force of this *toro* made one tremble for the life of every one in the arena, and the *picadors* were kept busy from the moment it dashed from the *toril.* Several pairs of *banderilles d'honneur* were presented by certain societies or *toro* clubs, and these were placed by the two *matadors* themselves, "Guerrita" courteously waiving his right of precedence and allowing the dashing little "Minuto" to come forward in a role in which he was sure to shine. His pair were placed "au cuarteo," and the quick movement with which he approached the raging *toro* and plunged them deep in— one wondered how he could reach up so high—raised a furor. Still, "Guerrita's" much greater finish and poise could not but take the color out of this really remarkable little *torero's* most effective efforts. His *banderillas* were placed so differently, with such quiet repose and exact regard for form, that the people simply went wild over him. For the *estocada* "Guerrita," with nerve which made one hold one's breath, folded his *muleta* and arranged it as he wished beneath the eyes of the bull. There were two or three passes— it is necessary to get the *toro* in a certain position for a successful *estocada*— and "Guerrita's" voice rang out, "This is for France! I tell you he is going to die!" and a moment later it rolled over and expired at his feet.

The last of the six bulls had been disposed of by "Minuto"; the *toreros* had gathered their brilliant *capas* about them, and had filed away, accompanied by the cheers of the people and the music of the band. Everybody was talking of the splendid success of this *corrida,* and I was standing there, feeling as if I had dreamed of what had taken place, although in my hand was one of the *banderillas,* posed for me by Antonio Guerra, to be carried to my far-off home as tangible proof that I had really witnessed a *corrida.* I was amazed at the perfect condition of the men who had taken such active part in the proceedings. Vaulting over high stone walls to escape the horns of the bull, running, using all of their force during the play of *banderillas* and sword, yet not one hair on their heads was ruffled; their immaculate linen and tight-fitting costumes were as free from stain or injury as if they had never stirred.

"Guerrita" (and his *cuadrilla*) lingered a few days at Nimes, and dined with us one evening. "Minuto," whom I met, and who posed for me before his departure, proved attractive, and was extremely courteous in manner.

This little informal gathering gave me still better opportunities to weigh the peculiarities of the greater of the two *matadors,* and my impressions concerning his unusual intelligence and strength of character were confirmed. Several who knew him well told me of his virtues as the best of husbands and of fathers, and assured me that his life was in all respects a moderate, well-governed one. He cares, it is said, but little for the excitement of social life, being always far more ready to sit and talk over his beloved art with congenial friends than to be made the hero of the hour at club or café. His distaste for over-convivial and not too sober admirers goes so far that he has been constantly known to call for water and wash his hands after being forced to submit to the grasp of such as are unpleasant to him. The quarters secured for him at Nimes proved uncomfortable, and his departure was somewhat hastened by this fact. Why did he not move to one of the other hotels? There were several that were excellent. He could not leave his men. They were as badly placed as he, and he was not willing to establish himself in comfort while they were suffering; as it seemed impracticable to move so large a party of men for so short a time, it would be better to pass on to Marseilles, en route for Beziers, where there would be another *corrida* on Sunday next.

"Guerrita" is a wealthy man, and in his own country he is simply idolized, but his tastes remain simple, and he is particularly free from an air of superiority towards those of his comrades who are less famous than himself. Many people find his manner forbidding, and he has the reputation of being plain-spoken and brusque, if not ungentle; but there were little touches which made me believe that this to me wholly agreeable straightforwardness indicated much genuineness of feeling, and the reserve of his nature, which was very strong, doubtless led to his often being misunderstood. The evening we dined together he expanded into a very different being from the "Guerrita" of the arena. He ate of the simplest food by choice, scarcely touched wine, and—for a Spaniard, most marvelous of all instances of renunciation—did not light the accustomed cigarette until the ladies at the table insisted on his doing so. Some one had gathered together a few yellow and red flow-

ers for the centre of the table, and to lay one at each napkin by way of bou-
tonniere. "Guerrita" was the first to take his up, lifting it quietly to see if it
had perfume, and fastening it in the exquisitely embroidered shirt peculiar
to the *torero*. The action and the manner showed a certain unexpected refinement of feeling, and his fastidiousness in several respects struck me as suggestive. Much was said concerning the *corrida,* and I was gravely pronounced an
aficionada, and asked if I believed many Americans would care to witness
the scene. I could truly say that I believed Señor Guerra's art must meet with
recognition all over the world, and that my countrymen were not slow to appreciate genius. Could *corridas* be given in New York? I thought our laws
would prevent this. But such laws might possibly be overcome. I turned to
the quiet figure by my side, and asked, "And if it could be so arranged, Señor
Guerra, would you come?" He looked me quickly in the face to see if I was
jesting, and answered decisively—quite sternly, in truth—"Yes, I will come."
Some one at the table raised a glass and proposed a toast to Señor Guerra's
first *corrida de toros* in Nueva York; so we drank to this solemnly, I almost felt
as if his coming was a *fait accompli.*

　　There are extenuating features of the *corrida,* and, like every other sport
in the world, it has two very clearly defined sides. It certainly develops qualities which are valuable and rare. But, at all events, I shall never forget the
wonderful drama in the old Roman amphitheatre at Nimes, nor the meeting
with "Guerrita," most justly famous as the very King of *Matadors.*

Excerpts from Shadows of the Sun

by ALEJANDRO PÉREZ LUGÍN

TRANSLATED BY SIDNEY FRANKLIN

　　Sidney Franklin of Brooklyn has been my friend for twenty-five
years. He is a man of great charm, ingenuity and several talents. He could have
been a top ranking *matador,* if he had not been so grievously wounded just as he
was entering the ranks of stardom. His facile imagination and picturesque expression, added to his ease in the language of his profession, added up to equipment
for writing. I saw him often when he was translating Pérez Lugín's *Currito de la
Cruz* into *Shadows of the Sun.* I tried to be of some consolation during his infancy
of authorship, but he had better professional care. I was a news correspondent.
Ernest Hemingway was a famous author and extremely generous with his time

for friends. Nobody will ever know, probably, what his help meant to Sidney. Both are modest men, in different ways.

Franklin certainly took on a large task for his first book. Alejandro Pérez Lugín, known as Don Pío, had died in 1926. He was a famous bullfight critic and newspaperman. The translation came off well. The beginning of a young bullfighter is told in the first chapter, and presented here.

Franklin also wrote a book on his own life, *Bullfighter from Brooklyn*. I have heard him tell the story many times, with variations. I have seen him act it out during one almost entire night at the Embassy in Madrid for Ambassador Claude G. Bowers, Franklin D. Roosevelt, Jr., Arthur Krock of *The New York Times*, and other wide-awake and rapt spectators. With his histrionic talent, the performances of his life, leavened with true comedy sense, are rare blends of pantomime and monologue.

We talked about doing the story of his life together, and he got so far as to dictate a few pages of notes to my assistant, Kay Hansen. Then he disappeared on some project into Mexico. It is just as well. It would have been too hilarious an undertaking. I am sure he acted it out as he was writing. I present also in this book his story of how he found out who Hemingway was. Literature has too few episodes of its kind.

At the sound of the bugle-call marking the entrance of the third bull, "Copita" twitched nervously. Turning to the youngster who, serious and abstracted, was sitting next to him in that terrifically hot front-row seat, he started with:

"Here's where we're going to see if you're any good, Curro!" and as Curro neither moved nor answered, "Copita" added:

"What the hell's the matter with you? Got lead in your pants already?"

"Nah."

"It can't be anything else. What are you waiting for?"

Ill at ease, he continued watching the performance, which, although the most important of the famous *corridas* during the Sevillian Fair of April, was extremely dull. It seemed as though all the component parts were in accord to bore the ever-patient public once more. The bulls were of the legendary, dangerous Miura herd, and the *matadors*—who were being extremely prudent and wishing they had never even heard of that fatal breed—were showing their distaste for such stock plainly, as could be observed by the unanimous disgust displayed by the masses that filled the stands.

While the mules were dragging out the bull that had just been killed in such a disgraceful manner by Lunares, "Copita" became serious and once again turned to the kid at his side.

"Now get this. Are you going in or not? I tell you that you'll never live long enough to wait for the kind of bull you want, and nobody's going to drag it up here and put it in your lap. . . . Now listen. . . . Say—what the hell's the matter with you? Can't you talk?"

"Let me alone, will you?"

226   **Excerpts from "Shadows of the Sun"**

"Let you alone? All right, that's all," he answered as gruffly as he could, "I'll let you alone! This is the end. When we leave here we go by footmobile. I'll take you back to the orphanage, where you belong. I hope the Mother Superior pardons you, and I'll tell her not to whack the lights out of you, so you won't run away again. Because there's no use. You're no good for this sort of thing anyway—but it's my own fault! I should have known as much when I took you to Tabladilla (the open corrals just outside Seville where the bulls are displayed preceding each performance) and watched you running around there. I thought it was funny you couldn't find a bull you liked out of all those there. The Murube bulls were skinny; the Colomas, too small; the Parlades, blah . . . and the 'Cid' right here at my side had to go and pick the only real bulls of the lot: the Miuras! Let God look after us and protect us! And me, 'Copita,' me a damn fool called 'Copita,' with all my knowledge of bulls and of the world, sucked in by a kid. What made me squander my last three bucks on a couple of sweltering first-row seats? Just so that this little dear could see a nice performance, and then go home to his mama? . . . The hell with it! It's your own fault, 'Copita,' let this be a lesson to you! The hell with it."

In this strain he continued heckling the boy until, tired of hearing him, Curro burst forth:

"But—can't you please shut up?"

"And on top of that he wants me to shut up. I'll shut up. The only reason I'm not leaving right this minute is that I don't want Manuel Carmona to believe he's boring me to death with his lousy performance. Christ, what a bunch of bandits in bullfighters' suits. But, by God, even though he is so lousy, I, Joaquín Gonzales 'Copita,' tell you now, once and for all, that Manuel Carmona is the Emperor, King, Pope, Sun, Moon and the Stars; well if you don't like that, he's the greatest *matador* that ever lived. . . . Listen to that—whistling their heads off at him. What do those bums want?"

Nobody paid the slightest attention to the monologue carried on by "Copita." The stands seethed with impassioned disputes, insulting shrieks, deafening whistling, demonstrations against the reigning lord of bullfighting. Some were vainly offering a weak defense for the greatest *matador* of all, who just then was experiencing one of the most trying moments of his career. Carmona was being violently insulted by the frantic crowds who were taking advantage of that awful moment in vengeance for the numerous occasions on which they were forced to applaud the great *matador*.

At a *corrida,* as at a literary gathering, the grievous sin of success is unpardonable. The applauding multitude, intoxicated with enthusiasm and admiration, gives itself over the very next moment to the perverse pleasure of pulling down and trampling upon the idol they have just raised to the very limits of the skies, with the clouds as his pedestal. Maybe the *matadors,* those great dominators of multitudes, knowing their power over the public, that public which is their fiercest antagonist, nourish their vanity by listening to its terrific grumblings and insults. After these weak indications of its momentary superiority over its dominator the hysterical mob docilely submits to its despotic master.

Here and there, some good friend or admirer of Carmona dared to lift his voice in defense of his idol. Other Carmonistas, at other times so vociferous in their praises, were now indifferent and shrinking from the deafening insults that were exploding all over the ring. The more charitable spectators limited themselves to the explanation—with secret complacence—that Carmona was sweating a number of strange substances unknown to the science of anatomy. Some affirmed that he was sweating ink; others sustained the possibility of its being shoe polish; still others contested that it might be fish glue, since the odors resembled those of the chemicals used in the shoe industry.

A handful of weary assistants surrounded the *matador* and were visibly spoiling the already impossible bull. The animal kept the ground before it clear, although no one attempted an approach. The more valorous ones limited themselves to extending their capes via long distance. This cowardice exasperated the indignant spectators even more.

"You've got to get up close! get up there right near it!" some enthusiasts yelled, with the facility for the most intricate manoeuvres one feels while seated in the stands.

"Get a shotgun!" vociferated an anti-Carmonista, standing in his seat.

Meanwhile poor Carmona was employing the thousands of precautions known to him against his extremely difficult enemy.

"An elephant gun for a great *matador* to kill that poor little bull with!"

"I wish to Christ that were true!" some of Carmona's assistants heard him say. He was the only one of the entire group who was at ease.

"What do you mean a rifle!" commented another anti-Carmonista. "He wouldn't even dare with that!"

"That Miura sure is tough!"

"And he certainly has softened up Carmona."

"What the devil do you all want?" clamored "Copita." "What do you expect a *matador* to do with an animal like that?"

The bugle-call advising the *matador* that the first fifteen minutes allotted for the killing were up threw the public into a still greater frenzy. Some demanded that the steers be brought out immediately without the necessary three-minute lapse. Others, tired of yelling, began throwing everything within reach at the unfortunate *matador*. A furious rain of oranges, cushions and bottles fell into the ring.

"*Matador,* they've given you the first signal," one of his *banderilleros* said.

"Get ahead of him and fix his attention. I'm going to try and kill him from the rear, or with the half turn. I won't let them have the fun of seeing the buzzard go out alive."

The indignation of the multitude was rising rapidly, so that Carmona, convinced of the impossibility of getting rid of the animal by any other means, despatched it in his most despicable and able manner.

There was no branch of the Carmona family tree that escaped the violent insults of those in the stands. Nor was there any part of his anatomy that wasn't blasphemed. At least ten editions of the most voluminous dictionary of blasphemy were consumed in the short time in which Carmona crossed the ring to the barrier where his sword handler awaited him. The *matador*, careful not to appear as satisfied as he felt at having saved himself from untold dangers, washed his hands in the little stream of water provided for him. After drying them with a towel, he sat down on the stepping-board of the barrier, and, now showing his calm, asked his assistants:

"Have you any idea what they're yelling about?"

"So you feel that good?" said "Carita," who was the next *matador* in turn.

"Don't be a fool!" answered Carmona. "Look how much better off you are now. Don't you see I left them all hoarse?"

"Carita" timidly looked up at the stands. "Yeah, hoarse! They're just getting their second wind now! I wonder what their lungs are made of!"

Carmona was soon to find out the extent of their hoarseness.

Although apparently indifferent, Carmona was thinking the same thoughts as his companion. The riot in the stands was beginning to take on serious proportions while the disgusted and preoccupied *matador* was awaiting the disagreeable moment of facing the next bull. But, what the hell! He already knew that when the effervescent nervousness of the moment was past, those who were now whistling and shouting with such vehemence, in days to come would smilingly recall the incident as proof of Carmona's greatness: his keeping calm through most trying moments made the most difficult antagonist appear inconsequential. They could shout as much as they wanted to now. But if he had his choice . . . what a pleasure he would get out of wringing some necks! . . . I don't mind their getting sore at the show, he thought, but what business have they trying to mix in a man's family, just because he hasn't had any luck! . . .

As though divining his thoughts, the public continued insulting the whole troupe, together with all his ancestors. It looked as though the demonstration and the insults would last throughout the rest of the performance. To expect that "Carita" or Lunares would distract the indignant public would be looking for the impossible. Carmona hoped they would. No one knows how interminable a performance can be, when once the public ire is brought to the boiling-point.

"Copita" and "Currito" were the only persons detached from all these happenings. When the bull had circled the ring once, "Currito" turned toward "Copita" and almost whispered:

"Let's have it!"

"You mean now?" asked "Copita," terrified.

"Yes, now!" he answered simply.

"But, you damn fool, don't you see that that's the red one?"

"That's why!" replied "Currito" calmly.

"All right, here goes, and may God help you. Everything comes in bunches!" concluded Joaquín, busying himself with the nervous exchange of something he had hidden under his jacket, for just such an occasion. Since this red bull had been on display in the corrals at Tabladilla, it had served as the basis of frightened discussions by all the *matadors*—even to the extent of those who were not to take part in the performance. "Copita" felt that the kid was going to be one of those freaks of genius; what we would call a *matador* of extremes—either very good or rotten. There could be no halfway about him. Recalling the hushed voices of the different groups when referring to this particular red Miura, and the rare occasions on which he himself had ever accidentally gotten close to an animal in his *corridas* of yesteryear, "Copita" suddenly went cold.

From Triana to San Bernardo, from the Delicias to the Alameda de Hércules, at the casinos, among those drinking aperitifs at the cafés on Las Sierpes and La Campana, in fact everywhere, in all those parishes of bull-fight followers, the red Miura had been talked about. They had discussed with awe its size and its probable "ideas," and the mention of its name caused eyes to look toward the door, in a quick survey of possible means of exit in case the bull should suddenly appear.

The legendary inmate of Tabladilla had already given occasion for alarm. On the eve of this *corrida,* some claimed, a most docile Swiss cow presented herself unexpectedly in the Café de la Perla, on the Plaza Nueva just at the time every one was out for the afternoon stroll. She stuck her inoffensive head in the door, looking curiously about her. With a single shriek of panic, according to the story, all the drinkers had disappeared as though by enchantment.

"The red Miura!!!" shouted all in unison, hurling themselves through windows and doors, overturning and destroying tables and chairs and everything else breakable.

Some clawed their way up columns as cats climb trees. Almost everybody fled. Some carried the table water-bottles along with them in their haste. An hour later, the cow returned to its barn. Order was restored. Sheer force was necessary to drag the chef out of the enormous water-tank into which he had jumped for refuge. His teeth were chattering more from fear than cold. That was how the boys told it at the café.

During those days nobody was free from the preoccupation of the red Miura.

"I wonder what's in Don Eduardo's mind! What could be his idea in sending that bull?"

"He probably wants to get revenge on somebody!"

"Did you notice how big it is?"

"Yeah, as big as a locomotive!"

"And what small horns! . . . Just reach from here to Lima!"

"And made of candy!"

"Yeah, and did you notice its neck? Good night, did you notice how it goes in and out like an accordion?"

"What do you mean an accordion? That's a whole orchestra! Why, that neck's automatic! That's a real gift, for the one who has to take it on!"

At the drawing for the bulls that morning, all the *banderilleros* and *picadors* whose respective *matadors* had especially entrusted them with the difficult task of arranging the lots to be drawn, had almost come to blows.

Fearful lest the red Miura fall to their lot, neither footmen nor horsemen could agree on the manner of pairing it off with the other animals. After several hours of discussing weights, sizes, and longitude of horns, when the drawing had been completed, it was found to be in "Carita's" lot. His assistants were panic-stricken. The others let out a sigh of relief.

"I don't know why you feel that way about it!" the promoter said, ignoring the murderous looks in his direction. "Just on account of an ordinary bull! There's barely a hair's difference between that one and the others! I'd like to bet anybody that it weighs less! You'll all see after the *corrida!*"

"I'd give plenty for it to be over," murmured El Sauce, one of "Carita's" *picadors,* whose bones were already aching in anticipation of the performance.

"He's right!" yelled another *torero,* suddenly realizing that his lot appeared to be swelling momentarily . . . also his fear. "I'll bet you that our black one is bigger than all the others!"

"And my speckled one!"

"Well, I'll trade you if you want to!" cut in "Carita's" *picador.*

"Not with me! Luck is luck and I don't want to mess it up. Maybe I'd spoil it for myself! A blind beggar can see our black one is bigger, fatter, much heavier and has longer horns!"

"Can you beat that? The next thing you'll be telling me is that they're sugar candy, made by the Sisters of San Leandro!"

Each and every one of them razzed the breeder's representative before leaving.

"My regards to your boss! What a sender."

"He likes us all right. He stabs us in the back."

". . . no matter what I do with this one or that one!" a *picador* of "Carita" was saying, irreverently shuffling all the saints on the calendar.

One may readily imagine "Carita's" feelings when he learned of the gift that had fallen to his lot. Until time to dress for the *corrida,* all his friends —as though in obedience to an assignment—would ask by way of greeting:

"But is it true that you drew the red one? Man, what a class of luck! . . .

The above comments will give the reader some idea of the enormous anticipation, the curiosity, and the emotion aroused in the solidly packed stands immediately before the entry of the already notorious red Miura.

Excerpts from "Shadows of the Sun"   **231**

A prolonged "aa-aa-ah!" . . . of admiration and fear greeted the entrance of the beautiful brute. Once in the ring, it appeared even larger than in the corrals at Tabladilla.

"Look how he gains size in the ring!" said one of the *toreros* seated among the spectators, feeling comfortably terrified compared to those in the ring, who were prudently keeping to the barrier, feebly shaking their capes. A long way ahead of the red bull's charge, they precipitously scaled the barrier, seeking the safety behind it.

The irate multitude whistled deafeningly. Cowards! Wretches!

As Manuel Carmona started to take his position in the ring, it was quite natural that the public vent its wrath on him, as though he were to blame for the panic displayed by his companions.

"I hope you all eat it and choke on it!" the *matador* said.

At that particular moment, a boy carrying a *muleta*—a "capitalist," so called because when arrested for jumping into the ring he was liable to a fine of fifty pesetas—suddenly appeared in the arena from nowhere. Running behind the bull from which all the *toreros* were fleeing, he kept calling in a childish voice to attract its attention.

He was nothing but a kid, skinny, shabby, and apparently resolved on suicide. His extreme youth horrified the spectators. They insulted the *toreros* more than ever. They insulted the policemen stationed behind the barrier for the sake of public safety. They insulted the bull-ring servants. They insulted everybody for not having impeded what looked like an imminent suicide. The lad kept running after the bull which seemed to be mowing the arena clean, arrogant in sensing itself supreme.

"But, don't you see he's only a kid, a child? that he'll be gored to pieces!" the stands yelled compassionately at the police, who dared no greater heroism than lifting a cowardly leg toward the barrier, seemingly undecided as to their next step—it might be fatal.

"Copita" was the only one who indignantly protested the sympathetic attitude of the public.

"Shut up, will you, you bunch of pansies!"

"But don't you see he's only a kid?"

"What if he is a kid! If he wants to fight, let him!"

The boy wanted to fight! Quickly and decidedly he went toward the gate of the bull's entry, where the red Miura, having tired somewhat from running around the ring, had stopped to get its bearings. Before "Currito" —having broken through all the bull-ring servants—could reach the bull, one of "Carita's" *banderilleros* tried to grab him.

"Hey! Where do you think you're going?"

"Currito" squirmed out of the man's grasp. Pulling an enormous shimmering knife—a knife, indeed, rather a tremendous and terrifying machete from the folds of the *muleta* in which it was hidden, he shook it at the *banderillero*.

"Don't come any nearer, or I'll cut your gizzards out!"

As every one gasped, the *banderillero* stopped short. "What's the matter with you?" he said, amazed and shocked.

"That kid is crazy!" someone shouted. "Let God look after him!"

The boy lost no time. Taking advantage of the liberty in which he found himself, he went directly to the bull. Carrying the folded *muleta* in his left hand, and the enormous blade, as though it were a sword, in his right, he stopped at a convenient distance from the elephantlike Miura.

No one breathed.

"Here it goes," shouted the youngster in an effeminately childish voice that resounded impressively in the profound and emotional silence of the arena, for Señor Manuel Carmona, the greatest *torero* in Spain!

Then, straightening his thin, urchin's body in a challenge, he attracted the attention of his enemy.

"Heh, toro!"

"Yo for my brave kid!" "Copita" shouted.

As the bull did not move, the boy calmly advanced a step and shaking the red cloth, again defied the beast, which raised its head as though shocked at the audacity of such an insignificant being.

"Heh, toro!"

If it were possible for it to be quieter it was now even more silent in the stands—the silence of fear. For the third time they heard the thin challenging voice of the kid. The terrible Miura seemed to be in doubt as to what was facing him—not to know whether this thing facing him was worth destroying.

"Heh! toro! toro!"

The spectators gasped with fear, as with a terrific rush the Miura charged the boy. Instinctively, they jerked back in their seats, jostling their neighbors. Women screamed, covering their faces with fans or hands.

"He'll kill him!" everybody shrieked.

Before they could finish the sentence, a joyous shout, a sigh of relief, a roar of admiration and triumph, developed into a thunder of amazement and enthusiasm.

"Olé!" came the ritual shout; the great, spontaneous deep-throated exhalation of triumph.

The boy had calmly awaited the impetuous rush of the beast, and gracefully bent his body in the precise movement necessary to allow the animal barely to graze him.

"Copita's" eyes were wet. Only once before in his life had he actually cried. That was when his *matador* was stretched on a cot between two small-town doctors who stood helpless and horror-stricken, looking at the man who had been destroyed by a bull in a country ring.

"I knew it! I knew it!" he said.

The lull preceding great events reigned anew in the stands. Curiosity and concern held everybody in suspense. "Currito," indifferent to those present, sure of himself, all attention fixed on that which he was doing—

as a fencer who returns to the attack after a parry—challenged the bull from his new position with the aplomb and skill of a seasoned performer. The body which previously had appeared so grotesque, now became the essence of rhythm and grace. Offering the red cloth to the brute, he slowly drew it all the way past his body in that beautifully classical and emotional manoeuvre known as the *pase natural*. Before the spectators could recover from the amazement of what they had just witnessed, he made them jump in their seats with a series of passes so slow, graceful and rhythmic that he seemed to have the bull tied to his *muleta,* apparently subjugating the beast to the dictates of its impervious conductor.

"He's mastered him! He's hypnotized!"

Then occurred that phenomenon of mirage which is produced by great events in the arena—the plaza moved. It was seen to have moved. The swaying of the nervous spectators actually gave the impression that the plaza was tottering. No one could refrain from outbursts. Everybody applauded excitedly, the women with greater enthusiasm than the men.

"*Olé* for you! *Olé!*" they yelled, their eyes brimming with tears.

From all over the arena, hats, fans, jackets, vests and cigars rained copiously.

"What a boy!"

"Look at him, my God, look at him!"

"Copita," hanging halfway over the rail, which he was shaking furiously—without his hat, his pigtail fallen loose, eyes starting from his head, face almost purple with congestion—was shouting as though mad:

"My fighter! My fighter! *Olé* my fighter!" He struck the man beside him on the head, biting his own hands nervously and jumping violently with the excitement caused by each new pass, in a frenzy of enthusiasm and joy.

"You're the greatest! The greatest! You've got the key to the Bank of Spain in your hands! You know it! You know it! There's no one else! No one else!" and turning toward the Giralda, the gracefully lace-like tower which stood beautifully erect against the clear sky of that spring afternoon, he passionately yelled to it:

"Come down and see this for yourself! Come on!"

Meanwhile, the boy, the Kid, as every one had nicknamed him, having resolutely opposed the interference of all the *toreros,* calmly and smilingly continued playing with the beast and death. His grace and valor seemed to paralyze the other *toreros* with admiration, especially when the Miura, in an extremely close pass, believing the body already on its horns, carried away as a trophy the front of the Kid's dirty jacket.

"*Viva la Alameda Vieja!*" shouted a section of the ring.

"Hurray for Triana!" exclaimed others.

Obeying local pride and desirous of assigning the glory of being the birthplace of a new idol to their respective districts, other shouts were heard in honor of the *barrios* of San Bernardo, Puerta del Osario, and la Macarena.

Just as the Greek cities claimed the birthplace of Homer, the Spanish disputed the baptism of Cervantes, or Pontevedra and Genoa the birth of Columbus, the Sevillian fans began to argue in the stands in defense of the historic, geographic and genealogic facts sustained by each, although none of them knew the Kid.

"He must be from Triana, like Antonio Montes and Juan Belmonte!"

"That genius from Triana? He must be from the Alameda like the 'Gallos,' 'Carita Ancha,' and Fuentes. You have to drink in the *fuente del Pato* to be able to perform like that!"

Whether the Alameda or Triana, the la Carne or Santa Cruz, battles with canes and bottles were going at full tilt in the upper part of section seven and the centre of section five. Even the most sedate section of the shady side, occupied by the intelligent Sevillian fans, was in a state of chaos, almost necessitating the proclamation of martial law in order to calm the tumult, for which the local police were momentarily inadequate.

"I'm going to take you two to the station, so you'd better stop it right now," ordered a municipal policeman in the sunny section, "because that kid is from la Carne, just like the late José Claros, 'Pepete'!"

"Did you say from la Carne? Your partner just told me he's from the Alameda."

"He did? What does he know!" answered the policeman.

"More than you!" replied his companion. "That Kid drinks in the Pato fountain."

"The Kid is from la Carne, that's where he got those guts——!"

A good-natured, fat sergeant imposed silence on his subordinates, ordering them to conduct the belligerents to the station, and stating, to dispel all doubts, that the Kid was from Triana; he was positive of it.

"You are?"

"Of course; I was there when he was born!"

"That lets us out! Come on, Manuel. Obey your superiors!"

Entirely unaware of the uneventful happenings around him, "Currito" continued manoeuvring gracefully and valorously on his knees as well as on foot. He was so close and so enthused that one might say he was satisfying an innate joy in demonstrating his aptitudes as a *torero*, doing all he had hoped to do on jumping into the arena.

Then a woman's shout was heard above the noise of the stands. "Currito" heard it and as he turned he gave "Carita's" peons the opportunity of attracting the animal to another section of the ring.

"Hurray for you and your whole family!"

Hearing this cry, the Kid, who had stopped working the bull for a moment, turned in the direction from which the shout had come, and smiled very sadly. Considering the vehemence and certainty with which mob sentiment is established and defined, this was interpreted as courtesy and modesty; thus augmenting the already thunderous applause.

But then a danger greater than the bull became apparent to "Currito":

it was the police. As soon as they were sure that the red Miura was far enough away, they jumped into the ring with drawn sabres, resolved on capturing the Kid and his machete. They would take him to jail where, according to custom, unless some one interested in his plight made a timely appearance to intercede on his behalf, the fuzzy beginnings of his pigtail would be shaved off.

When "Currito" saw them approaching, he fled in the prescribed manner of the perfect *"capitalista"* in the direction where the bull was at that moment on the verge of charging a *picador,* but it was too late. The police, knowing the code, anticipated this movement and, cutting off his escape, grabbed him.

"Let's have that weapon!" one of them demanded angrily as soon as they had a good hold on him.

"But it can't even cut butter!" answered the Kid, eagerly surrendering the tremendous blade, hoping they would overlook the *muleta.* "It's only a piece of wood!"

"By God, it is wood, at that!" said Traguete, one of the police interpreters who had been most terrified at the idea of entering the ring, as he heroically grabbed the weapon while his companion held the Kid from behind.

Offended by the absurdity of the situation, he threatened the Kid with the pseudo-knife, as though he intended piercing him through and through.

"I ought to cut out your damned heart for this!"

Loudly demanding the Kid's freedom, the spectators rose in a wave of indignation. What! that cop trying to harm our hero! and twenty thousand discordant voices demanded the head of Traguete; no matter how sporting or popular a policeman might be, he had no right to do that! "Out with him! Kill him! Lynch him! Out with him!" they shouted, the same terms they used to abuse poorly performing *picadors.*

To calm their anger and deflect this outburst, Traguete broke the blade over his knee and held up to the crowd two pieces of wood covered with silver paper.

The stands broke into laughter.

The Kid was clever!

On top of being such a good *torero,* and so valiant, the Kid was witty! That was the finishing touch. He was made. When the Kid, followed by the policemen, reached the barrier, some one in the first row threw five shining silver *duros* to him.

"Here, plucky, this is so you can get yourself a new jacket!"

There is no enthusiasm as contagious as that at the *corridas.* Those immediately round about imitated their neighbor and threw coins at the Kid. Those farther on did the same. "Currito," being called from all sections at once, was obliged to circle the ring, followed by the policemen; in acknowledgment not only of glory and the tremendous applause, but also a more prosaic though Heaven-sent shower of money . . . silver and coppers wrapped in paper, and even some five-*duro* notes. The golden rain was so copious that he was unable to gather it by himself. The policemen were obliged to help him—even a *guardia* can be courteous. Using their hats as receptacles, as years ago the *banderilleros* used the hats they wore when fighting to collect cigars thrown to their fortunate *matadors,* they accompanied the Kid on his triumphal march around the arena.

"What a troupe!" yelled the cynics from the stands.

"Traguete, you're perfect in that role! You look just like the dead 'Lagartijo'! The only difference is that you talk!" Becoming seriously absorbed in his role, Traguete paid no attention. When his hat became filled, he took one end of the *muleta,* and giving the other end to "Currito," they pooled in it all the coins that kept raining into the ring.

"Well done, Traguete! Now don't grab any for yourself!"

Having finished the collection, "Currito" and his *guardias,* hats in hands, bowed before the mayor's box. After giving the *muleta* to his peon, "Currito" demanded pardon.

"Yes! Sí! Sí! You're pardoned!" decreed the mass.

The mayor and his two secretaries answered the Kid by throwing four or five *duros* to him.

More applause followed as the Kid bowed in gratitude.

"Here, take this and go back to your seat," said the treasurer, turning over the *muleta* filled with money.

"Currito" responded gallantly by dipping his hand in the *muleta* and generously offering the *guardias* a handful of coins. Traguete pompously refused, seemingly hurt and indignant, while saying between his teeth:

"Not here! I should say not! Later, alone, we'll have a couple of drinks . . . and whatever you say, *torero!"*

On the way to his seat the Kid passed near Carmona who, leaning against the barrier, called him.

"Listen, *niño,* after the *corrida* I want you to come to my home. I want to make you a gift for your dedication. You've been fine, . . . and you've helped me out. It was a good *quite."*

Shaking his hand cordially, "Currito," happy and awed, was too shy to speak.

"Copita" received him with an embrace that almost crushed him. For some time tears kept the veteran *banderillero* speechless.

"Didn't I tell you, Señor Joaquín?" questioned "Currito." Later, self-satisfied, "I did all right, didn't I?"

"You couldn't possibly be better, sweetheart! like the very angels!" answered "Copita" happily. Turning to the curious spectators and proudly convinced of his prophetic powers, he exclaimed: "Señores, I am the greatest *aficionado* in the world and its four hundred provinces!"

A shout attracted every one's attention. The bull had suspended "Carita" by a leg. According to the wiseacres in the stands, he had been gored while going in to kill because of his professional pride. Had it not been for the perfect execution of the killing and its rapid effects, the bull would have mangled him beyond recognition. While the red Miura was swaying on its feet before falling dead, "Carita's" peons carried him to the infirmary . . . his trousers in shreds and bathed in blood . . . amid thunderous applause.

Word soon came back by a bull-ring servant that the wound was not as serious as it had appeared.

"*Nada!* Just a little scratch! He sure had a narrow escape! All he loses is tomorrow's *corrida*, Sunday in Madrid, and the fair in Jerez!"

An old aficionado . . . a señor with a tobacco-stained white mustache, a Cordoban hat, big spectacles, and speaking with a frightened twang . . . came over to "Currito." Shaking his hand, he said as though delivering a sentence:

"Boy, you've just caused the downfall of a conceited pup . . . . God bless you!"

A four-masted schooner was never blown by more favorable trade winds than our friend "Copita" on leaving the *plaza de toros* that memorable afternoon. He was supremely happy. Making his way through the sea of Andalusian hats that flooded the *Calle* Aureola, and emptied into the cafés and taverns of *Calle* Adriano, he stepped haughtily along, basking in the reflection of "Currito's" glory.

Envious aspirant fighters on *Calle* Aureola watched him pass and said:

"God looks after lunatics!"

"Any of us could do the same with a bull as noble as that!"

"Copita" didn't hear them nor did he care. Who could now dispute his ability to recognize a diamond in the rough?

Besides, "Currito's" triumph practically assured "Copita's" future. The Calvary of his past life rushed by in review.

Now things were going to be different. "Copita," having lost the hope of shining in his own light, turned all his energies toward discovering and developing a future star. He knew that once he made a discovery, his services would be indispensable.

His experience with men and *toreros* would serve him well. He had learned a great deal during his apprenticeship in small-time rings. He knew that this little fellow's heart was in the right place, and would not fail him as so many other ingrates had. Those who had neglected to follow his advice were now forgotten and starving.

The future looked good to "Copita." As they passed the saddle-shops on *Calle* Adriano, filled with dickering customers, he pointed out the sample harness on a wooden show-horse and exclaimed to "Currito":

"That's the kind of trappings your horses will wear! . . . If we weren't in a hurry I'd go in right now and order the outfits for your carriage, for next year's fair! . . ."

"Currito" walked at his side, modestly and contentedly, as though the admiration of the group that followed were not meant for him. People stopped and stared as they recognized him, pointing him out to one another. The *corrida's* enthusiasm knows no bounds, and he was flirted with as though he were a young girl.

"Hurray for you! . . ."

"*Viva los toreritos finos! . . .*"

"God bless your mother!"

"Hurray for the little man with loads of guts! . . ."

"You'd better tie up your pigtails, all you false idols, there's a new barber in town with a big pair of scissors! . . ."

But he of the scissors was attentive only to the animated conversation of a friend of his, who was waiting for him. When he saw "Currito," this boy hugged him excitedly and impatiently asked him:

"You were swell, weren't you? . . . All the applause was for you! . . . Truly? . . . And didn't they make some noise! . . . A real earthquake! . . ."

"Gasusilla!" jubilantly yelled "Currito," effusively returning his friend's embrace. "It was all mine! It was all for me! I was pretty good, wasn't I?"

"Colossal! Phenomenal!" "Copita" happily corroborated. "There's no more applause left in Seville for anybody. And don't forget it, Gasusa! Today is the beginning of a new epoch: the golden age of bullfighting! It's me that's telling you, me, Joaquín Gonzales, 'Copita,' the greatest aficionado in the world and ten leagues all around here. On these matters, brother, I'm an authority!"

As he said this, he proudly wrote his name in the air, as though affixing his signature thereto.

Gasusa did not wait to hear more. Turning to a group of kids who were awaiting him, he chestily told them:

"Did you hear that? He's been colossal! Something that's never been seen before in Seville! The public jumped into the ring and carried him around on their shoulders!"

Without awaiting more details, they hurriedly scattered through the town, as though going to a fire, eager to be the first ones to spread the glad news in their respective *barrios*.

"There's a new *fenómeno*! A kid from the Alameda has caused a riot! He jumped into the ring when everybody was scared stiff and they gave him an ear! He killed a bull superbly, and if it weren't for him, 'Carita' would be dead! He saved 'Carita's' life, and Carmona wanted to make him a full *matador* right there!"

"More than ten thousand *duros*, eye witnesses later testified, were thrown him in gold and big bills! I threw him one of five hundred *pesetas* myself! . . ."

When Gasusa had given all this information to his companions, he turned to "Currito" with a flood of impatient questions, barely allowing time for answers.

Excerpts from "Shadows of the Sun" 239

"Did you pass it *al natural?* and *al cambio?* and *al molinete?* Did you get down on your knees? Was it the red one? Did you grab its horn? Did you pass it by your chest?"

"It was the red one! And I did everything!"

"They wore their hands out up to the elbows applauding him," corroborated "Copita." Taking advantage of Gasusa's company, he asked him to help carry the *muleta.* "Here, grab a hold, it's heavy!"

All of "Copita's" friends and acquaintances, even those who at times feigned not to know him, hailed him affectionately that afternoon.

"Well met—congratulations—Joaquín!"

"Thank you!" answered "Copita" serious and dignified, lifting his hat with a stiff hand as he did when applauded in the ring.

Some veteran *banderilleros* and *picadors,* in their haste to get aboard the speeding band wagon, recalled their sufferings when comrades.

"Joaquín, don't forget me! I've always been your friend, and you're going to be the boss now—*el amo!*"

"I'll do what I can!" responded "Copita" without promising anything.

Other aficionados, hangers-on of the semi-professional class—apprentice fighters—valuing the friendship of this newly budding star, attempted to open a conversation. Cleverly and diplomatically playing his role, "Copita" cut them short. He took care to offend no one; he never knew when he might need them.

He politely told them that what they had seen that afternoon was nothing in comparison to what they would see in the near future. The Kid had managed the cape and the *muleta* to perfection, because he, Joaquín Gonzales, "Copita," "knew more about these things than any one else."

He stated firmly that his protégé would soon start cleaning up all the existing false idols. "Copita" shook his followers off politely, and continued on his way. For the first time in his life, he refused to be treated to a drink.

"Just a minute, we'll be right back!"

"Copita" was busy. He had no time to lose. He knew from experience that the co-operation of his friends on the outside was just as necessary for success as the performance of the *torero* in the ring.

"Now," he told the Kid on leaving the plaza, "it's my turn to *torear!* The *torero*—Don Luis Mazzantini used to say—performs two hours in the ring and twenty-two hours outside. You'll see!"

When they reached the corner of *Calles* García Vinuesa and Atarfe, he stopped a moment. Satisfying himself that the people he wanted to see were there, he started resolutely toward them. Just outside the wide portal of the newspaper *El Liberal,* were standing the editor and some linotypists, whose habit it was on *corrida* days to watch the procession of homeward-bound *toreros.*

"Good afternoon, Don José and company!" greeted "Copita" while passing, lifting his hat very courteously to the editor.

Suddenly, as though the thought had just struck him, he retraced his steps and casually pointing to the *muleta* the kids were carrying, addressed Laguilla.

"Hi there, Don José! I wonder if you could change this fortune into something easier to carry! It's more difficult to manage than a bunch of Miuras!"

"I suppose so," answered Laguilla. "Come inside a minute." He called the treasurer—"Hey there, Martínez!" They mounted to the press-room. After brushing off all the papers on one of the desks there, they emptied the *muleta* of its precious burden.

"Lord, what a bunch of dirty cracks there must be in those!" exclaimed "Copita," trying to ingratiate himself as he pointed to the pile of newspapers.

While the treasurer and his assistant counted the money, "Currito" and Gasusa were silently absorbed in looking at the photographs of famous people which covered the walls. The editor, always on the lookout for news of the moment, overwhelmed "Copita" with questions. The astute *banderillero* cleverly gave the most convenient answers.

The child was Sevillian and an orphan. The best ever. A born artist. Better than anybody else. "Copita" knew about these things very well; he wasn't easily fooled. In fact he was never fooled. As an aficionado, everybody knew "that he really knew about these things."

"You'll soon see. The si-plus-ultra of the profession!"

He meant the ne-plus-ultra; but "Copita" superstitiously preferred saying "yes" instead of "no."

"Antonio Reyes here, can tell you how much I know about these things!" he answered as dulcetly as he could, having spied the man who wrote bullfight criticisms under the name of Don Criterio coming into the room. Don Criterio—stout, reddish, smiling, his clothes spotlessly clean, wearing a small flexible green hat, boots highly polished, and a handkerchief lining his collar in order to keep it clean, was one of the great taurine critics of the day. A few lines in his column were enough to make or break a *matador*.

"Just a minute, Joaquín, is that the Kid there?" asked Don Criterio, as he gave a bunch of proofs to one of the press-boys.

"The very same, Don Antonio! Is he good or is he good?"

"Well, he's got the essentials! If he only does the same professionally, in full uniform in the ring. . . ."

"The same? Much better! You know that I understand about these things; well, I'm telling you that he's the highest Pope of all the Popes in *tauromaquia.*"

After cracking a few jokes, he changed his tone and humbly begged the critic:

"Please, whatever you do, Don Antonio, treat us like friends! A few favorable words from you and you know that by tomorrow the Kid will be famous! A few of your spicy words is an order for the promoters!"

"Since when do beginners ask favors? How times have changed! The kids of today are born knowing more than their elders!"

"But this Kid," protested "Copita" offended, "isn't a beginner! He's a finished artist! I'm telling you because——"

"Yeah, I know, you know all about these things!"

"Yes, sir, I'll say I do!"

They had finished counting the money. Seven hundred and fifty-three *pesetas*, sixty *céntimos*, and one counterfeit *duro*.

"Can you beat that!" indignantly exclaimed the *banderillero*. "Can you imagine how that tramp must have shown off when he threw this counterfeit coin into the ring? Give it to me!" He took the coin. "I'd hate to see any one get stuck with this! . . . I know who I'll stick with it tonight!"

They bade each other farewell.

"What's your name, youngster?" the editor asked the Kid.

" 'Currito de la Cruz.' "

"What *barrio* are you from?"

"Where do you think an artist like him can be from?" quickly interposed "Copita." "From the Alameda Vieja! Where the good ones come from! You'll soon be asking me for his photograph, to stick up there on the wall with the others!"

Going through the door, he again begged Laguillo and Don Criterio:

"Give the promoters a little hint. After what he did this afternoon, the Kid's reappearance will be a sell-out! Con Dios, señores."

Again at the bottom of the stairs, he insisted:

"Don José! . . . It's up to you! . . ."

"Good afternoon!" Currito answered simply on leaving.

"And regards!" broke in Gasusa.

"I'm at your service and thanks for the regards," ceremoniously answered Laguillo. "But who are you?"

"Me? Nobody! I'm just 'Currito's' confidential *banderillero!* his most dependable assistant. You can say that I place *banderillas* swell *al cambio!*"

"I'll take care of everything! You can depend on me!"

"Copita" took the kids to a ready-made clothes bazaar, frequented by beginning fighters. At these bazaars anything from the beginners' muslin cape to the first decent suit of clothes could be acquired. He bought "Currito" a drill jacket to replace the one torn by the red Miura. The suit that he would have to wear in accordance with his new status could be bought later. There were many important things to be done now.

"When do we eat?" put in Gasusa, justifying his nickname which meant "The hungry one."

"First we got to go to Manuel Carmona's house," "Currito" reminded him.

"Later, when we've finished with everything," answered "Copita." "We didn't get so much today after all; there won't be enough for everybody. That's the way the *toreros'* friends are. You're popular? Millions! When you get a bad run, no one knows you!"

Going out of his way, "Copita" took the Kid by the places where the most intelligent fans generally congregate. As the day wore on, less and less importance was conceded to the afternoon's events. Thus on crossing in front of the Borrachería of the Calle Tetuán, they were barely noticed. The occupants of the chairs on the narrow sidewalk were more interested in flirting with the women and discussing horses, hare-racing, and cockfighting. Some ex-*toreros* were busy courting their aristocratic friends in the possibility of chiselling from them what they had been unable to earn in the bullrings. On the Campana it was even worse. There, conceited fighters, sitting in the Café de Paris, didn't even see them. As for those sitting behind the plate glass of the aristocratic Fiambrera, and to those in the neighboring Cervecerría Inglesa, the ragged trio did not exist.

"The dirty bums!" grumbled "Copita." "It won't be long before you'll all be coming to see me with your hats in your hands! . . . Let's go home, kids!"

At a brisk pace he took them toward the Alameda de Hércules, near which on the Calle del Hombre de Piedra, "Copita" and "Currito" lived: a miserable room in a *posada*. A faded sign over the entrance to the patio declared it to be the Casa de Vecinos de San Antonio Bendito—home of the neighbors of San Antonio the Blessed. The doors and walls of the façade were covered with signs, signs of the tenants' dislike for the proprietor: We be Long tothe unIOn,—HuRr ay forthE unIoNOf tenANts,—to HELl withE oWn ERaNd hIs DoG,—weWaNt fIftY oFf,—OuT wiThE oWnEr —to which was added—aNd HiS dOg.

The Corral, as these lodgings are called—because of the large patio in the center which is generally equipped with stalls for all sorts of animals, causing the surrounding rooms to reek with the stench of the stable—was tenanted by very poor people. Their poverty was indicated by the shredding straw and threadbare cretonne curtains which vainly sought to hide the interior from prying eyes.

Forming a garden in the center, were a pair of pompous banana trees and a number of flower pots, put there by the tenants to color their drab surroundings. At the inner extremity water gurgled from a blue and white mosaic fountain. Pots of all sizes and descriptions containing flowers, hung from the walls surrounding each door. Alternating with the pots, were bamboo bird cages the inmates of which never went hungry even though their owners very often did. These details gave the corral a jubilant and happy air, in contrast with life's miseries—as though a cheerful exterior could blot out the poverty that existed inside.

Tired men and emaciated women came and went. They were poor but clean. Young and old, the women wore a flower in their hair. Some sat on the doorstep for a while before entering. Nobody sang or laughed. Occasionally, sour disputing voices were heard; women fighting with their shiftless husbands.

"You're drunk, you tramp! Judas! If you hadn't spent it all drinking in the saloons. . . . I wish they'd all burn down! . . ."

Jauntily "Copita" entered the patio with the two kids. He was disappointed because no one made a fuss over him.

"Granny!" called Joaquín lifting the straw curtain of one of the rooms. The interior was very poor but clean. The entire furniture consisted of a much-scrubbed pine table, three run-down chairs, and a very faded old bureau on which, as though forming an altar, rested a print of Nuestro Padre Jesús del Gran Poder in a cheap frame. Illuminating the print was a flickering night-taper, near which stood a little bunch of aromatic flowers in a broken glass. A few photographs barely distinguishable because of the inexorable action of time and the offenses of flies, and a photograph of the Virgen de la Esperanza de San Gil—la Macarena—completed the adornment of the room.

From a very small room, which with this parlor and a tiny dark kitchen, constituted her palace, emerged a wrinkled old woman, her clothes spotless, and also wearing a carnation in her sparse white hair.

"Granny!" happily repeated "Copita," patting her arms tenderly. "Everything has come out fine! A sensation the like of which has never been seen in Seville before! We're going to be rich! Didn't I tell you, Mother? I'm going to dress you up like a queen on her throne!"

"Blessed be the Name of God!" the old woman said. "I've been praying for it long enough. You haven't been hurt, 'Currito,' have you? I'm glad; really and truly I'm glad, but more so if you've brought something to eat."

"You bet your life we have! Look at this! A million so you can eat whatever you want," "Copita" said. "Here, take this." Ostentatiously he gave her a couple of *duros*.

"Bring it here, sonny! I've been waiting for you as though you were the doctor; I've been hearing noises in my stomach and I'm afraid it wants to run away, bored from doing nothing."

"That's all over, now!"

"I hope that's true; but I've been disappointed so many times. . . ."

"Don't blaspheme, Mother!"

"Give her some more money so she can buy what she wants; a silk dress, gold earrings! . . . " proposed "Currito."

"Whoa there, a little slower, niño!" interrupted "Copita." "The procession is long and the candle short! We'll do everything we can, but we've got to watch ourselves. Now, Mother, fix us up something to eat! Go out and get four *reales* of fried fish, from the Europa; a little bit of mountain ham and a bottle of wine. Make it quick, we're in a hurry."

"Don't worry, sonny, I'll be quick. I'm nearly dead for it myself."

Meanwhile "Copita" and the two boys pulled out the three chairs and sat down in the patio. They awaited their dinner there. Because of the momentous events of the day, they needed more fresh air than the hole-in-the-wall afforded. A spicy odor of something frying began to float through the corral and stimulated their appetites. Kitchen-fan in hand, some women impatiently stuck their heads from their doors as though waiting for some tardy arrival. Others went as far as the street and even approached the corner, hoping to discover their man amongst those in the tavern.

Night fell, a Sevillian night, a spring night—clear, warm, fragrant with roses, orange blossoms and acacia in bloom. From the street a shrill whistle was heard as a young fellow stopped in front of the corral. From one of the rooms scurried a dark young girl, slim from youth and hunger, her enormous black eyes shining brilliantly in the darkness of the night. A woman's shrill voice called her.

"Come here and finish eating!"

"I don't want any more, Mother!"

Close by the door, she carried on a flirtation with the young fellow who had whistled, eating him with her eyes, and drinking his words; the best food —the only food she wanted—for her seventeen Aprils.

Our friends were entirely indifferent to the happenings around them, paying attention only to those things which concerned themselves. While they were waiting for their food, and again, after having finished it, "Copita" repeated for the hundredth time to the enthralled boys, the almost legendary history of Manuel Carmona. Unique artist, and popular idol that he was, he held in his hands the power to open wide the doors of the bull-fighting profession to "Currito."

"A great *torero* and a fine man," summed up "Copita," getting up from the table, as he concluded his story. "But he's very hard to understand, and has very little to do with anybody," he added, finishing his wine and wiping his mouth with the back of his hand, which he dried on the cloth that served as table cover.

"Let's go, kids!"

"So long, Mother!"

"Where are we going, *Señor* Joaquín?" asked "Currito."

"To Manuel Carmona's."

"Give my regards to Teresa," said Granny.

In Seville at night were heard the hoofbeats and tinkling bells of spirited horses, richly adorned in Andalusian style, drawing carriages filled with women, on the way to the merriment of the fair. Women who could afford it were proudly wrapped in their classic Spanish shawls. Parents saw themselves in their children, who gracefully wore the shawl drawn around them in Sevillian style or were topped off with the pretty Spanish mantilla, carnations forming a pedestal for their high combs. The castanets seemed impatient in their hands, ready to roll off the Andalusian gypsy music, and their ears were filled with the pleasing homage of compliments.

At the doors of the Teatro del Duque a large group of country people were waiting out the intermission. They overflowed into the table space of the café and stopped traffic so that the exasperated clanging of the tram-bell failed to open passage. Cafés and picnic-grounds were filled to capacity. Illuminated patios presented to the eye the poetry of their flowers. Hilarity exploded everywhere, filling the air with gaiety.

On the corners newswomen lazily announced the evening newspapers in tired voices. Some poorly dressed individuals were reading laboriously in a chorus by the light of the store windows.

"*Liberal! Correo! Noticiero! Unión! Revista de toros!* Riot against Manuel Carmona!"

In idolatrous indignation "Currito" proposed to Joaquín the purchase of all the newspapers to silence the irreverent announcement. The *banderillero* laughed aloud.

"Let them yell, Kid; his crown won't lose any of its brilliance. Tomorrow they'll be yelling applause and ears. The bulls give and take, and a *torero* who knows his business"—putting his index finger to his eye—"doesn't pay any attention to what they say . . . excepting when it's convenient. You'll learn soon!"

At a good pace they turned their steps toward the Calle de Placentines, where Carmona lived. His home was almost a palace. The façade was brilliantly whitewashed, with a base about a meter wide of brilliantly colored Andalusian tiles, iron bars on the lower floor windows, and the classic crystal lookout window in the wide door which was spiked with large antique nails blackened by time. The entrance driveway was paved with little pebbles and Tarifa tiles, in checker-board design; the baseboard was of metallic reflecting tiles with heraldic designs in the center; a hand-carved screen in the interior, near which—high up in the corner—was a little window with beautifully forged iron bars and on the side—under an overhanging tiled roofing —the Virgen del Rocío done in Triana tiles, feebly illuminated by a little oil lamp.

Carmona's arrogance, together with his natural inclination and his inborn good taste, were the causes of his living in this aristocratic section, fleeing disdainfully the more popular *barrios*. He was great because he had it in him, without the necessity of backbiting in order to impose his will in the ring.

"When I'm with the bull . . ." he would always begin.

When "Currito" found himself inside this imposing portal before which he had so often timidly stopped, humble and vaguely nostalgic, he was queerly moved. The same heart which had beat so calmly and courageously in the ring that afternoon quickened with emotion when the voice of a distant caller broke the silence.

An elderly maidservant, with a flower in her hair, pushed aside the screen and mounted the stairs to announce them. She left them in the insultingly white patio which boasted no other furnishings than an enormous Triana ceramic flower pot containing a tall palm, in the center.

From a window in the gallery that circled the first floor she called them.

"You may come up now. Please close the screen after you!"

"You wait for us outside," "Copita" ordered Gasusa mounting the stairs.

Gasusa made a grimace behind his back and not paying any attention followed them. He did not remove his cap, busily patting down the shaggy hair that protruded from under it. He was interested only in his own personal appearance.

"Take your hats off, they'll think you haven't any manners," urged "Copita" in a low voice, when they caught up with him in the corridor of the gallery.

As they arrived at an interior corridor where Carmona was entertaining some friends, "Copita" raised his hat to the level of his face and greeted the group most cordially:

"Good evening to you, gentlemen!"

A Story of the Arena

by RUBÉN DARÍO

Rubén Darío (1867–1916). One of the greatest poets in the Spanish language, and a major poet in any language. He dominated his epoch and brought fresh vitality and music into Castilian literature. He was born in Nicaragua, but lived many years over the Americas and Europe. In this translation, I have tried to convey the spirit of this poetic dialogue, with the knowledge that his music and magic must always stay in the radiant boundaries of its original language.

America. A bull ring. Afternoon. The sun shines brightly in a cloudless sky. There is a multitude in the amphitheatre. In the arena, after the death of several bulls, the group of bullfighters prepares to leave triumphantly. The chief gladiator, near a bloody path in the sand, is graceful, dressed in blue and gold, *muleta* and sword under his arm. The *banderilleros* are dressed in yellow and silver. The spangles of the *picadors'* jackets mirror the splendor of the afternoon. There were left in the stalls of the bull ring: a beautiful, brave bull, and an ox. The trumpet sounds.

The Crowd

Another bull! Another bull!

The Ox

Do you hear:
Prepare for the charge, with hide and horns;
Your time has come. Go, in fury to the lances and *banderillas*
that await you,
To the applause for your executioner; death, at last.
And above, the calm and solitary contemplation of the imperturbable sky.

I, ridiculous and insignificant, am the patient slave. I am the
humble eunuch.
My head carries the yoke and hauls over the stony roads the carts
whose wheels creak, and on the high loads of rustling hay
sometimes the strong workers sing.
My pensive eyes, to the poet,
Bring thoughts of mysterious lives ruled by an enigma. I am
content to dream. I am a philosopher.
If I suffer
Lashes and blows, I reflect that God has given me this lot:
I can frighten the flies with my tail.
And I know that the slaughter house exists not far away.

The Bull

The prairie! Liberty!
Air and sun! I was the master of the plains
where the wind carried my bellow,
the trumpet sounded by a titan of great power.
With my budding horns
I wandered once in a sea of green leaves
Near the banks of a transparent stream
where I slaked my thirst with noisy satisfaction.
Later I was the beautiful king of the
sabre horns.
The mountains echoed my voice,
and my symmetry, superb and awesome
Would make legendary heroes burn with envy.
More than once the indomitable storm
sank its fists in the shuddering oak
under the warm sky of summer, but only breathed as
its fire passed my nostrils.

Afterward were the fights. Once the puma
caught its claws in my flank,
and I buried my horns in its bowels.
After the sultry day, the soft breeze of night, sweet
sleep.
I tasted the dawn, and welcomed the aurora of daybreak
that festooned my head in rose and pearl:
I saw the phalanx of Triton arising and plunging through
the clouds in helmets of gold,
and around the shining chariot
the pale stars faded into day.
Now I have mystery, derision, and death. . .

The Ox

You poor declaimer! You are at the gate-way to life,
And, a smiling sphinx appears.
Hope may sometimes appear behind despair.
The star hides, disappears, dies.
But man is here, the powerful traitor.
Fear him.
I was once on my prairie superb as you.
Over the grass I bellowed proudly.
Today I live mutilated. I eat. I get fat. I bow
my head.

The Bull

Very well: for you the fresh pasture, a tranquil life,
water in the trough, and an approaching old age.
For me the red cape of the bullfighter,
the challenge and the ridicule,
the hoarse roar of the crowd, the sand where I plant
my feet. The *torero* with his deft and graceful deceit,
and in my flesh buries the barb of the gay *banderilla*,
blood-colored insect of steel;
the tempest in my lung,
the gasping that ripples the dust,
the thirst of death in uncontrollable instinct,
my muscles of bronze that the blood swells in seething
abundance of life;
in my eyes two raging flames,
fury flows through maddened nerves,
that pound like a hot surf in my throat;
the clarion of the bizarre gate keeper

who arouses the dangerous throng;
the *matador* who buries the sword to its hilt in my strength;
the quartette of garlanded mules
that will drag away my bleeding and lifeless body;
the pageant and applause for the kill
When the steel pierces my heart.
Oh, there is no greater tragedy!
For me, when the blade of that cold sword brings
death;
and then derision, the crude sacrifice, the awful death
rattle of the last agony . . . .
Meanwhile the wide and sacred sky
remains serene, and, far above,
The golden mighty sun
Turns to the west
In godly exaltation . . .

The Crowd

Another bull!

The Ox

Hush! Die! Your time has come!

The Bull

Horrible sentence! Yesterday, the air, the sun; today the
executioner. . . .
What is worse than this martyrdom?

The Ox

Impotence!

The Bull

What is blacker than death?

The Ox

The yoke!

Excerpt from Blood and Sand

by VICENTE BLASCO-IBÁÑEZ

Vicente Blasco-Ibáñez, 1867–1928, was an old-fashioned melo-dramatist in fiction. He slashed and tried to slay the things he considered public evils. He attacked, at various times, war, the church, class consciousness, people who drink, bullfights, and other ancient institutions.

Blood and Sand, 1908, his novel on bullfighting, has a great fighter as protagonist. Juan Gallardo was a man of talent for the *corrida,* who rose to the top rank of stardom. He was killed trying to justify the faith of the people in his fame after his ability had deserted him. The author, through a mouth-piece apologist, likens the *corrida* to the Inquisition, and indulges in long dissertations on violent entertainments, such as boxing, fox hunting, and other sports that endanger the participants.

He had evangelical zeal for colorful descriptive expression. His portrayal of the moods and surroundings of a reigning celebrity begins his novel. Excerpts from that chapter picture the environment effectively. The translation is from the Dell Publishing Company version.

Chapter One: King of the Matadors

Juan Gallardo breakfasted early as was his custom on the day of a bull-fight. A little roast meat was his only dish. Wine he did not touch, and the bottle remained unopened before him. He had to keep himself steady. He drank two cups of strong black coffee and then, lighting an enormous cigar, sat with his elbows resting on the table and his chin on his hands, watching with drowsy eyes the customers who, little by little, began to fill the dining-room.

For many years past, ever since he had been "recognized" as a master *matador* in the bull ring of Madrid, he had always lodged at the same hotel in the Calle de Alcalá, where the proprietors treated him as one of the family, and waiters, porters, kitchen scullions, and old chambermaids all adored him as the glory of the establishment.

There also had he stayed many days, swathed in bandages, in a dense atmosphere of iodoform and cigar smoke, as the result of two bad gorings—

but these evil memories had not made much impression. With his Southern superstition and continual exposure to danger he had come to believe that this hotel was lucky—*a buena sombra*—and that while staying there no harm would happen to him. The risks of his profession he had to take, a tear in his clothes perhaps, or even a gash in his flesh, but nothing to make him fall forever, as so many of his comrades had fallen. The memory of their fate disturbed his happiest hours.

On these days, after his early breakfast, he enjoyed sitting in the dining room watching the travelers, foreigners, or people from distant provinces, who passed him by without a glance, but who tuned with curiosity on hearing that the handsome young fellow with clean-shaven face and black eyes, dressed like a gentleman, was Juan Gallardo, the famous *matador,* called familiarly by everybody El Gallardo.

In this atmosphere he whiled away the wearisome wait until it was time to go to the Plaza. Those hours of uncertainty, in which vague fears rose from the depths of his soul, making him doubtful of himself, were the most painful in his profession. He did not care to go out into the street—he thought of the fatigues of the *corrida* and the necessity of keeping himself fresh and agile. Nor could he amuse himself with the pleasures of the table, on account of the necessity of eating little and early, so as to arrive in the Plaza free from the heaviness of digestion.

He remained at the head of the table, his head resting on his hands, and a cloud of smoke before his eyes, which he turned from time to time with a self-satisfied air in the direction of some ladies who were watching the famous *torero* with marked interest.

His vanity as an idol of the populace made him read praises and flatteries in those glances. Forgetting his anxieties, with the instinct of a man accustomed to adopt a proud bearing before the public, he drew himself up, flicked the ashes of his cigar from his coat sleeves, and adjusted the ring which, set with an enormous diamond, covered the whole joint of one finger, and from which flashed a perfect rainbow of colors as if its depths, clear as a drop of water, were burning with magic fires.

He thought with pleasure of his well-cut suit, the cap which he usually wore about the hotel now thrown on a chair close by, the fine gold chain which crossed the upper part of his waistcoat from pocket to pocket, the pearl in his cravat, which seemed to light up the swarthy color of his face, and his Russia leather shoes, which showed between the instep and the turned-up trouser openwork embroidered silk socks, like the stockings of a cocotte. An aroma of English scents, sweet and vague, but used in profusion, emanated from his clothes and from the black, glossy waves of hair which he wore curled on his temples, and he assumed a swaggering air. For a *torero* he was not bad. Where was there a man more distinguished or more attractive to women?

But suddenly his chin again sank onto his hand, and he puffed hard at his cigar. His gaze lost itself in a cloud of smoke. He thought with impatience of the twilight hours, longing for them to come—of his return from the bull-fight, hot and tired, but with the relief of danger overcome, his appetites awakened, a wild desire for pleasure, and the certainty of a few days of safety and rest. If God still protected him as He had done so many times before, he would dine well, drink his fill, and then go in search of a girl who was singing in a music-hall, whom he had met during one of his journeys, without, how-ever, having been able to follow up the acquaintance. In this life of rushing from one end of Spain to the other, he never had time for anything.

Several enthusiastic friends who, before going to breakfast in their own homes, wished to see the *matador,* had by this time entered the dining room. They were old fans of the bull ring, anxious to form a small coterie and to have an idol. They had made the young Gallardo "their own *matador,*" giv-ing him sage advice, and recalling at every turn their adoration for such older *matadors* as "Lagartijo" or "Frascuelo." They spoke to him with pa-tronizing familiarity, and he, when he answered them, placed the respect-ful don before their names, with that traditional separation of classes which exists between even a *torero* risen from a social substratum and his admirers.

These people joined to their enthusiasm their memories of past times, in order to impress the young *matador* with the superiority of their years and ex-perience. They spoke of the "old Plaza" of Madrid, where only "true" *toreros* and "true" bulls were known, and drawing nearer to the present times, they trembled with excitement as they remembered "Frascuelo," who always wore black in the ring.

Other enthusiasts kept coming into the dining-room, men with untidy clothes and hungry faces, obscure reporters of papers only known to the bull-fighters, whom they honored with their praise or censure, and who appeared as soon as the news of Gallardo's arrival got about, besieging him with flat-teries and requests for tickets. The general enthusiasm permitted them to mix with the other gentlemen, businessmen and public functionaries, who discussed bullfighting affairs with them hotly without being troubled by their shabby appearance.

All of them, on seeing the *matador,* embraced him or clasped his hand, to a running accompaniment of questions and exclamations:

"Juanillo! . . . How is Carmen?"

"Quite well, thank you."

"And your mother—the Señora Angustias?"

"Fine, thanks. She is at La Rincona."

"And your sister and the little nephews?"

"In good health, thanks."

"And that funny fellow, your brother-in-law?"

"Well, also. As great a talker as ever."

"And a little family? Is there no hope?"

"No—not that much——" And he bit his nails in expressive negation. "And your own family? Are they also quite well? Come along, I am glad to meet you. Sit down and have something."

Next he asked about the bulls he was going to fight in a few hours, because all these friends had just come from the Plaza, after seeing the separation and boxing of the animals, and with professional curiosity he asked for news from the Café Inglés, where *matadors* and their admirers congregated.

It was the first bullfight of the spring season, and Gallardo's enthusiastic followers had great hopes of him as they called to mind all the articles they had read in the papers, describing his recent triumphs in other plazas in Spain. He had more engagements than any other *torero*. Since the Easter *corrida,* the first important event in the bullfighter's year, Gallardo had gone from place to place killing bulls. Later on, when August and September came round, he would have to spend his nights in the train and his afternoons in the ring, with scarcely breathing time between them. His agent in Seville was nearly frantic—overwhelmed with letters and telegrams, and not knowing how to fit so many requests for engagements into one man's calendar.

The evening before this he had fought at Ciudad Real and, still in his splendid dress, had taken the train to arrive in Madrid in the morning. He had spent a wakeful night, boxed up in the small sitting space that the other passengers, by squeezing themselves together, managed to leave for the man who was to risk his life on the following day.

The enthusiasts admired the courage with which he threw himself on the bull at the moment of killing it. "Let us see what you can do this afternoon," they said with the fervor of zealots, "the fans expect great things from you. You will lower the *moña* of many of our rivals. Let us see you as dashing here as you were in Seville!" (The *moña* is the knot of hair, dressed with ribbons, worn at the back of the head by *toreros,* principally to lessen the shock of a fall. The *moña* was only "lowered" when a *torero* retired finally from the ring, whether because of age or inefficiency.)

His admirers dispersed to their breakfasts at home in order to go early to the *corrida.* Gallardo, finding himself alone, was making his way up to his room in his nervous restlessness when a man holding two children by the hand pushed open the glass doors of the dining-room. He smiled happily when he saw the *torero* and advanced, dragging the children along and scarcely noticing where he placed his feet.

Gallardo recognized him. "How are you, my friend?"

Then came all the usual questions as to the welfare of the family, after which the man turned to his children, saying solemnly, "Here he is. You are always asking to see him. He's exactly like his portraits, isn't he?"

The two youngsters stared religiously at the hero whose portraits they had so often seen on the walls of their poor little home, a supernatural being whose exploits and wealth had been their chief admiration ever since they had begun to understand the world.

"Juanillo, kiss your godfather's hand." And the younger of the two rubbed a red cheek against the *torero's* hand, a cheek newly polished by his mother in view of this visit.

Gallardo caressed his head abstractedly. This was one of the numerous godchildren he had about Spain. His fans forced him to stand godfather to their children, thinking in this way to secure their future, and appearing at baptisms was one of the penalties of his fame. This particular godson reminded him of bad times at the beginning of his career, and he felt grateful to the father for the confidence he had placed in him when others were still doubtful of his merits.

"And how about your business, friend?" inquired Gallardo. "Is it going on better?"

The aficionado shrugged his shoulders. He was making a living, thanks to his dealings in the barley market—just making a living, nothing more.

Gallardo looked with sympathy at his threadbare Sunday-best clothes.

"Would you like to see the *corrida*, friend? Well, go up to my room and tell Garabato to give you a ticket. Good-by, my dear fellow. Here—buy something for the kids." And while the little godson again kissed his right hand, with his other hand the *matador* gave the man a couple of *duros*.

The father dragged away his offspring with many grateful excuses. Gallardo waited so as not to meet them in his room. Then he looked at his watch. Only one o'clock! It still was a long time till the bullfight.

As he came out of the dining room and turned toward the stairs, a woman wrapped in an old cloak came out of the hall-porter's office and deliberately barred his way.

"Juaniyo! Juan! Don't you know me? I am the Señora Dolores, mother of poor Lechuguero."

Gallardo smiled at this little dark, wizened, excitable woman, whose eyes burned like live coals—the eyes of a witch. At the same time, knowing what would be the outcome of her chatter, he raised his hand to his waistcoat pocket.

"Misery, my son! Poverty and sickness! When I heard you were bullfighting today I said, 'I will go and see Juaniyo; he will remember the mother of his poor comrade.' How smart you are! All the women are crazy about you, you rascal! I am very badly off, my son. I have had nothing to eat today. They keep me, out of pity, in La Pepona's house—she is from our province. Come round there, they would love to see you. I dress the girls' hair and run errands for the men. If only my poor son were alive! You remember Pepiyo? Do you remember the afternoon he died?"

Gallardo put a *duro* into her hand and did his best to escape from her prattle; by this time she was showing signs of imminent tears.

Damned witch! Why did she come and remind him, on the day of a *corrida*, of poor Lechuguero, the companion of his early years, whom he had seen killed almost instantly, gored to the heart, in the Plaza of Lebrija, when the two were bullfighting as *novilleros*. Nasty hag of evil omen!

He pushed her aside, but she, flitting from sorrow to joy, broke out into enthusiastic praises of the brave boys, the good *toreros,* who carried away the money of the public and the hearts of the women.

Excerpt from "Blood and Sand"   **255**

"You deserve to have the Queen, my hero! The Señora Carmen will have to keep her eyes wide open. Some fine day a beauty will steal you. Can't you give me a ticket for this afternoon, Juaniyo? I am dying to see you kill!"

The old woman's shrill voice and noisy flattery diverted the attention of the hotel servants and enabled a number of idlers and beggars who had collected outside the entrance, to burst into the hall. Boys with bundles of papers under their arms waved their caps and greeted Gallardo boisterously.

"*Olé* El Gallardo. Long live Gallardo!"

The more daring seized his hand, shaking it roughly and pulling it about, excited to be touching this national hero whose picture they had all seen in every paper. They shouted, "Shake his hand. He won't mind! He's a good fellow." Their devotion made them almost kneel before the *matador*.

There were also other admirers, just as insistent, with unkempt beards and clothes, who shuffled round their idol in shoes that had seen better days. They swept their greasy sombreros toward him and called him "Don Juan," in order to show the difference between themselves and the rest of that irreverent, excited crowd. Some of them asked for a small donation, others, more impertinent, asked, in the name of their love of the sport, for a ticket for the *corrida*—fully intending to sell it immediately.

Gallardo defended himself laughingly against this avalanche which jostled and overwhelmed him, and from which the hotel servants were quite unable to save him.

He searched through all his pockets until he finally turned them out empty, distributing silver coins to the greedy hands held out to clutch them.

"That's all! There is no more. Leave me alone, my friends."

Pretending to be annoyed by this popularity, which actually flattered him greatly, he suddenly opened a way through them with his muscular, athletic arms, and ran upstairs, bounding up with the lightness of a wrestler, while the servants, freed from the restraint of his presence, pushed the crowd toward the door and swept them into the street.

Gallardo passed the room occupied by his servant Garabato, and saw him through the half-open door, busy amid trunks and boxes, preparing his master's clothes for the *corrida*.

Alone in his own room, the happy excitement caused by his admirers vanished. The bad moments of the days of a *corrida* returned to him; the anxiety of those last hours before going to the Plaza. Fierce bulls of Miura and a Madrid audience. The danger, which when facing him seemed to intoxicate him and increase his daring, was torture to him when alone—something supernatural, fearful and intimidating from its very uncertainty.

The fatigue of his previous bad night seemed suddenly to overcome him. He longed to throw himself on one of the beds at the end of the room, but again anxiety shut out the desire to sleep. He walked restlessly up and down the room, lighting another Havana from the end of the one he had just smoked.

What would be the result for him of the Madrid season just about to be-gin? What would his enemies say? What would his professional rivals do? He had killed many Miura bulls—after all they were only like any other bulls—still, he thought of his comrades fallen in the arena—nearly all of them vic-tims of animals from this herd. Cursed Miuras! No wonder he and other *matadors* demanded a thousand *pesetas* more in their contracts each time they fought with bulls of this breed.

He wandered nervously about the room and finally threw himself into an armchair, as if suddenly weak. He looked often at his watch—not yet two o'clock. How slowly the time passed!

The need for distracting his mind made him search the inside pocket of his coat and take out of his wallet a letter which gave out a strong, sweet scent.

Standing by a window, through which entered the dull light of an in-terior courtyard, he looked at the envelope which had been delivered to him on his arrival at the hotel, admiring the elegance of the handwriting in which the address was written—so delicate and well shaped.

Then he drew out the letter, inhaling its indefinable perfume with de-light. Ah! These people of high birth who had traveled much—how they re-vealed their breeding even in the smallest details!

Gallardo, as though he still carried the pungent odor of the poverty of his early years, perfumed himself abundantly. His enemies laughed at this athletic young fellow who by his love of scent belied the strength of his sex. Even his admirers smiled at his weakness.

Certain cocottes whose acquaintance he had made during a journey to the plazas in the South of France had given him the secret of combining and mixing rare perfumes—but the scent of that letter! It was the scent of the person who had written it—that mysterious scent so delicate, indefinable, and inimitable, which seemed to emanate from her aristocratic form, and which he called "the scent of the lady."

He read and reread the letter with a smile of delight and pride. It was not much, only half a dozen lines—A greeting from Seville, wishing you good luck in Madrid. Congratulations in advance on your expected triumph.

Friend Gallardo, it began, in a delicate handwriting which made the *torero's* eyes brighten, and it ended Your friend, Sol, all in a coldly friendly style, addressing him formally as *usted* with an amiable tone of superiority, as though the words were not between equals, but fell in mercy from on high.

The *torero* could not hold back a certain feeling of annoyance.

"What a woman!" he murmured. "No one can upset her! See how she writes to me as *usted! Usted*—to me!"

But pleasant memories made him smile with self-satisfaction. That cold style was for letters only—the ways of a great lady—the precautions of a woman of the world. His annoyance soon turned to admiration.

"How clever she is! A cautious little devil!"

While Gallardo was admiring his letter, his servant Garabato passed in and out of the room, laden with clothes and boxes which he spread on a bed.

He was very quiet in his movements, and seemed to take no notice of the *matador's* presence.

For many years he had accompanied the *torero* to all his bullfights as sword carrier. He had begun bullfighting at the same time as Gallardo, but all the bad luck had been for him and all the advancement and fame for his companion.

He was dark, swarthy, and of poor muscular development, and a jagged, badly healed scar crossed his wrinkled, flabby, old-looking face like a white scrawl. It was a goring he had received in a bullfight and had nearly been his death, and besides this terrible wound, there were others which disfigured parts of his body which could not be seen.

By a miracle he had emerged with his life from his passion for bullfighting, and the cruel part of it was that people used to laugh at his misfortunes, seeming to take a pleasure in seeing him trampled and mangled by the bulls.

Finally he gave up and decided to become the attendant and confidential servant of his old friend. He was Gallardo's most fervent admirer, though he sometimes took advantage of this intimacy to allow himself to criticize and advise. "Had he been in his master's place he would have done better under the circumstances."

Gallardo's friends found the wrecked ambitions of the sword carrier an unfailing source of merriment, but he took no notice of their jokes. Give up bulls? Never! So that all memory of the past should not be erased, he combed his coarse hair in curls above his ears, and preserved the long, sacred lock, the pigtail of his younger days, the hallmark of the profession which distinguished him from other mortals.

When Gallardo was angry with him, his noisy, impulsive rage always threatened this braid. "You dare to wear a pigtail, you idiot? I'll cut off that rat's tail for you!"

Garabato received these threats resignedly, but he revenged himself by retiring into the silence of a superior being, and only replying by a shrug of his shoulders when, on returning from a bullfight after a lucky afternoon, Gallardo exclaimed with almost childish vanity, "What did you think of it? Really, wasn't I splendid?"

In consequence of their early comradeship he always retained the privilege of addressing his master as *tú*. He could not speak otherwise to the maestro, but the *tú* was accompanied by a grave face and an expression of genuine respect. His familiarity was something like that of their squires toward the knights errant of olden days.

From his neck to the top of his head Garabato was a *torero*, but the rest of his person seemed half tailor, half valet. Dressed in a suit of English cloth —a present from his master—he had the lapels of his coat covered with pins while several threaded needles were fastened to one of his sleeves. His dark withered hands manipulated things with the gentleness of a woman.

When everything that was necessary for his master's toilet had been placed upon the bed, he passed the numerous articles in review to make sure that nothing was missing. After a time he came and stood in the middle of the room, without looking at Gallardo, and, as if he were speaking to himself, said in a hoarse and rasping voice:

"Two o'clock!"

Gallardo raised his head nervously, as if up to now he had not noticed his servant's presence. He put the letter away, and then walked lazily to the end of the room, as though he wished to postpone the dressing time. "Is everything there?"

Suddenly his pale face became flushed and violently distorted and his eyes opened unnaturally wide, as if he had just experienced some awful shock. "What clothes have you put out?"

Garabato pointed to the bed, but before he could speak, his master's wrath fell on him, loud and terrible.

"Damn you! Don't you know anything about the profession? Have you just come from the cornfields? *Corrida* in Madrid—bulls from Miura—and you lay out red clothes like those poor Manuel, 'el Espartero,' wore! You are so idiotic that one would think you were my enemy! It would seem that you wished for my death, you villain!"

The more he thought of the enormity of this carelessness, which was equivalent to courting disaster, the more his anger increased. His eyes sparkled with rage, the whites of his eyes became bloodshot, and he seemed ready to fall on the unfortunate Garabato with his big rough hands.

A discreet knock at the door cut the scene short.

"Come in."

A young man entered, dressed in a light suit with a red cravat, carrying his Cordovan felt hat in a hand covered with large diamond rings. Gallardo recognized him at once. His anger was instantly transformed to a smiling amiability, as if the visit was a pleasant surprise to him.

It was a friend from Bilbao, an enthusiastic aficionado. That was all he could remember about him. His name? He knew so many people! What was his name? All he knew was that most certainly he ought to call him *tú*, as this was an old acquaintanceship.

"Sit down. This is a surprise! When did you arrive? Are you and your family well?"

His admirer sat down, with the joy of a devotee who enters the sanctuary of his idol, with no intention of moving from it till the very last moment, delighted at being addressed as *tú* by the master, and calling him Juan at every other word, so that the furniture, walls, or anyone passing along the hall outside should be aware of his intimacy with the great man. He had arrived that morning and was returning on the following day. The journey was solely to see Gallardo. He had read of his exploits. The season seemed opening well. This afternoon would be a good one. He had visited the bulls' enclosure in the morning and had noticed an almost black animal which assuredly would give great sport in Gallardo's hands—

The master hurriedly cut short the fan's prophecies.

"Pardon me. Please excuse me. I will be right back."

Leaving the room, he went toward an unnumbered door at the end of the hall.

"What clothes shall I put out?" asked Garabato, in a voice more hoarse than usual, from his wish to appear submissive.

"The green, the tobacco, the blue—anything you please." And Gallardo disappeared through the little door, while his servant smiled with malicious revenge. He knew what that sudden rush meant, just at dressing time— "The relieving of fear" they called it in the profession, and his smile expressed satisfaction at seeing once more that the greatest masters of the art and the bravest suffered from anxiety, just as he himself had done when he went down into the arena in different towns.

When Gallardo returned to his room, he found a new visitor. This was Doctor Ruiz, a popular physician who had spent thirty years attending *toreros* who fell wounded in the Plaza of Madrid.

Gallardo admired him immensely, regarding him as the greatest exponent of universal science, but at the same time he allowed himself affectionate jokes at the expense of the Doctor's good-natured character and personal untidiness.

He was of low stature and prominent paunch, broad-faced and flat-nosed. When he stood up, his protuberant and flabby stomach seemed to shake under his ample waistcoat as he spoke. When he sat down this same part of his anatomy rose up to his thin chest.

"He is a simpleton," said Gallardo—"A learned man certainly, as good as they come, but a little touched in the head. He will never have a *peseta*. Whatever he has he gives away, and he takes whatever people choose to pay him."

Two great passions filled his life—the revolution and bulls. That vague but tremendous revolution which would come, leaving in Europe nothing that now existed, an anarchical republicanism that he did not trouble to explain. The *toreros* spoke to him as a father, he called them all by the familiar *tú,* and it was sufficient for a telegram to come from the farthest end of the Peninsula for the good doctor instantly to take the train and rush to heal a goring received by one of his "lads."

He embraced Gallardo on seeing him after his long absence. "Oh! You fine fellow!" He thought the *matador* looked better than ever.

"And how about that republic, Doctor? When is it going to come?" asked Gallardo. " 'El Nacional' says that we are on the verge, and that it will come one of these days."

"What does it matter to you, you rascal? Leave poor Nacional in peace. He had far better learn to be a better *banderillero* (the man who fixes the darts into the bull). As for you, you ought to go on killing bulls. We have a fine little afternoon in prospect. I am told that the herd——"

But when he got this far, the young man who had seen the selection of bulls and wished to give news of it, interrupted the doctor to speak of the dark bull which had caught his eye, and from which the greatest wonders might be expected. The two men who, after bowing to each other, had sat together in the room for a long time in silence, now stood up face to face, and Gailardo thought that an introduction was necessary, but what was his friend's name? He scratched his head, frowning, but his indecision was short.

"Listen here. What is your name? Pardon me—you understand I see so many people."

The youth smothered beneath a smile his disappointment at finding himself forgotten by the master and gave his name. When he heard it, Gallardo felt all the past recur suddenly to his memory and repaired his forgetfulness by adding after the name "a rich mine owner in Bilbao," and then presented "the famous Dr. Ruiz"; and the two men, united by the enthusiasm of a common passion, began to chat about the afternoon's herd, just as if they had known each other all their lives.

"Sit down," said Gallardo, pointing to a sofa at the far end of the room. "You won't disturb me there. Talk and pay no attention to me. I am going to dress." And he began to take off his clothes, down to his undergarments.

Seated on a chair under the arch which divided the sitting room from the bedroom, he gave himself over into the hands of Garabato, who had opened a Russia leather bag from which he had taken an almost feminine toilet case.

In spite of his being already carefully shaved, Garabato soaped the *matador's* face and ran the razor over his cheeks with the speed that comes with daily practice. After washing himself, Gallardo resumed his seat. The servant then sprinkled his hair with brilliantine and scent, combing it in curls over forehead and temples, and then began to dress the sign of the profession, the sacred pigtail.

With infinite care he combed and plaited the long lock which adorned the back of his master's head; and then, interrupting the operation, fastened it on the top of his head with two hairpins, leaving its final dressing for a later stage. Next he must attend to the feet, and he drew off the fighter's socks, leaving him only his undershirt and spun-silk drawers.

Gallardo's powerful muscles stood out beneath these clothes in superb swellings. A hollow in one thigh betrayed a place where the flesh had disappeared owing to a gash from a horn. The swarthy skin of his arms was marked with white wheals, the scars of ancient wounds. His dark, hairless chest was crossed by two irregular purple lines, record also of bloody feats.

Excerpt from "Blood and Sand"   261

On one of his heels the flesh was of a violet color, with a round depression like the mold for a coin. All this fighting machine exhaled an odor of clean and healthy flesh blended with that of women's pungent scents.

Garabato, with an armful of cotton wool and white bandages, knelt at his master's feet.

"Just like the ancient gladiators," said Dr. Ruiz, interrupting his conversation with the Bilbaon. "See! You have become a Roman, Juan."

"Age, Doctor!" replied the *matador*, with a tinge of sadness. "We are all getting older. When I fought both bulls and hunger at the same time, I did not need all this. In those days I had feet of iron."

Garabato placed small tufts of cotton between his master's toes and covered the soles and the upper part of his feet with a thin layer of it; then, pulling out the bandages, he rolled them round in tight spirals, like the wrappings of an ancient mummy. To fix them firmly he drew one of the threaded needles from his sleeve and carefully and neatly sewed up their ends.

Gallardo stamped on the floor with his bandaged feet, which seemed to him firmer in their soft wrappings. In the bandages he felt them both strong and agile. The servant then drew on the long stockings, thick and flexible, which came halfway up the thigh. This was the only protection for the legs under the silk of the fighting dress.

"Be careful of wrinkles! Garabato, I don't want to wear sacks." And standing before the looking-glass, endeavoring to see both back and front, he bent down and passed his hands over his legs, smoothing out the wrinkles for himself.

Over these white stockings Garabato drew others of pink silk which alone remained visible when the *torero* was fully dressed, and then Gallardo put his feet into the pumps which he chose from among several pairs which Garabato had laid out on a box—all quite new and with white soles.

Then began the real task of the dressing. Holding them by the upper part, the servant handed him the fighting knee-breeches made of tobacco-colored silk, with heavy gold embroidery along the seams. Gallardo slipped them on, and the thick cords, ending in gold tassels, which drew in the lower ends, hung down over his feet. These cords which gather the breeches below the knee, constricting the leg to give it artificial strength, are called *los machos*.

Gallardo swelled out the muscles of his legs and ordered his servant to tighten the cords without fear. This was one of the most important operations, as a *matador's machos* must be well tightened; and Garabato, with nimble dexterity, soon had the cords wound round and tucked away out of sight underneath the ends of the breeches, with the tassels hanging down.

The master then drew on the fine lawn shirt held out by his servant, the front covered with zigzag crimpings, and as delicate and thin as a woman's garment. After he had fastened it, Garabato knotted the long cravat that hung down dividing the chest with its red line till it lost itself in the waistband of the drawers. Now remained the most complicated article of clothing, the waist-sash—a strip of silk over four yards long which seemed to take up the whole room, and which Garabato handled with the mastery of long experience.

The bullfighter went over to stand near his friends at the other end of the room, fastening one end of the sash to his waist.

"Now then, pay attention," he said to his servant, "and do your little best."

Turning slowly on his heels he gradually approached his servant, while the sash which he held up rolled itself round his waist in regular curves and gave it a more graceful shape. Garabato, with quick movements of his hand, changed the position of the band of silk. In some turns the sash was folded double, in others it was completely open, and always adjusted to the *matador's* waist, smooth and seemingly like one piece without wrinkles or unevenness. In the course of his turning, Gallardo, scrupulous and very difficult to please in the adornment of his person, several times stopped his forward movement, to step a few paces back and rectify the arrangement.

"That is not right," he said ill-humoredly. "Take more care, Garabato!"

After many halts, Gallardo came to the last turn, with the whole length of silk wound round his waist. The capable valet had put stitches and pins all round his master's body, making his clothing literally all one piece. To remove them scissors would be required.

Gallardo sat down again and Garabato, taking hold of the pigtail, removed the pins from it, and fastened it to the *moña,* the bunch of ribbons like a black cockade, which reminded one of the old *redecilla,* or net headdress, of the earliest days of bullfighting.

The master stretched himself, as if he wished to put off getting finally into the rest of his costume. He asked Garabato to hand him the cigar he had left on the bedside table, inquired what the time was, and seemed to think that all the clocks had gone fast.

"It is still early. The lads have not yet come. I do not like to go to the Plaza early. Every tile in the roof seems to weigh on me when I am waiting there."

At this moment a hotel employee announced that the carriage with the *cuadrilla,* or troupe, was waiting for him downstairs.

The time had come! There was no longer any pretext for delaying his departure. He slipped the gold-embroidered waistcoat over the silk sash, and above this the jacket, a piece of dazzling embroidery in very high relief, as heavy as a piece of armor and flashing with light like live coals. The tobacco-colored silk was only visible on the inside of the arms, and in two triangles on the back. Almost the whole fabric was hidden beneath a mass of golden tufts and gold-embroidered flowers with colored precious stones in their petals. The epaulets were heavy masses of gold embroidery, from which hung innumerable tassels of the same metal. The gold work reached the extreme edge of the jacket, where it ended in a thick fringe which quivered at every step. At the gold-edged openings of the pockets appeared the corners of two silk handkerchiefs which, like the cravat and sash, were red.

Excerpt from "Blood and Sand" 263

"Give me *la montera.*"

Out of an oval box Garabato took with great care the small round hat with black frizzed border and pompons which stood out on either side like large ears. Gallardo put it on, being careful that his *moña* should remain uncovered, hanging symmetrically down his back.

"Now the cape."

From the back of a chair Garabato took the cape called *la capa de paseo,* the gala procession cape, a princely mantle of silk, the same color as his clothes, and, like them, covered with gold embroidery. Gallardo slung it over one shoulder and then looked at himself in the glass, well satisfied with the effect.

"Not bad. Now to the Plaza."

His two friends took their leave hurriedly in order to find a cab and follow him. Garabato tucked under his arm a large bundle of red cloth, from the ends of which projected the pommels and buttons of several swords.

As Gallardo descended to the vestibule of the hotel, he saw that the street was filled with a noisy, excited crowd, as if some great event had just happened, and he could hear the buzz of a multitude whom he could not see through the doorway.

The manager and all his family ran up with outstretched hands as if they were speeding him on a long journey.

"Good luck! May all go well with you!"

The servants, abandoning all social distinctions, also shook his hand. "Good luck, Don Juan!"

He turned round, smiling on every side, heedless of the anxious looks of the women of the hotel.

"Thanks, many thanks. So long!"

He was another man now. Now that he had slung his dazzling cape over his shoulder, an untroubled smile lit up his face. He had the moist pallor of a sick man, but he laughed with the joy of life, and, going to meet his public, he adopted his new attitude with the instinctive facility of a man who has to put on a fine air before his audience. He swaggered arrogantly as he walked, puffing at the cigar in his left hand, and swayed from his hips under his gorgeous cape, stepping out firmly with the pride of a handsome man.

"Now then, gentlemen! Make way, please! Many thanks! Many thanks!"

As he opened a way for himself he tried to protect his clothes from contact with the dirty crowd of ill-dressed but enthusiastic rowdies who crowded round the hotel door. They had no money to go to the *corrida,* but they took advantage of this opportunity of shaking hands with the famous Gallardo, or even of touching some part of his clothing.

Close to the pavement was waiting a wagonette drawn by four mules, gaily decorated with tassels and little bells. Garabato had already hoisted himself onto the box seat with his bundle of cloth and swords. Behind sat three *toreros* with their capes on their knees, all wearing bright-colored clothes, embroidered as profusely as those of the master, only with silver instead of gold.

Gallardo was obliged to defend himself with his elbows against the outstretched hands, and, amid the jostling of the crowd, he managed at last to reach the steps of the carriage. Amid the general excitement he was finally unceremoniously hoisted into his seat from behind.

"Good afternoon, gentlemen," he said curtly to his *cuadrilla*.

He took the seat nearest to the step so that all could see him, and he smiled and nodded his acknowledgment of the cries and shouts of applause.

The carriage dashed forward with all the strength of the spirited mules and filled the street with a merry tinkling. The crowd opened to let the team pass, but many hung on to the carriage, in imminent danger of falling under its wheels. Sticks and hats were brandished in the air. A wave of enthusiasm swept over the crowd. It was one of those contagious outbursts which at times sway the masses, driving them mad and making them shout without knowing why.

"*Olé* El Gallardo! . . . Viva España!"

Gallardo, still pale but smiling, saluted and repeated, "Many thanks." He was moved by this outburst of popular enthusiasm, and proud of the fame that made them couple his name with that of his country.

A crowd of rough boys and disheveled girls ran after the carriage as fast as their legs could carry them.

For an hour now the Calle de Alcalá had been a stream of carriages, between banks of crowded foot-passengers, all hurrying to the outskirts of the town. Every sort of vehicle, old or modern, figured in this confused and noisy migration. The trams passed along, crowded bunches of passengers overflowing onto their steps. Omnibuses took up fares at the corner of the Calle de Sevilla, while the conductors shouted, "Plaza! Plaza!" Mules covered with tassels, drawing carriages full of women in white mantillas and bright flowers, trotted along gaily to the tinkling of their silvery bells. Motor horns shrieked and coachmen shouted. Newspaper sellers hawked leaflets giving a picture and history of the bulls which were going to fight, or the portraits and biographies of the famous *toreros*. Now and then a murmur of curiosity swelled the dull humming of the crowd.

Between the dark uniforms of the Municipal Guard rode showily dressed horsemen on lean, miserable nags, wearing gold-embroidered jackets, wide beaver sombreros with a pompon on one side like a cockade, and yellow padding on their legs. These were the *picadors*, who from the backs of horses would attack the bulls with lances. Rough men of wild appearance, each carried, clinging to the crupper behind his high Moorish saddle, a kind of devil dressed in red, the *monosabio*, the servant who had taken the horse to his house and whose function at the bullfight it was to strip the harness off dead horses and sprinkle sand over the pools of blood.

The *cuadrillas* passed by in open carriages. The gold embroidery of the *toreros* flashing in the afternoon sun seemed to dazzle the crowd and excite all its enthusiasm. "There's Fuentes!" "That's 'el Bomba'!" cried the people, pleased at having recognized them.

From the top of the Calle de Alcalá, the whole length of the broad, straight street could be seen lying white under the sun with its rows of trees beginning to turn green under the breath of spring. The balconies were black with onlookers and the roadway was only visible here and there amid the swarming crowd which, on foot and in carriages, was making its way toward the fountain, La Cibeles.

From this point the ground rose between lines of trees and buildings and the vista was closed by the Puerta de Alcalá outlined like a triumphal arch against the blue sky on which floated a few flecks of cloud like wandering swans.

Gallardo sat in silence, replying to the people only with his fixed smile. Since his first greeting to the *banderilleros* he had not uttered a word. They also were pale and silent with anxiety for the unknown. Now that they were among *toreros* they had laid aside as useless the swagger that was necessary in the presence of the public.

A mysterious inspiration seemed to tell the people of the coming of the last *cuadrilla* on its way to the Plaza. The group of ragamuffins who had run after the carriage acclaiming Gallardo had lost their breath and had scattered amid the traffic, but all the same, people glanced behind them as though they felt the proximity of the famous *torero* and slackened their pace, lining the edge of the pavement so as to get a better view of him.

Women seated in the carriages rolling along turned their heads as they heard the tinkling bells of the trotting mules. Dull roars came from various groups standing on the pavement. These must have been demonstrations of enthusiasm, for many waved their sombreros while others greeted him by flourishing their sticks.

Gallardo replied to all these salutations with a wooden smile. With his thoughts far away, he took little notice of them. By his side sat "el Nacional," the *banderillero* in whom he placed most trust, a big, hard man, older by ten years than himself, with a grave manner and eyebrows that met between his eyes. He was well known in the profession for his kindness of heart and sterling worth, and also for his political opinions.

"Juan, you will not have to complain of Madrid," said "el Nacional"; "you have taken the public by storm."

But Gallardo, as if he had not heard but felt obliged to give vent to the thoughts that were weighing on him, replied, "My heart tells me that something will happen this afternoon."

As they arrived at Cibeles, the carriage stopped. A great funeral was passing through the Prado in the direction of Castellana and cut through the avalanche of carriages coming from the Calle de Alcalá.

Gallardo turned still paler as he looked with terrified eyes at the passing of the silver cross and the procession of priests who broke into a mournful chant as they gazed, some with aversion, others with envy, at the stream of godless people who were rushing to amuse themselves.

The *matador* hastened to take off his *montera*. His *banderilleros* did the same, with the exception of "el Nacional."

"Curse you!" cried Gallardo. "Take off your cap!"

He glared at him as if about to strike him, fully convinced, by some confused intuition, that this impiety would bring down on him the greatest misfortunes.

"All right, I'll take it off," said "el Nacional," with the sulkiness of a thwarted child, as he saw the cross moving off. "I'll take it off, but it is to the dead man!"

They were obliged to stop for some time to let the funeral cortege pass.

"Bad luck!" murmured Gallardo, his voice trembling with rage. "Who can have thought of bringing a funeral across the way to the Plaza? Curse them! I said something would happen today!"

"El Nacional" smiled, and shrugged his shoulders. "Superstition and fanaticism! God or Nature don't trouble about these things!"

These words, which increased the irritation of Gallardo, seemed to dispel the grave preoccupation of the other *toreros,* and they began to laugh at their companion, as indeed they always did when he aired his favorite phrase, "God or Nature."

As soon as the way was clear the carriage resumed its former speed, traveling as fast as the mules could trot and passing all the other vehicles which were converging on the Plaza. On arriving there it turned to the left, making for the door which led to the yards and stables, but compelled to pass slowly through the compact crowd.

Gallardo received another ovation as, followed by his *banderilleros,* he alighted from the carriage, pushing and elbowing his way in order to save his clothes from the touch of dirty hands, smiling greetings everywhere and hiding his right hand which everybody wished to shake.

"Make way, please, gentlemen! . . . Many thanks."

The great courtyard between the main building of the Plaza and the boundary wall of its outbuildings was full of people who, before taking their seats, wished to get a close view of the bullfighters. On horseback, mounted high above the crowd, could be seen the *picadors* and the *alguaciles,* or ringmasters, in their seventeenth-century costumes.

On one side of the courtyard stood a row of single-story brick buildings, with vines trellised over the doors and pots of flowers in the windows. It was quite a small town of offices, workshops, stables, and houses in which lived stablemen, carpenters, and other servants of the bull ring.

The *torero* made his way laboriously through the various groups, and his name passed from lip to lip amid exclamations of admiration. "Gallardo!" "Here is El Gallardo!" "*Olé!* Viva España!"

And he, with no thought but that of the adoration of the public, swaggered along, serene as a god and gay and self-satisfied, just as if he were attending a fete given in his honor.

Suddenly two arms were thrown round his neck and at the same time a strong smell of wine assailed his nostrils.

"A real man! Three cheers for the heroes!"

It was a man of good appearance, a tradesman who had breakfasted with some friends, whose smiling vigilance Gallardo thought he had escaped but who were watching him from a short distance. He leaned his head on the *matador's* shoulder and let it remain there, as though he intended to drop off into a sleep of ecstasy in that position. Gallardo pushed and the man's friends pulled and the bullfighter was soon free of this intolerable embrace, but the tippler, finding himself parted from his idol, broke out into loud shouts of admiration.

"*Olé* for such men! All nations of the earth should come and admire *toreros* like this, and die of envy! They may have ships, they may have money, but that's all rot! They have no bulls and no men like this! Hurrah, my lads! Long live my country!"

Gallardo crossed a large whitewashed hall in which his professional companions were standing surrounded by admiring groups. Making his way through the crowd around a door, he entered a small, dark, and narrow room, at one end of which lights were burning. It was the chapel. An old picture called "The Virgin of the Dove" filled the back of the altar. On the table four tapers were burning, and several bunches of dusty, moth-eaten muslin flowers stood in common pottery vases.

The chapel was full of people. The aficionados of humble class assembled in it so as to see the great man close at hand. In the darkness some stood bareheaded in the front row, while others sat on benches and chairs, the greater part of them turning their backs on the Virgin, looking eagerly toward the door to call out a name as soon as the glitter of a gala dress appeared.

The *banderilleros* and *picadors,* poor devils who were going to risk their lives the same as the maestros, scarcely caused a whisper by their presence. Only the most fervent aficionados knew their nicknames.

Presently there was a prolonged murmur, a name repeated from mouth to mouth.

"Fuentes! It is El Fuentes!"

The elegant *torero,* tall and graceful, his cape loose over his shoulder, walked up to the altar, bending his knee with theatrical affectation. The lights were reflected in his gypsy eyes and fell across the fine, agile, kneeling figure. After he had finished his prayer and crossed himself he rose, walking backward toward the door, never taking his eyes off the image, like a tenor who retires bowing to his audience.

Gallardo was more simple in his piety. He entered with *montera* in hand, his cape gathered round him, walking no less arrogantly, but when he came opposite the image, he knelt with both knees on the ground, giving himself over entirely to his prayers and taking no notice of the hundreds of eyes fixed on him. His simple Christian soul trembled with fear and remorse. He prayed for protection with the fervor of ignorant men who live in continual danger and who believe in every sort of adverse influence and supernatural protection. For the first time in the whole of that day he thought of his wife and his mother. Poor Carmen down in Seville waiting for his telegram! The Señora Angustias, undisturbed with her fowls at the farm of La Rinconada, not knowing for certain where her son was fighting! And he, here, with that terrible presentiment that something would happen that afternoon! Virgin of the Dove, give a little protection! He would be good, he would live as God commands.

His superstitious spirit being comforted by this empty repentance, he left the chapel still under its influence, with clouded eyes that did not see the people who obstructed his way.

Outside in the room where the *toreros* were waiting he was saluted by a clean-shaven gentleman, in black clothes in which he appeared ill at ease.

"Bad luck!" murmured the *torero,* moving on. "As I said before, something will happen today!"

It was the chaplain of the Plaza, a bullfighting enthusiast, who had arrived with the holy oils concealed beneath his coat. He was priest of the suburb of La Prosperidad and for years had maintained a heated controversy with another parish priest in the center of Madrid as to who claimed a better right to monopolize the religious service of the Plaza. He came to the Plaza accompanied by a neighbor, who served him as sacristan in return for a seat for the *corrida.*

The priest entered the chapel with the air of being scandalized by the behavior of the public. All had their heads uncovered, but they were talking loudly, and some even smoking.

"*Caballeros,* this is not a café. You will do me the favor of going outside. The *corrida* is about to begin."

This news caused a general exodus, during which the priest took out the hidden oils and placed them in a painted wooden box. He, too, having concealed his sacred deposit, hurried out in order to reach his seat in the Plaza before the appearance of the *cuadrillas.*

The crowd had vanished. Nobody was to be seen in the courtyard but men dressed in silk and gold embroidery, horsemen in yellow with large beavers, ringmasters on horseback, and the servants on duty in their liveries of blue and gold.

In the doorway called De Caballos, under the arch forming the entrance to the Plaza, the *toreros* lined up for the procession with the promptness which comes of constant practice. In front the maestros, some distance behind them the *banderilleros,* and beyond these again, in the courtyard outside, the clattering rear guard, the stern, steel-clad squadron of *picadors,* smelling of hot leather and manure, and mounted on skeleton horses with a bandage over one eye. In the far distance, like the baggage of this army, fidgeted the teams of mules which were to drag out the carcasses, strong, lively animals with shining skins, their harness covered with tassels and bells, and their collars ornamented with a small national flag.

At the other end of the archway, above the wooden barricade which closed the lower half, could be seen a shining patch of blue sky, the roof of the Plaza, and a section of the seats with its compact, swarming mass of occupants, among which fluttered fans and papers like gaily colored butterflies. Faint harmonious sounds floated on the waves of air, betokening distant music, guessed at rather than heard.

Along the sides of the archway could be seen a row of heads—those of the spectators on the nearest benches, who peered over in their eagerness to get the first possible glimpse of the heroes of the day.

Gallardo took his place in line with the other *matadors*. They neither spoke nor smiled, a grave inclination of the head being all the greeting that they exchanged. Each seemed wrapped in his own preoccupation, letting his thoughts wander far afield, or, perhaps, with the vacuity of deep emotion, thinking of nothing at all. Outwardly this preoccupation was manifested in an apparently unending arrangement and rearrangement of their capes. All their faces were pale, not with a dull pallor, but with the bright, hectic, moist shine of excitement. Their minds were in the arena, as yet invisible to them, and they felt the irresistible fear of things that might happen on the other side of a wall, the terror of the unknown, the indefinite danger that is felt but not seen. How would this afternoon end?

From beyond the *cuadrillas* was heard the sound of the trotting of two horses, coming along underneath the outer arcades of the Plaza. This was the arrival of the *alguaciles* in their small black capeless mantles and broad hats surmounted with red and yellow feathers. They had just finished clearing the ring of all the intruding crowd and now came to place themselves as advance-guard at the head of the *cuadrillas*.

The doorways of the arch were thrown wide open, as also were those of the barrier in front of them. The huge ring was revealed, the real Plaza, an immense circular expanse of sand on which would be enacted the afternoon's tragedy, one which would excite the feelings and rejoicings of fourteen thousand spectators. The confused, harmonious sounds now became louder, resolving themselves into lively, reckless music, a noisy, clanging triumphal march that made the audience move hip and shoulder to its martial air. Forward, fine fellows!

The bullfighters, blinking at the sudden change, stepped out from darkness to light, from the silence of the quiet arcade to the roar of the ring, where the crowd on the tiers of benches, throbbing with excitement and curiosity, rose to its feet en masse, in order to obtain a better view.

The *toreros* advanced, dwarfed as soon as they trod the arena, by the immensity of their surroundings. They seemed like brilliant dolls on whose embroideries the sunlight flashed in iridescent hues, and their graceful movements fired the people with the delight that a child takes in some marvelous toy. The mad impulse which agitates a crowd, sending a shiver down its back for no particular reason, affected the entire Plaza. Some applauded, others, more enthusiastic or more nervous, shouted, the music clanged, and in the midst of this universal tumult, the *cuadrillas* advanced solemnly and slowly from the entrance door up to the presidential chair, making up for the shortness of their step by the graceful swing of their arms and the swaying of their bodies.

They felt themselves different men as they advanced over the sand. They were risking their lives for something more than money. Their doubts and terrors of the unknown had been felt outside the barricades. Now they trod the arena. They were face to face with their public. Reality had come. The longing for glory in their barbarous, ignorant minds, the desire to excel their comrades, the pride in their own strength and dexterity, all blinded them, making them forget all fears, and inspiring them with the daring of brute force.

Gallardo was quite transfigured. He drew himself up as he walked, wishing to appear the tallest. He moved with the arrogance of a conqueror, looking all round him with an air of triumph, as though his two companions did not exist. Everything was his, both the Plaza and the public. He felt himself at that moment capable of killing every bull alive on the broad pasture lands of Andalusia or Castile. All the applause was meant for him, he was quite sure of that. The thousands of feminine eyes, shaded by white mantillas, were fixed on him only, of that there could be no manner of doubt. The public adored him, and while he advanced smiling with pride, as though the ovation were intended for himself alone, he cast his eyes along the rows of seats, noticing the places where the largest groups of his followers were massed, and ignoring those where his comrades' friends had congregated.

They saluted the president, *montera* in hand, and then the brilliant parade broke up, peons (*banderilleros, chulos,* and others who participate on foot) and horsemen scattering in all directions. While a ringmaster caught in his hat the key thrown to him by the president, Gallardo walked toward the barrier behind which his most enthusiastic supporters stood, and gave into their charge his beautiful cape which was spread along the edge of the palisade, the sacred symbol of a faction.

His most enthusiastic followers stood up, waving their hands and sticks, to greet the *matador,* and loudly proclaiming their hopes. "Let us see what the lad from Seville will do!"

And he smiled as he leaned against the barrier, proud of his strength, repeating to all:

"Many thanks! He will do what he can."

It was not only his supporters who showed their high hopes on seeing him; everywhere he found adherents among the crowd, which anticipated deep excitement. He was a *torero* who promised hule—excitement—and such hule was likely to lead to a bed in the infirmary.

Everyone thought he was destined to die, gored to death in the Plaza, and for this very reason they applauded him with homicidal enthusiasm, with a barbarous interest.

Gallardo laughed at the ancient aficionados who judged it impossible that an accident should happen if a *torero* conformed to the rules of the art. Rules indeed! He ignored them and took no trouble to learn them. Bravery and audacity only were necessary to ensure victory. Almost blindly, with no other rule than his own temerity, no other help than his own bodily faculties, he had made a rapid career for himself, forcing outbursts of wonder from the people and astonishing them with his mad courage.

He had not, like other *matadors*, risen by regular steps, serving long years as peon and *banderillero* at the maestros' side. The bulls' horns caused him no fear. "Hunger gores worse," he said. The great thing was to rise quickly, and the public had seen him commence at once as *matador*, and in a few years enjoy an immense popularity.

It admired him for the very reason that a catastrophe was so certain. It was inflamed with a horrible enthusiasm by the blindness with which this man defied death, and paid him the same care and attention as are paid to a condemned man in the chapel. This *torero* was not one who held anything back; he gave them everything, including his life. He was worth the money he cost. And the crowd, with the brutality of those who watch danger from a safe place, admired and hallooed on the hero. The more prudent shrugged their shoulders, regarding him as a suicide playing with fate, and murmured, "As long as it lasts . . ."

Amid a clash of kettledrums and trumpets the first bull rushed out. Gallardo, with his working cloak devoid of ornament hanging on his arm, remained by the barrier, close to the benches where his supporters sat, disdainfully motionless, as though the eyes of the whole audience were fixed on him. That bull was for someone else. He would give signs of existence when his own bull came out. But the applause at the cloak play executed by his companions drew him out of this immobility, and in spite of his intentions he joined in the fray, performing several feats in which he showed more audacity than skill. The whole Plaza applauded him, roused by the delight they felt at his daring.

When Fuentes killed his first bull, and went toward the presidential chair saluting the crowd, Gallardo turned paler than before, as though any expression of gratification that was not for him was a studied insult. Now his turn had come; they would see great things. He did not know for certain what they might be, but he was disposed to startle the public.

As soon as the second bull came out, Gallardo, thanks to his mobility and his desire to shine, seemed to fill the whole Plaza. His cape was constantly close to the beast's muzzle. A *picador* of his own *cuadrilla*, the one named Potaje, was thrown from his horse, and lay helpless close to the horns. The maestro, seizing the fierce beast's tail, pulled with such herculean strength that he forced it to turn round till the dismounted rider was safe. This was a feat that the public applauded wildly.

When the play of the *banderilleros* began, Gallardo remained in the passage between the barriers awaiting the signal to kill. "El Nacional" with the darts in his hand challenged the bull in the center of the arena. There was nothing graceful in his movements, nor any proud daring, "simply the question of earning his bread." Down in Seville he had four little ones, who, if he died, would find no other father. He would do his duty and nothing more, stick in his *banderillas*, like a journeyman bullfighter, not desiring applause, and trying to avoid hissing.

When he had stuck in the pair, a few on the vast tiers applauded, while others, alluding to his ideas, found fault with the *banderillero* in jesting tones. "Quit politics and strike better!"

And "el Nacional," deceived by the distance, heard these shouts, and acknowledged them smilingly like his master.

When Gallardo leaped again into the arena, the crowd, hearing the blare of trumpets and drums which announced the final death stroke, became restless and buzzed with excitement. That *matador* was their own, now they would see something fine.

He took the *muleta*—that square of red silk fastened to a wand, used to irritate the bull and to throw over his eyes as he charges—from the hands of Garabato, who offered it to him folded from inside the barrier, and drew the rapier, which his servant also presented to him. Then with short steps he went and stood in front of the president's chair, carrying his *montera* in one hand. All stretched their necks, but no one could hear the *brindis*. (The *matador* has to declare before the president in whose honor—man or woman—he will kill the bull. There is an ancient formula used: "I dedicate this bull to so and so—either I will kill him or he will kill me." He then throws his *montera* on the ground behind him and fights the bull bareheaded.) The proud figure with its magnificent stature, the body thrown back to give more strength to his voice, produced the same effect upon the onlookers as the most eloquent oration. As he ended his speech, giving a half-turn and throwing his *montera* to the ground, noisy enthusiasm broke out. *Olé* for the lad from Seville! Now they would see real sport! And the spectators looked at one another, mutely promising each other tremendous happenings.

Silence fell on the crowd, a silence so deep that one would have thought that the Plaza had suddenly become empty. The life of thousands of people seemed concentrated in their eyes. No one seemed even to breathe.

Gallardo advanced slowly toward the bull, carrying the *muleta* against his stomach like a flag, and with sword waving in his other hand, swinging like a pendulum to his step.

Turning his head for an instant, he saw he was being followed by "el Nacional" and another peon of his *cuadrilla,* their cloaks on their arms ready to assist him.

"Go out, everybody!"

His voice rang out in the silence of the Plaza reaching up to the farthest benches, and was answered by a roar of admiration.

He remained completely alone close to the beast, and instantly there was again silence. Very calmly he unrolled the red *muleta,* and spread it, advancing a few steps at the same time, till he flung it almost on the muzzle of the bull, who stood bewildered and frightened at the man's audacity.

The audience scarcely dared to breathe, but admiration flashed in their eyes. What a man! He ws going up to the very horns. . . . He stamped impatiently on the sand with one foot, inciting the animal to attack, and the enormous mass of flesh, with its sharp defenses, fell bellowing upon him. The *muleta* passed over its horns, which grazed the tassels and fringes of the *matador's* costume. He remained fixed in his place, his only movement being to throw his body slightly back. A roar from the masses replied to this pass of the *muleta:* "*Olé!*"

The animal turned, once more attacking the man and his scarf, and the pass was again repeated amid the roars of the audience. The bull, each time more infuriated by the deception, again and again attacked the fighter who repeated the passes with the *muleta,* scarcely moving off his ground, excited by the proximity of danger and the admiring acclamations of the crowd, which seemed to intoxicate him.

Gallardo felt the wild beast's snorting close to him. Its breath moist with saliva fell on his face and right hand. Becoming used to the feeling, he seemed to look on the animal as a good friend who was going to let himself be killed, to contribute to the fighter's glory.

At last the bull remained still for a few instants as if tired of the game, looking with eyes full of somber reflection at this man and his red cloth, suspecting in his limited brain some stratagem that, by attack after attack, would lead him to his death.

Now! Gallardo caught the *muleta* with a circular sweep of his left hand, rolling it round the stick, and raised his right to the height of his eyes, standing with the sword bending down toward the nape of the bull's neck. A tumult of surprised protest broke from the crowd: "Don't strike! . . . No! . . . No!"

It was too soon. The bull was not well placed, it would charge and catch him. He was acting outside all rules of the art. But what did rules or life itself signify to that reckless man!

Suddenly he threw himself forward with his sword at the same instant that the beast fell upon him. The encounter was brutal, savage. For an instant man and beast formed one confused mass, and thus advanced a few paces. No one could see which was the conqueror—the man with one arm and part of his body between the two horns, or the bull lowering his head and fighting to catch on those horns the brilliantly colored golden puppet which seemed to be slipping away from him.

At last they separated. The *muleta* remained on the ground, and the fighter, his hands empty, emerged staggering from the impetus of the shock, till some distance away he recovered his balance. His clothes were disordered, and the cravat floating outside the waistcoat was gashed and torn by the bull's horns.

The bull continued its rush with the impetus of the first charge. On its broad neck the red pommel of the sword, buried up to the hilt, scarcely could be seen. Suddenly it stopped short in its course, rolling with a painful curt-seying motion, then folded its forelegs, bent its head till its bellowing muzzle touched the sand, and finally subsided in convulsions of agony.

It seemed as though the whole Plaza were falling down, as if all its bricks were rattling against one another, as if the crowd were going to fly in panic, when all rose suddenly to their feet, pale, trembling, waving their arms. Dead! What a sword thrust! They had all thought for a second that the *matador* was impaled on the bull's horns, all thought they would certainly see him fall bleeding on the sand, but now they saw him standing there, still giddy from the shock, but smiling! The surprise and astonishment of it all in-creased their enthusiasm.

"Oh! the brute!" they roared from the benches, not finding any better word with which to express their unbounded astonishment. "What a savage!"

Hats flew into the arena. Overwhelming rounds of applause ran like a torrent of hail from bench to bench, as the *matador* advanced through the arena, following the circle of the barriers, till he arrived opposite the presi-dential chair.

Then as Gallardo opened his arms to salute the president, the thunder-ing ovation redoubled, all shouted claiming the honors of the *maestría*—com-plete knowledge—for the *matador*. "He ought to be given the bull's ear.... Never was the honor better deserved. ... Sword-thrusts like that are seldom seen." And the enthusiasm waxed even greater when one of the attendants of the Plaza presented him with a dark, hairy, bloody triangle; it was the tip of one of the beast's ears.

The third bull was already in the arena, and still the ovation to Gallardo continued, as if the audience had not recovered from its astonishment, and nothing that could possibly happen during the rest of the *corrida* could be of the slightest interest.

The other *toreros,* pale with professional jealousy, exerted themselves to attract the attention of the public, but the applause they got sounded weak and timid after the outburst that had preceded it.

Soon violent disputes arose between the rows of seats. The supporters of the other *matadors* who by this time had recovered from the wave of enthu-siasm which had swayed them together with everyone else, began to justify their former spontaneous outbursts by criticizing Gallardo.

"Very brave ... very daring ... suicidal," but that was not art. On the other hand the worshipers of the idol who were even more vehement and brutal, and who admired his audacity from innate sympathy, were rabid with the rage of zealots who hear doubts cast on the miracles of their own particular saint.

Excerpt from "Blood and Sand"   **275**

Suddenly there was a commotion in some section of the amphitheater. Everybody stood up, turning their backs on the arena, and arms and sticks were flourished above the sea of heads. The rest of the audience forgot the arena, and concentrated their attention on the fracas, and the large numbers painted on the walls of the inside barrier, which distinguished the blocks of seats.

"A fight in number three!" they yelled joyfully. "Now there's a row in number five!"

Finally the whole audience caught the contagion, and stood up, each trying to look over his neighbor's head, but all they were able to see was the slow ascent of the police, who pushed a way for themselves from bench to bench, and finally reached the group where the disturbance was going on.

"Sit down!" shouted the more peaceable, who were prevented from seeing the arena, where the *toreros* were continuing their work.

The general tumult was gradually calmed, but the audience seemed to have its nerves overstrained, and gave vent to its feelings, by uncalled-for animosity, or contemptuous silence toward certain of the fighters.

The crowd, exhausted by its previous outburst of emotion, regarded all that followed as insipid, and so diverted its boredom by eating and drinking. The refreshment sellers of the Plaza walked round between the barriers, throwing up the articles asked for with marvelous dexterity. Oranges flew like golden balls up to the very highest benches. Bottles of soft drinks were opened, and the golden wine of Andalusia shone in glasses.

Soon a current of curiosity ran round the seats. Fuentes was going to fix *banderillas* in his bull, and everyone expected something extraordinarily dexterous and graceful. He advanced alone into the middle of the Plaza, the *banderillas* in his hand, quiet and self-possessed, moving slowly. The bull followed his movements with anxious eyes, astonished to see this man alone in front of him, after the previous hurly-burly of outspread cloaks, cruel pikes sticking into his neck, and horses which placed themselves in front of his horns, as if offering themselves to his attack.

The man hypnotized the beast, approaching so close as even to touch his pole with the *banderillas*. Then with short tripping steps he ran away, pursued by the bull, which followed him as though fascinated to the opposite end of the Plaza. The animal seemed cowed by the fighter, and obeyed his every movement, until at last, thinking the game had lasted long enough, the man opened his arms with a dart in each hand, drew up his graceful slim figure on tiptoe, and advancing toward the bull with majestic calm, fixed the colored darts in the neck of the surprised animal.

Three times he performed this feat, amid the acclamations of the audience. Those who thought themselves connoisseurs now had their revenge for the explosion of admiration provoked by Gallardo. This was what a true *torero* should be! This was real art!

Gallardo stood by the barrier, wiping the sweat from his face with a towel handed to him by Garabato. Afterward he drank some water, and turned his back on the arena so as not to see the prowess of his rival. Outside the Plaza he esteemed his rivals with the fraternity established by danger; but once they trod the arena they all became his enemies and their triumphs pained him like insults. This general enthusiasm for Fuentes which obscured his own great triumphs seemed to him like robbery. On the appearance of the fifth bull, which was his, he leaped into the arena, burning to astonish everybody by his prowess.

If a *picador* fell he spread his cloak and drew the bull to the other end of the arena, bewildering it with a succession of cloak play that left the beast motionless. Then Gallardo would touch it on the muzzle with one foot, or would take off his *montera* and lay it between the animal's horns. Again and again he took advantage of its bewilderment and exposed his stomach in an audacious challenge, or knelt close to it as though about to lie down beneath its nose.

Under their breath the old aficionados muttered "monkey business! . . . Tricks that would not have been tolerated in former days!" But amid the general shouts of approval they were obliged to keep their opinion to themselves.

When the signal for the *banderillas* was given, the audience was amazed to see Gallardo take the darts from "el Nacional," and advance with them toward the bull. There was a shout of protest. "That one with the *banderillas!*" They all knew his failing in that respect. *Banderilla* play was only for those who had risen in their career step by step, who before arriving at being *matadors* had been *banderilleros* for many years by the side of their masters, and Gallardo had begun at the other end, killing bulls from the time he first began in the Plaza.

"No! No!" shouted the crowd.

Doctor Ruiz yelled and thumped inside the barrier. "Don't do it, lad! You know well enough what they want. Kill!"

But Gallardo despised his audience, and was deaf to its advice when his daring impulses came over him. In the midst of the din he went straight up to the bull, and before it moved—*¿as!* he stuck in the *banderillas.* The pair were out of place and badly driven in. One of them fell out with the animal's start of surprise, but this did not matter. With the tolerance that a crowd always has for its idol, excusing, even justifying, his shortcomings, the spectators watched this daring act smilingly. Gallardo, rendered still more audacious, took a second pair of *banderillas* and stuck them in, regardless of the warnings of those who feared for his life. This feat he repeated a third time, badly, but with such dash that what would have provoked hisses for another produced only explosions of admiration for him. "What a man! . . . How lucky and fearless he is!"

The bull carried four *banderillas* instead of the customary six, and those were so feebly planted that it scarcely seemed to feel the discomfort.

"He is still fresh!" shouted the aficionados from the benches, alluding to the bull, while Gallardo with his *montera* on his head, grasping rapier and *mu-*

leta in his hands, advanced toward him, proud and calm, trusting to his lucky star.

"Out—all of you!" he cried again.

He turned his head, sensing that someone was still close to him regardless of his orders. It was Fuentes, a few steps behind him, who had followed him with his cloak on his arm pretending not to have heard, but ready to rush to his assistance, as if he foresaw some accident.

"Leave me, Antonio," said Gallardo half angrily, and yet respectfully, as if speaking to an elder brother.

His manner was such that Fuentes shrugged his shoulders, disclaiming all responsibility. Turning his back, he moved slowly away, certain that he would be suddenly required.

Gallardo spread his cloth on the very head of the wild beast, which at once attacked it. A pass. *"Olé!"* roared the enthusiasts. The animal turned suddenly, throwing itself again on the *torero* with a violent toss of its head that tore the *muleta* out of his hand. Finding himself disarmed and attacked, the *matador* was obliged to run for the barrier, but at this instant Fuentes's cloak diverted the animal's charge. Gallardo, who guessed during his flight the cause of the bull's sudden distraction, did not leap the barrier, but sat on the step and remained there some moments watching his enemy a few paces off. His flight ended in applause for this display of calmness.

He recovered his *muleta* and rapier, carefully rearranged the red cloth, and once again placed himself in front of the bull's head, but this time not so calmly. The lust of slaughter dominated him, an intense desire to kill as soon as possible the animal which had forced him to flee in the sight of thousands of admirers.

He scarcely moved a step. Thinking that the decisive moment had come, he squared himself, the *muleta* low, and the pommel of the rapier raised to his eyes.

Again the audience protested, fearing for his life.

"Don't strike! Stop! . . . Oh-h-h!"

An exclamation of horror shook the whole Plaza, a spasm which made all rise to their feet, their eyes jumping, while the women hid their faces or convulsively clutched at the nearest arm.

As the *matador* struck, the sword glanced on a bone. This mishap retarded his escape, and caught by one of the horns he was hooked up by the middle of his body, and despite his weight and strength of muscle, this well-built man was lifted, then twirled about on its point like a helpless dummy until the powerful beast with a toss of its head sent him flying several yards away. The *torero* fell with a thump on the sand with his limbs spread wide apart, like a frog dressed up in silk and gold.

"It has killed him! . . . He is gored in the stomach!" they yelled from the seats.

But Gallardo picked himself up from the cluster of men who rushed to his rescue. With a smile he passed his hands over his body, and then shrugged his shoulders to show he was not hurt. Nothing but the force of the blow and a sash in rags. The horn had only torn the strong silk belt.

He turned to pick up his killing weapons. None of the spectators sat down, as they guessed that the next encounter would be brief and terrible. Gallardo advanced toward the bull with a reckless excitement, as if he disbelieved the powers of its horns now he had emerged unhurt. He was determined to kill or to die. There must be neither delay nor precaution. It must be either the bull or himself! Everything became red to him, and he only heard, like a distant sound from the other world, the shouts of the people who implored him to keep calm.

He only made two passes with the help of a cloak which lay near him, and then suddenly, quick as thought, he threw himself on the bull, planting a thrust which his admirers described as "like lightning." He thrust his arm in so far that as he drew back from between the horns one of them grazed him, sending him staggering several steps. But he kept his feet, and the bull, after a mad rush, fell at the opposite side of the Plaza, with its legs doubled beneath it and the top of its head touching the sand, until the *puntillero* came to give the final dagger thrust.

The crowd seemed to go mad with delight. A splendid *corrida!* Gallardo didn't steal their cash, he paid back their entrance money with interest. The aficionados would have enough to keep them talking for three days at their evening meetings in the cafés. What a brave fellow! What a savage!

"He's the finest *matador* in the world! If anyone dares to deny it, I'm here, ready for him."

The rest of the *corrida* scarcely attracted any attention. It all seemed colorless after Gallardo's great feats.

When the last bull fell in the arena, a swarm of boys, low-class fans, and bull-ring apprentices invaded the arena. They surrounded Gallardo, and escorted him from the president's chair to the exit door. They pressed round him, anxious to shake his hands, or even to touch his clothes, till finally the wildest of them seized the maestro by the legs, and hoisting him on their shoulders, carried him in triumph round the arena and galleries as far as the outbuildings of the Plaza.

Raising his *montera,* Gallardo saluted the groups who cheered his progress. With his gorgeous cape around him, he let himself be carried like a god, erect and motionless, above the sea of Cordovan hats and Madrid caps, from which issued enthusiastic rounds of cheers.

When he was seated in his carriage, passing down the Calle de Alcalá, hailed by the crowds who had not seen the *corrida* but who had already heard of his triumphs, a smile of pride, of delight in his own strength, illuminated his face, which was perspiring and pale with excitement.

"El Nacional," still anxious about his master's accident and terrible fall, asked if he was in pain, and whether Doctor Ruiz should be summoned.

"No, it was only a graze, nothing more. The bull that can kill me is not born yet."

But as though in the midst of his pride some remembrance of his former weakness had surged up, and he thought he saw a sarcastic gleam in "el Nacional's" eye, he added:

"Those feelings come over me before I go to the plaza. Something like women's fancies. You are not far wrong, Sebastián. What's your saying?— 'God or Nature'; that's it. Everyone comes out of it as best he can, by his own skill or his own courage; there is no protection to be got from either earth or heaven. . . . You have talents, Sebastián; you ought to have studied for a profession."

On arriving at his lodging he found a crowd of admirers in the lobby waiting to embrace him. Upstairs he found his room full of friends. Gentlemen who imitated the rustic speech of the peasantry, slapping him on the back and saying, "You were splendid . . . absolutely first class."

Gallardo freed himself from this warm reception, and went out into the passage with Garabato.

"Go and send off the telegram home. You know—'nothing new.' "

The Album of Roberto Domingo

Roberto Domingo, 1883–1956, was a unique and magnificent artist. He was the creator of bullfight art before he had seen a bullfight, before he had seen Spain and before he was sixteen years old. He was born in Paris, the son of Spanish painter, Francisco Domingo.

The young artist moved to Madrid in his early manhood. Although he was a versatile stylist, his fame was established as an interpreter of bullfight subjects. He did everything from line drawings for newspapers to paintings. Domingo was an enthusiastic aficionado and a delightful companion in tauromachian talk. His studio was around the corner from my news office in Madrid. The Cafe León was between. My information on the bulls was deepened and broadened by his wise and painstaking observations of the fiesta in the *tertulias,* intimate social gatherings, of our time. The twentieth-century tauromachian illustrators owe a lot to Don Roberto and his eloquent lines. This gallery of drawings shows noted bullfighters in famous passes and phases of the *corrida* as interpreted by the artist.

The brave bull

The *picador* Atienga

Félix Rodríguez taking the bull in a *verónica*

A *verónica* by Gitanillo de Triana

Chicuelo in his creation, the *chicuelina*

Manolo Bienvenida placing *banderillas*

283

Nacional placing a pair of *banderillas* against the barrier

Niño de la Palma in a right-handed breast pass

Niño de la Estrella in a high pass

Manolo Bienvenida in a signature pass

285

Nicanor Villalta in a punishing right-handed pass

Armillita Chico in a natural pass

Gitanillo de Triana in a low testing pass

Belmonte in a high pass

Nicanor Villalta in a tremendous sword thrust

"Cagancho" posing at the kill

Fuentes Bejarano and a perfect kill

Excerpt from
Mars in the House of Death

by REX INGRAM

Rex Ingram was a world famous motion-picture director. He was also an artist and writer. Biographical information supplied me by our mutual friend, Pepo Romero, fine Mexican columnist, author and artist, reveal other facets of his character. He was a sculptor, a flier, a Foreign Legionnaire, a Moslem convert, and a linguist. He was a disciple of David Wark Griffith in Hollywood, and directed "The Four Horsemen of the Apocalypse" as well as other famous pictures. He died five years ago.

Mars in the House of Death is a novel about Spanish bullfighting. It might have been written by a Spaniard, so deep is his knowledge of the people, and so melodramatic is his story that could easily have happened just the way he wrote it. His picture of the youthful bullfighter apprentice is both touching and truly done.

Chuchito was staring up at bull-ring posters that splashed vivid colors across the dull brick walls inside the plaza. Some of these advertisements, coated with the dust of several seasons, had already begun to curl at the edges, but the more recent were a riot of color. They represented the aces of the bull ring executing the various passes in impeccable style: "el Gallo," Joselito, Belmonte and Rodolfo Gaona. Pepe pointed them out one by one, naming the maneuver depicted. Carlos Ruano Llopis had painted them. . . .

While they awaited the arrival of the bulls from the station, Chuchito was seeing a *plaza de toros* for the first time. Pepe had a friend on the premises, Manolo by name. This old *torero* had at one time been the Minotaur's confidential *banderillero*, and now lived on the ground floor of the *Museo Taurino*. In addition to his duties as *torilero* he also took care of the museum. He seemed to have keys to everything. Together the three of them made a tour of inspection that began with a visit to the small chapel where *matadors* bow the knee to La Macarena—Our Lady of Hope—before marching into the arena at the head of their *cuadrillas*. The dark *toril* where the bulls are kept until the *puerta de toros* is opened onto the arena filled Chuchito with apprehension. In its sepulchral obscurity the smell of dung and damp earth oppressed him. He half expected to be confronted with the ghostly specters of bulls that had died in the ring. The thought sent chills down his spine. An encounter with the supernatural was the last thing he wished for. In sunlight, and with a bull of flesh and blood, a man could take care of himself, but here in the dark! He breathed a prayer for protection to the Macarena Virgin, thankful that she was in the vicinity, and clutched the Minotaur's sleeve. He sighed with relief when Manolo struck a match, though not until they had emerged again into the sunlight did he feel completely at ease. . . .

There was still plenty of time. No sign yet of the bulls. They ascended the steps to the first floor of the museum and as they entered the principal *sala* the mounted heads of bulls that had distinguished themselves in the *corrida* looked down upon them from the walls. Within the cramped space of the exhibition room these heads seemed to have gained in size, the spread of their horns assuming proportions truly alarming in the narrow confines of their mausoleum.

Before the head of Perdigón the Minotaur paused, reciting the virtues of "el Espartero's" slayer with as much pride as though the great bull had come from the Villalbaso *ganadería* instead of from that of Don Eduardo Miura. Pepe had named his finest seed bull after this heroic animal—as municipalities name streets and public squares after the illustrious dead.

Farther on, the head of Señorito confronted them. Conqueror of a Bengal tiger, no less. No animal alive was a match for the fighting bulls of Spain, the Minotaur declared. More credit to the men who fought them. And certain addle-brained citizens still called the lion the king of beasts. Child's prattle! In proof of his assertion he pointed to the stuffed head of Caramelo, a trifle moth-eaten, but ferocious even in death and in spite of eyes of colored glass.

"Take a good look at this fellow, *chico*. There's a bull for you! When he had gored a tiger to death in Sevilla, they turned a lion loose on him. But it wasn't long before the beast's entrails were wrapped around Caramelo's horns."

"You saw it?" queried the boy, awed and open-mouthed.

The Minotaur was about to reply in the affirmative, but remembered in time that Manolo stood behind them.

"Madre de Dios, no!" he exclaimed—adding apologetically: "It was in 1849."

From room to room they wandered. About each exhibit the Minotaur had comments to make, anecdotes to relate.

"Here is 'Lagartijo.' I knew him well. A great artist who could kill well if he felt like it. Take a good look at that portrait. Woven in silk, no less."

They examined glass cases that displayed panoplies of estocs and *ban-*

derillas, lanceheads and short wicked-looking *puntillas* with which mortally wounded animals are dispatched. Everywhere were souvenirs of illustrious *matadors* of the past: the Romeros, "Pepe-Hillo," and "Costillares," who discovered a new and spectacular way of killing. . . . Next to Goya's etching of "Pepe-Hillo's" death was a photograph of Juan Belmonte, a *matador* with a special style of his own invention. Our Lady had endowed him with courage and cunning that made up for his physical defects. Below the picture of Belmonte hung an enlargement of the photograph Pepe had signed for Pablo at the *bodega* in Barcelona

At last they came to an engraving before which the Minotaur uncovered himself with almost the same respect he had accorded the Macarena Virgin.

"There he is. Take a good look at him, *chico*. There's the great *espada* who gave my grandfather the *alternativa*, the *matador* who revolutionized the art of bullfighting and wrote a book about it. His cape is preserved in the cathedral at Sevilla."

Chuchito gazed upon an engraving of Francisco Montes, the famous *torero* of the last century, better known as "Paquiro." This was the hero of so many of the Minotaur's fireside stories—the hero whose prowess increased at each telling until the boy had come to think of him with reverence. Long he studied the bewhiskered face with its mouth twisted up at one corner and eyes that avoided his own. . . . So this was what he looked like, "Paquiro!" Not at all as Chuchito had imagined him. The whiskers and the unfamiliar *montera*, so unlike the flat-crowned headgear worn by modern *matadors*, bothered him. He had pictured "Paquiro" as a glorified more robust edition of Pepe, and he missed the Minotaur's beetling brows and massive shoulders. . . . Below the portrait a sword and *muleta* and a blood-rusted *puntilla* were displayed under glass. A card stated that they had served "Paquiro" in one or more of his triumphant *corridas*.

These, Pepe declared, were souvenirs that merited the respect accorded the relics of sainted personages. . . .

Basta! . . . They must be going. The Minotaur replaced his hat and propelled Chuchito toward the stairway, followed by Manolo.

In the circular passage between the arena and the adjoining buildings a crowd had gathered, waiting for the arrival of the bulls and eager to assist—from the safety of the railed gallery above the corral—at the free spectacle of the unloading.

The rattle of iron wheels on the stone-paved street outside greeted Pepe and Chuchito as they stepped from the doorway of the museum. The first boxcar was hauled in by a horse. Shouting orders at the driver, Lázaro followed them. When he saw Pepe, he approached with raised arms. He was late, there was no denying it, but what could a man do? Valencia was getting to be as bad as Madrid. With all these trams and motorcars people no longer had any respect for a horse-drawn vehicle—not even when it contained a fighting bull!

Through Manolo's kitchen they took a short cut to the corrals. The boxcars were unhitched, and when the first of them had been pushed against the narrow entrance of the unloading enclosure until the doors of each were flush, the enclosure door was pulled up. Along the railed-off runways on the top of the walls *corraleros* were busy untangling ropes that worked on pulleys and controlled the gates leading from the unloading corral to those adjoining it. Inside the entrance the plaza carpenter was busy with his hammer, knocking the wedges from their staples to release the door of the boxcar. The last of them removed, he stopped discreetly behind a *burladero*. When the Minotaur, standing to one side of the entrance, raised his hand, Lázaro moved instinctively closer to the nearest shelter. The men on top of the boxcar let down the door, and with a crash of horns against wood and hoofs against feeding pail a bull leaped from darkness into the glare of sunlight. In the middle of the corral it pulled up snorting, and with such abruptness that its hoofs slid from under it. Its entrance was met with yells and challenges from the aficionados safely installed behind the rails of the gallery above. Scarves were waved; hats, coats and capes enticed it to attack. A newspaper floated down and shouts greeted the beast's frenzied efforts to tear it to pieces.

The Minotaur had not moved. With hoarse inarticulate sounds he addressed the bull, counseling calm. Between him and the *burladero*, watching the antics of the gallery bullfighters with scorn, stood Chuchito. When the *corraleros* hauled on the ropes and the door to the adjoining corral slid back he seconded Pepe and Lázaro in their efforts to drive the beast toward it, with unerring aim striking the horns with lumps of hard clay. . . .

When the fourth bull crashed out of its boxcar Chuchito stepped back. Here was one to be accorded respect!

Suddenly from his boyish lips broke an oath. Leaping the height of a man to reach a fluttering scarf, the bull had splintered a horn against the perforated iron flooring of the gallery. The crowd backed against the wall, scanning the exits anxiously. Another such onslaught might land the animal in their midst! . . . Forgetting caution, Chuchito rushed into the middle of the enclosure. Outraged feelings brought the tears to his eyes.

"*Hijo de puta!*" he shouted at the owner of the scarf. "Down here in the corral with you, *valiente!* Here is the place to show your courage!"

This insult brought roars of laughter and applause and the person addressed did his best to efface himself in the crowd. Chuchito turned toward the bull, as though moved by a desire to console it, to excuse such behavior on the part of one belonging to the same species as himself. But the beast had already charged into the next corral, Pepe close on its heels to ascertain the extent of the damage. The door slid back behind them.

A well-known journalist whose articles had first drawn attention to a score of popular *toreros* elbowed himself forward. He leaned over the balcony:

"*Bravo, torerito!* When the time comes you'll do credit to the *corrida,* to the tradition of 'Paquiro.' . . . Before you receive the *alternativa* come and see me."

The eminent man beamed with approbation and kindly humor. His card fluttered down. Chuchito picked it up. He made a pretence of reading it and removed his hat in the manner of a *matador* saluting the president of the *corrida.*

"*Gracias, Excelencia.* I shall remember," he replied with grave dignity.

In the evening Pepe and Chuchito dined with Manolo in a small restaurant frequented by *toreros.* The patrón was a *matador* who had been forced by the amputation of a leg to seek other means of livelihood. Since he had been a brave conscientious man, members of the profession flocked to his tavern, their appreciation of him warmed by the knowledge that they had no longer reason to fear his competition. His wife occupied herself with the cuisine, and here one could enjoy all the dishes for which Valencia is famous. Daily shipments of sea food arrived from the port, and for three *pesetas* a man could gorge himself and wash his repast down with a bottle of local wine—the *vino del país.*

A *torero,* Pedro Morera, joined them. He came from a village near the *ganadería* and as a boy had worked for Pepe. He had just graduated from the status of *novillero* or fighter of immature bulls—or bulls otherwise ineligible for the formal *corridas*—to that of *matador de toros* and was very proud of himself. Pedro's swarthy face was commonplace enough, and gold front teeth—souvenirs of a tossing—did not enhance it. But these and his salmon-pink shirt made a favorable impression on Chuchito.

During the meal bull-raising formed the subject of conversation, and Chuchito's astute comments surprised the *matador.* Before the repast was over they were friends.

When the check was brought, Pedro wanted to pay for all, but Pepe would not permit this; he was the host. Before leaving, Pedro produced a couple of tickets for the bullfight. Knowing that Pepe and Chuchito did not need them, he offered them to Manolo. Though tempted by the possibility of a resale, Manolo could not forgo the pleasure of stating that in his official capacity he had the privilege of viewing the *corridas* from the arena itself; in fact, no bullfight could proceed without him: as *torilero* he kept the key to the bull pens. . . . This was obviously Pedro's first *corrida* in Valencia!

"A brave killer, but clumsy with the cloth," said Pepe when Pedro had gone.

"That may be," said Manolo. "But when a *torero* kills the way they say he does, people will always pay the price of admission on the chance of seeing him gored."

Before quitting Valencia, Pepe took Chuchito to visit Don Eusebio Pilar, the journalist who had tossed him his card from the balcony. That incident was one to be taken advantage of: it warranted a call. Not many were fortunate enough to attract the attention of such a person.

They found Don Eusebio at the offices of *El Pueblo,* a republican journal known for the revolutionary editorials that had caused the exile of its director, Vicente Blasco-Ibáñez.

Entering by a side door, they passed through rooms where great presses, with the rhythmic tempo of a slow waltz, were spewing out copies of the latest edition.

When the Minotaur had been announced, a spectacled yellow-toothed typesetter, sleeves protected by black alpaca cuffs, led the way up an iron stairway to the editorial sanctum.

They found themselves in a vast hall of which the distinguishing feature was an immense column that rose through the floor from the basement and supported the roof. It made Chuchito think of a stick of sugarcandy reproduced on a huge scale. The hall vaguely suggested a church, but instead of the Stations of the Cross, souvenirs of the exiled (*patrio*) hung from the walls. Behind a carved baroque desk of black wood, at which many of his most famous books had been written, first editions of the master's works were stacked behind sliding glass doors. A portrait bust of him, a literal likeness of no sculptural merit, surmounted the bookcase, and above it, covering the wall, was a large poster representing Valencia as a woman wearing the red bonnet of Liberty. The signature was Joaquín Sorolla's; the date, 1911. . . . Fellows with the courage of their beliefs, these Valencians, thought Pepe, noting it. . . . Choice pieces of bric-a-brac, scattered about indiscriminately lost their effectiveness in the surrounding space, and everywhere hung framed announcements of the author's novels, diplomas from institutes of learning, and illuminated testimonials from various societies. Chuchito passed these and the autographed pictures of men of letters without a second glance. A terra cotta representing the Rape of Europa, the work of the sculptor Carpeaux, was absorbing his attention when Don Eusebio came in from the patio.

"On Saturday you were too busy with your bulls to notice me," he said, greeting Pepe. "But this young *mayoral* and I became acquainted."

He held out his hand to Chuchito.

"*Buenos días,* Excelencia," said the boy, impressed more than ever by the bearded gentleman in these surroundings. . . .

At the novelist's desk, in a chair that looked like a stage throne, Don Eusebio suggested a minister of state, and when he spoke to Chuchito,

Chuchito, intent on missing no word, edged forward until he was in danger of slipping off his seat.

"My greatest claim to fame," said the journalist, "is that I picked Pepe's nom de guerre: 'El Minotauro.' . . . Can you think of a better name for him?"

"No, indeed, Excelencia," agreed Chuchito, mystified, but eager to fall in with any opinions the great man might express.

"A week," said the journalist in reply to Pepe's query as to the length of his stay in Valencia. "I'm here visiting the family of my exiled confrere. . . . The son is growing up. His father has a political career in mind for him. You never can tell—one of these days he may represent Valencia in the Cortes."

Don Eusebio, leaning closer to Pepe, lowered his voice:

"By that time Ibáñez's dream may have come true: a republic in Spain."

"If God is willing," said Pepe. "For my own part, I'm all for the change. What Spain needs is new blood, red blood, at the helm of things."

Refrescos in tall glasses were brought in, and Chuchito became the subject of conversation. Pepe told something of the boy's life and predicted a great career for him in the bull ring. When the time came he was determined that Chuchito should step into the ring with a knowledge of bulls as complete as his own—"And yours, amigo," he hastened to add.

Yes, Chuchito would be raised on the *ganadería,* and under Pepe's tutelage reach fame by the direct route. Not like himself, who had been forced to get his first experience in the rural *capeas,* or trespassing the ranges at night to draw a beast from the herd and play it in the moonlight with coat or cape. . . . When Chuchito entered the arena, it would be with his own *cuadrilla* behind him, not as a peon in the *cuadrilla* of another *matador.*

"At present he has a remarkable asset: that peculiar courage which is really not courage at all, but incomprehension of fear," said the journalist looking at Chuchito. "This in itself is a quality that permits mere man to dominate a fighting bull. You possessed it yourself to an unusual degree, Pepe. Among our *matadors* today few do, fine artists though some of them are, and, on occasion, good killers."

"Fear," remarked the Minotaur, "as I have observed it in other *matadors,* is generally due to lack of education."

"Education?" Don Eusebio raised an eyebrow.

The Minotaur was not a talkative man, but on the subject of tauromaquia he could talk lengthily and with authority and, by the simple expedient of raising his voice, without interruption.

"Nothing else, *amigo.* People who know bulls the way I do have no need to be afraid of them. . . . We've all seen *toreros* bring down the hats and flowers with their first *suertes* and leave the bull ring dodging cushions and bottles because the bull didn't keep on acting the way he should, and they hadn't the education to make him. . . . And when a *torero* isn't sure of himself, he loses control and the bull dominates the *corrida*. That's when the gorings happen; for dominating the bull isn't only the art of bullfighting, it's the *torero's* only chance of keeping a whole skin—and without education he can't do it. . . . An educated *torero* knows what kind of bull he has drawn after he has taken it into his cape. When it's cowardly or suspicious he makes it frank and confident by working closer to it, by deceiving it, by making it believe that it's the master, that one more charge will end everything; this is where education comes in. The lack of it sends more *toreros* to hospitals than fear ever did. For my own part neither bulls nor cows ever bothered me—I understood them too well. . . . The educated *torero* has his off days, but fear is not the cause of them."

Don Eusebio smiled.

"I see what you mean, Pepe. There's no doubt that knowledge gives confidence, but not, in the case of a *torero,* to the complete exclusion of fear —which, after all, is largely a matter of temperament. Imaginative people are more subject to it than practical beings like yourself; and I've a feeling that the boy, for all his fearlessness, has imagination. When you spoke of education I thought, of course, you were referring to school education."

"School? . . . Whether you believe it or not, Don Eusebio, there are young fellows who have attended school for three years and can't tell a heifer from a bullock."

"But there are schools and schools, Pepe. I refuse to believe that such abysmal ignorance pervades them all."

With a smile the journalist turned to Chuchito, who had been sipping at his *refresco* in silence.

What was the Minotaur doing about the boy's education—that other, more prosaic, yet equally essential education? . . . His nephew, was he not? Was there a school near the *ganadería?*

"Not within ten miles of it," said Pepe. "But he can already spell out words from the *Almanac of Bullfighting.* Later on we'll try him at Cervantes and your own articles."

Don Eusebio got up. He patted Pepe affectionately on the back, not displeased at the bracketing of his name with that of the other man of letters. Before they left he took the Minotaur's right hand and lifted the arm, but Pepe could get it no higher than his chest without raising the shoulder too. The goring that ended his career had left him with only the partial use of it.

"Ah, well, Pepe," said Don Eusebio, "at least you have the satisfaction of knowing that while you lasted you upheld our best traditions."

Pepe sighed. These words from the man whose praise assured a *matador's* career, whose ridicule could break it, touched him more deeply now than in the days when he had read them above the journalist's signature.

"I'm schooling the boy to pick up where I left off," he said.

"I believe you will succeed, Pepe. But keep in mind what I mentioned about that other schooling," said Don Eusebio, opening the door.

Excerpt from

Bullfighter from Brooklyn

by SIDNEY FRANKLIN

Shortly after my debut in Madrid, a duke who was the King's uncle became one of my most outspoken admirers. He formed a caravan of about twenty cars which traveled with me all over the country. Each car belonged to some titled person. These people were in the habit of doing most of their business at the fairs, much in the manner of those of our big businessmen who prefer to discuss their projects on the golf course.

The duke always got my advance schedule from Argomaniz and we could take to the road for tours of a month or so before returning to Madrid. His party would reserve a floor or two in the swankiest hotel in each city or town we would visit. We carried our own chef. And before long I had to have a chef prepare food exclusively for me. I couldn't take the rich banquets as a steady fare. My stomach definitely affected my performances.

Internationally famous artists who appeared at the fairs where I was booked entertained us privately in our suites after the theater. There were violinists, pianists, cellists, singers of many nationalities, and artists in many fields. Pavlova gave some performances for us I'll never forget. And so did Mary Garden, Farrar, Fritz Kreisler, Schipa, Pablo Casals, Andrés Segovia, and a great many others. They all gave brilliant performances. Practically all of the world-famous artists who toured Spain at that time entertained us privately at some time or another.

The day after returning from our first short trip around the country, I was sitting at a sidewalk table of the Café Gran Vía, just across from the Telephone Building. There were about twelve in our group. It was just before noon and it was one of those days for which Madrid is famous. The air was crystal clear. The sky was a brilliant blue without a wisp of a cloud in it. The usual mob were making things difficult for the traffic and police. We were having a pre-lunch Tío Pepe when I noticed a great big fellow talking quietly with our waiter. The waiter pointed me out to him and then came over and asked if I'd permit him to present "a *paisano* of mine" who wanted to speak with me.

"Bring him over," I said, reaching into my pocket for some change. By his appearance, this fellow looked as though he needed a handout. Since my first success in Seville I had been swamped with all sorts of requests and demands for money by Americans. Some had what I believed to be legitimate hard-luck stories. Some were wise guys who lived by their wits. And there were quite a few crackpots. This man hadn't shaved and he needed a haircut. He wore a shabby suit which looked as though it had forgotten what a tailor's iron felt like. Battered bedroom slippers were on his feet. He approached very meekly and in a very small voice asked if I were Sidney Franklin the *matador*. I rattled my pocket change in anticipation. But he didn't want money. Rather, he said, he'd like to know when he could speak with me.

"What about?" I asked.

He asked if I had received a letter from a Guy Hickock who was the Paris correspondent of the *Brooklyn Daily Eagle*. At first I didn't recall any such letter. But when he mentioned that it said something about my going to Pamplona to meet a certain Ernest Hemingway, I remembered it. "That's right," I said. "I remember this Hickock made some silly suggestion of that kind. Whoever this Hickock is, he doesn't seem to understand that for me to go to a place like Pamplona when I'm not appearing there would mean canceling engagements. And for what? I don't know Hickock. And I don't know who this fellow he mentions is either. The way my contracts run right now, I can't go anywhere unless I'm booked there."

"That's what I tried to explain to Hickock when he told me he was going to write to you," he said. "I know a little about these things. But you can see that Hickock doesn't understand anything about bullfighters or bullfighting. So please don't hold that against me."

"Why should I? What has all this to do with you?" I asked.

"I'm the fellow he mentioned," he said. "I'm Ernest Hemingway, the one he asked you to go to Pamplona to meet."

At this point Count de la Peña, who was sitting on my right, offered his chair to the fellow. After a quick glance at me to see if it would be all right, he asked my permission and sat down. "What'll you have?" I said.

He thought awhile then said he'd order what he wanted if I'd permit him to pay for this round. But that was out of the question. "That's quite all right," I said. "Just order what you want. I don't pay for it, and, for that matter, I don't know who does. But somehow everything gets taken care of at the right time. So go right ahead and order."

"I can't do that," he said. "It wouldn't be right."

"That's a strange thing to say," I said. "Why wouldn't it be right?"

"What I'd like to order is about the most expensive drink there is," he said. "And this is one of the very few places in Madrid where it can be had. No, on second thought, I guess I'll have a beer."

I clapped for the waiter. This seemed to be an entirely new line. I de-

Excerpt from "Bullfighter from Brooklyn"   **299**

cided to play along with him, just to see what his game was, so I insisted he order what he first had in mind.

He ordered Pernod and explained that it was really absinthe. Absinthe? I hazily recalled having heard something about it. It seemed to be shrouded in a certain mystery. Something like cocaine, heroin, or opium. They all evoked visions of the mysterious. Something to stay away from. I definitely wanted to see what this absinthe was like.

The way he handled his stemmed glass, the ice tray with the tiny hole in it which sits on top of the glass, and the way he dripped the water, all made me wonder just who this fellow really was. His language and manners definitely didn't go with his appearance. I had a strange feeling that he either had had means at some time and was now down on his luck, or was somebody so well known that he didn't want to be recognized. Maybe this could explain his appearance.

So I asked who he was and what he did.

He stated simply that he was Ernest Hemingway and an author.

"What kind of an author?" I asked. "Books, newspapers, magazines? Do you make a living at it?"

"I manage to get along," he said.

"Are you any good at it?" I asked. I never had heard of Hemingway or read anything that wasn't directly concerned with bullfighting, except *The Saturday Evening Post.* I had no idea that he had already written *A Farewell to Arms* and *The Sun also Rises* and was world-famous. When he offered to get me some of his books, I told him I wasn't interested. I had read so many pieces of tripe in English by people who said they were authors of repute that I had better use for my time. And far from being annoyed, he seemed to take my statement without the slightest feeling of any kind. So, at his own suggestion, we just ignored the fact that he was an author. More to our mutual interest, we began to discuss bullfighting.

As we chatted, I realized that this fellow had a choice selection of English terms for bullfighting which up until then I had been at a loss to translate. And he used them very casually, as though it were old stuff with him. Besides, he was the first person who spoke to me in American English who appeared to have a deep understanding of the business. Since I knew that someday I would want to write on the subject, this was a perfect opportunity to learn. I drew our conversation into channels which would show me just how much he knew about bullfighting. And, little by little, he amazed me. He was familiar with events and instances which only a deep and sincere student of the subject could know about. We kept up this discussion until someone remarked it was time for lunch.

Hemingway asked me if I'd permit him to invite me to lunch. He said he'd been looking forward to this moment ever since he first saw references to me in the professional journals. He'd been thinking for some time that he'd go to Mexico to see me perform. But now that I had come to Spain, he was glad he didn't have to go so far.

Truthfully, I didn't believe he had the means for anything like that. I listened with half an ear to whatever he said about himself.

When the subject of lunch was brought up, he immediately invited me to lunch. I explained I was in the habit of eating at home. I had one of the most wonderful cooks in the country, and Spain is noted for her good cooks. So I invited him to come home with me for lunch if he didn't mind Spanish cooking. Mercedes always prepared enough for six or eight guests who dropped in at almost every meal. I was sure he'd enjoy it.

He accepted so enthusiastically that I smiled to myself smugly. This must be his gag, I thought.

When we reached the house, Ernest stopped at the door. He said he wouldn't feel right accepting my invitation unless I let him bring some wine. For the moment I thought the idea silly because my pantry was loaded with quantities of packaged foodstuffs and wines given me by manufacturers who were fans. He seemed to know of a very good wine house near by and said it wouldn't take but a few minutes. So I told him to go ahead.

He finally came back with half-a-dozen different wines. Without the slightest suggestion of being prepossessing, he explained that each wine was noted for some particular quality and was at its best when used with certain types of food. He said I'd soon see that a particular wine would bring out the finer flavors in certain dishes. He did it in such a manner that I could tell he knew what he was talking about. I didn't know the first thing about wines. Here was an opportunity to learn something I had wanted to know about for a long time. I had begun to entertain on a scale I'd never known before. As a host I'd be expected to understand all the things a good host should know for the benefit of his guests.

We began lunch with smoked clams and mussels, *percebes* (a sea barnacle with a meaty stem), *cigalas* (a delicious long-armed large shrimp found only in Spanish waters), several kinds of Spanish olives, small cubes of a very special Spanish Serrano ham, anchovies, Spanish sausage, pickled artichoke hearts, and marinated herring bits. Ernest went into the pantry and prepared the Cinzano for that.

When we had had our fill of appetizers, Mercedes brought in the first course, a light vegetable soup. Ernest opened a light white wine.

We talked and talked about bullfighting.

And here was Mercedes with a vegetable course, *acelgas,* as only she knew how to prepare them. Ernest now opened another white wine. We ate slowly and talked and talked and talked.

Then Mercedes came in with a platter of *lenguado,* baked in butter with a lemon sauce. Here we call it filet of sole. I've never tasted any sole like the *lenguado* of Spain. And Ernest opened still another white wine for the *lenguado.*

I asked if he'd like to try some *calamares en su tinta,* baby squid done in a sauce made with their ink, which Mercedes had prepared for my approval. He said he'd love to try it to taste the real thing done by a cook who knew how. It was delicious, with a very rare flavor which can't be described. I made a note to have her repeat this several days later. And of course Ernest opened a very light red wine he said was especially good with *calamares*.

Then we had partridge in orange sauce. After that we had some wafer-thin slices of Serrano ham with a very light *amontillado*. And then dessert. While I was preparing the expresso coffee machine to make coffee under steam pressure, Ernest suddenly asked if I'd mind if he followed me around the country to watch me fight. By then I really liked the guy and didn't care what he looked like. But when he mentioned following me around the country, I looked to see if he really meant what he was saying.

"That's an expensive proposition," I said. "Do you realize the kind of money a thing like that would take?"

"I'll manage it, I guess," he said with some hesitancy. "But I don't want to do it if you don't approve."

"What has that to do with it?" I said. "Whether I approve or not, anyone who can afford it can go where he pleases. I can't stop anyone from coming to see me fight. You seem to know a lot about bullfighting and I don't know how long you've been in Spain. But do you know how expensive such a proposition would be?"

"I guess I can take care of the expenses," he said without the slightest sign of boasting.

"Let's not kid ourselves," I said. "In the first place, the travel part would cost you an arm and a leg. Then, when you got to a town where I was to appear, and since it would be right in the middle of the fair dates, unless you had reserved some accommodations from six months to a year in advance, you'd never be able to find a place to sleep standing up, much less in a bed!"

He was on the point of saying something, but hesitated. So I continued. "Let's say, for argument's sake, that you managed by hook or crook to get to these towns. It wouldn't be possible, but let's say you also were able to find some hole in the wall where you could stay so you wouldn't have to spend each twenty-four hours on the street. You may not know this, but since my first appearance in Sevilla, the moment my name appears on a card you can't find a ticket. If I didn't have it stipulated in my contract, even I couldn't get tickets to my own fights. Now how do you suppose you'd get in to see these fights after all the expense and trouble of getting to the places where they are held? Can you answer that?"

"That's not worrying me," he insisted. "All that bothers me is that I don't want you to feel annoyed at me for doing it. I guess I'll be able to manage everything. And even if I miss some of your fights, at least I'll have tried. On the level, what do you say?"

I particularly liked this fellow because he took a deep and sincere interest in my favorite subject, and I didn't want to offend him by constantly harping on expenses. So I told him I'd be in town for a day or so and would let him know where and when I was to appear. We were so engrossed in our discussion that I hadn't noticed Luis, who now was trying to attract my attention. He reminded me that I was supposed to meet Argomaniz at the Frontón Madrid. Then, for the first time, I suddenly realized what time it was. It was eight o'clock in the evening. We had been eating for five and a half hours! So I asked Ernest if he was free and if he'd like to accompany us to the *frontón*. He excused himself, claiming he'd already taken up more of my time than was right. Besides, if he intended to follow me around the country, he had a number of things which demanded his attention. But he promised to meet me at the *frontón* next evening when I'd be there again with my manager.

The following night, as soon as I had introduced him to my friends, we went to another box where we could be alone. I gave him my advance schedule for the next month and a half. He showed me a *kilométrico* with seven thousand miles in it but I brushed it aside.

"You won't need that," I said. "I've spoken with some of my friends who make up our traveling caravan. If you'd care to pack in with us, I guess we can find room for one more person in our some twenty-odd cars. If you don't mind sharing a room with Luis, my *mozo*, I can manage it so they can put an extra cot in it for you. How does that strike you?"

For a moment I thought he would burst into tears. His eyes watered. I don't know what may have caused it, but I saw his eyes wet. After some time he spoke very slowly.

"It's too much! I can't let you put yourself out like that for me! I couldn't accept anything like that unless you let me pay for my share of the expenses!"

"Look!" I said. "Let's not kid ourselves. The traveling, even with your *kilométrico*, would be very expensive. And you'd never be able to get accommodations. I don't pay for any of this and I don't know who does! I've tried to find out many times. But whenever I send Luis for an accounting, he always comes back and says he doesn't know who paid the bills. I like you and I really want to help you. You're the first guy I've ever spoken to in English who really knows something about all this. That's worth plenty to me. And here's another thing. The tickets I get are all spoken for. If you won't mind and would like to watch the fights from behind the fence, if you're not afraid to see them that close, I think I can arrange it. That's the only way you'd ever be able to see the fights. Now, what do you say?"

He finally accepted my invitation and left to make his arrangements.

The first few nights out of town we talked until about three in the morning. When he noticed me dozing off, he would go to his room quietly so as not to wake me. And although I didn't notice it at the time, later I marveled at how well he got along with all our hosts. I found out much later that he had known most of them intimately for a number of years. He never let on, and I was so absorbed in other things that I never guessed.

Excerpt from "Bullfighter from Brooklyn"   **303**

When we visited the great estates and hunted and fished, he outdid himself in teaching me the finer points of handling a gun and rod. He was an expert with both. Now and then he'd tell me stories of things he had done and places he had been. He never put himself in a good light. He was very unassuming. And the more I got to know him the more I liked him. He was definitely an outdoor man. There didn't seem to be a thing he didn't know about nature and sports. And once in a while our conversation would drift to a point where I'd stop him and ask who the hell he was! All he'd say was that he was an author, and a lousy one at that, and once in a while he did some newspaper reporting. He offered to get me some of his books to read so I could tell him what I thought of his stuff. But I told him that no matter how well he might write, he couldn't possibly add up in his writing to what I already thought of him as a person. So again we deliberately forgot about his writing and didn't mention it any more.

After the first week or so on the road, we reached a point where it began to bother me that he had to go to another room when I'd fall asleep during our discussions. So I had his cot or bed placed in my room to make things more convenient for him. And when we couldn't get the extra cot or bed, if I had a double bed in my room we just shared it.

He questioned me about past great *matadors*. Why was it, he wanted to know, that nowadays we didn't see such things as made "Guerrita" great? And Joselito? And "Frascuelo"? And Fuentes? He made me describe in detail exactly how each maneuver was done. And wouldn't it be a good stunt to try some of the specialties of former days once in a while? I promised to try a couple on the following day. In the next fight I did one or two of the passes which hadn't been seen in Spanish rings for more than fifty years. The effect on the critics and old fans was electric. It started a whole new series of endless discussions.

The press fell all over me. Who was I, anyway? And where did I really come from? Who taught me all these maneuvers since it wasn't possible I had seen them and only a few people alive actually had? They wanted to know all about my background. I must have Spanish blood in me. It couldn't be possible otherwise. And as though to show they knew more about me than I did, I began to get photostatic copies of what were purported to be birth certificates and baptismal papers which seemingly proved beyond any doubt that I was born in Sevilla, and then in Madrid, and then in Valencia or Bilbao or a dozen other places which had produced some famous fighters of the past.

All this proved that Ernest was right in his approach. So we worked out a series of signals between us. He would give me an indication of how things were going from the spectator's angle and what I should do next. Only he and I knew what was going on. This direction from him was the cause of my meteoric rise. My appearances were causing demonstrations which began to take on the dimensions of riots. Meanwhile, we spent more and more time in the country when we were inland, and yachting and fishing when we were near the coast.

I began to live in a goldfish bowl. I couldn't take a bath in privacy. I couldn't even go to the bathroom alone. They thought there was nothing strange about wanting to observe me at all times. By the time we had finished that second tour, my price had risen to fifteen thousand *pesetas* per fight. You can understand what this meant when I say that the top full professional *matadors* of the day were getting the long-established rate of twelve thousand *pesetas*. I was even naming the breeds I appeared with as well as the *matadors* on the cards.

When we got back to Madrid, Louise Whitney was waiting in my home for me. She said she had been ordered by the Ambassador to wait until she saw me and to make me promise to bring Ernest Hemingway to the embassy for tea.

"All Spain knows you've been traveling with Ernest Hemingway," she said. "And you can name anything you want if you'll only bring him to the embassy!"

"What do you mean, I've been traveling with Hemingway?" I said. "Don't be silly! He's been traveling with me as my companion on the whole trip!"

"What difference does it make who's been traveling with whom?" she said, annoyed. "The important fact is that the Ambassador wants you to bring him for tea!"

"The Ambassador wants him for tea?" I said incredulously. "Why, the poor fellow doesn't even have the clothes for such a thing!"

"The idea of such a thing!" Louise said impatiently. "I'm surprised at you, Sidney!"

"Let's quit horsing around, Louise," I said, exasperated. "I ought to know what I'm talking about! After all, we spent the last month and a half together."

"Well, it's apparent you don't even know who the man is!"

"Who is he?" I twitted. "All I know is that his name is Ernest Hemingway. I don't know what he does. He told me once or twice that he wrote, or something like that."

"Good Lord!" she said, throwing up her hands in genuine surprise. "You mean to stand there and tell me you don't know who Ernest Hemingway is? Can you really mean that?"

"Of course!" I said. "Who is he? Tell me! I'm waiting!"

"Why, he's only the greatest author of our time!" she said. "There are millions of people who would give their right arms just to see what he looks like in the flesh! Can it really be possible that the two of you have been together for more than a month and you don't know who he is?" she said.

As soon as Louise left, I hurried to the Hotel Victoria on Calle Victoria where Ernest said he would be staying. I sat down and told him what had happened and demanded that he tell me who he really was. He tried to tell me, but I couldn't grasp most of it. He just said he wrote and some people thought he wrote all right. Then he asked me if it would do me any good to have him accompany me to the embassy. I balked at that. I didn't want him to go solely because it might serve me in any way. The only way I'd agree to go with him would be because he really wanted to go for his own purposes. Otherwise we'd forget it and I'd tell them I couldn't find him. In the end, this was what he preferred.

Although I'm getting ahead of my story, we spent four months together that year and the whole eight months of the following season before I got up enough courage to read *A Farewell to Arms* and *The Sun also Rises*. After those two books, he couldn't write fast enough to keep me satisfied.

The Day I Fought With Belmonte

by BARNABY CONRAD

The day before the fight, I arrived at Castillo de las Guardas about seven o'clock from Sevilla with my two *banderilleros* and my sword handler. We looked over the Plaza de Toros first, to find out where the president's box and the entrances were. There were big posters all around advertising the fight. Below Juan Belmonte's name, I was billed as The California Kid—El Niño de California—which struck everyone, including me, as amusing. I guess it was Juan Belmonte's idea. Then we drove through the towered, fairy-tale town up to the bull breeder's *finca,* a three-hundred-year-old ranch that probably didn't look much different, with its courtyard, carriages and quaintly costumed farm hands, in the days when it was built. We arrived in time for dinner in the patio with the large family of the *ganadero,* and afterwards a guitar was produced and we sang. Chico wailed out a gypsy song, but stopped midway, saying he wasn't in voice; he was as nervous as though he were fighting the next day instead of just being my sword boy. Cascabel, a *banderillero,* did a stamping dance with Sona, the rancher's pretty sister, but we couldn't seem to clap in rhythm for him. I asked Manolo, my number one *banderillero,* to dance a *bulería,* but he said he wasn't in the mood. We were all jumpy and quarrelsome. We went to bed early.

I fell right to sleep but tossed restlessly and fought a hundred bulls before waking up at dawn, sweaty and tired and with a sinking feeling. I made myself go back to sleep. When I awoke again, the sun was pouring in the window; there was the good hot scent off the fields in my room and the swallows were wheeling and crying around the barn. What a fine day for everyone else, I thought; what a hell of a fine day. For the first time I asked myself if the glamor and excitement were really worth it.

Why was I, a twenty-three-year-old American vice-consul, signed to fight on the same program with Spanish professionals anyway? Well, mainly because I *was* American and *was* a vice-consul and they knew that my passion was bullfighting. Before graduating from Yale I had studied painting at the University of Mexico and become fascinated by the art and grace and color of the spectacle down there. After I imbibed a lot of *tequila* one day, some Mexican "friends" convinced me that I should jump in the bull ring during a fight. I did, using my raincoat as a cape. I made a few half-hearted passes at the bull, made a fool of myself and somehow got out alive. An amused professional, 19-year-old Félix Guzmán, took an interest in me and began to teach me what an intricate science bullfighting is. I hadn't really grasped the first fundamentals before I was in a practice ring with animals too large for me to handle. One of the very first days, a large half-breed bull charged unexpectedly and smashed my right knee. I lay there on the ground for what seemed a century, waiting for a horn to go in my back. It didn't because Félix jumped in the ring with no cape, struck the bull in the face, and when it left me to charge him, he out-sprinted it to the fence. I was carried out of the ring by the time the bull came back for me. Some months afterward Félix was gored terribly in the lung in the big bull ring and died two days later. I lost my enthusiasm for *"la fiesta brava."*

I was on a cane for a couple of years, and was still wearing a metal brace from ankle to hip, when the State Department sent me to Sevilla, Spain, as vice-consul. However, after six months of swimming and Andalusian sun, my leg got better, so much so that I began to think about fighting again. One day I was taken by some friends sixty kilometers out of town to a bullfight party at Juan Belmonte's ranch.

That first day when I fought on his ranch with the cow calves they were testing for bravery, I made myself ridiculous. I had intimated to everyone that I had been a pretty big bullfighter in Mexico—mainly to bolster my own courage—and I had half come to believe it. So when I got out in Belmonte's private ring and was shoved around by a small calf, it was humiliating. I couldn't blame it on a weak knee, either, for it was just lack of knowledge that made me miscalculate the angles of a calf's charge and get knocked down by the stubby horns time after time. Belmonte was amused, however. He liked the idea that an American wanted to bullfight. I guess he also liked the dumb stubborn way I kept going back at the calf with the cape, making the same clumsy mistake, getting knocked sprawling each time, and then taking a terrible pounding on the ground from the vicious little animals. He finally persuaded me to stop this masochism and began to show me what I was doing wrong. It seems I was trying to make the calf pass between me and the fence. Fighting cattle have a tendency to hook away from the fence, so that halfway through a pass, the animal would swerve and hit my legs. I never made that mistake again.

When my bruised body would let me walk without groaning—about a week—I went back for another lesson. This time I wasn't allowed in the ring, and I was just as glad. Belmonte had me practice for hours with just a cape and an imaginary bull. We started with the basic pass—the *verónica* —and he showed me how to hold the heavy scarlet cape, to keep my head down, my hands low, my footwork in rhythm with my arms. He would stand in back of me and work my arms like a golf pro until I learned to swing the cape smoothly. Then I graduated to a small boy hired to charge, holding a pair of sharp horns in front of him and simulating the action of a bull. He could not do anything that a fighting bull would not logically do, but if I made a mistake, such as holding the cape too far in front of my body or not fixing "the bull" properly after a series of passes, the boy would delightedly jab me in the legs. A bullfighter's performance is judged by his proximity to the horns, so now I had to think not only of manipulating the cape properly and gracefully but I also had to concentrate on working close to these sharp horns, yet making them miss me.

Sidney Franklin, the American *matador,* lived in the same hotel with me and he would help me with my homework in the Consulate patio. So would Belmonte's son and Carlos Arruza and "El Gallo," and Pepe Luis Vázquez and "Manolete" and "Cagancho"; I don't think anyone's been lucky enough to have better teachers.

After the *verónica* was more or less mastered, I had to learn the half-*verónica,* and the *chicuelina* pass where you turn in toward the bull after the horns go by your knee, and the spinning "lighthouse" pass, and the butterfly, and the many others.

Then the *muleta* was produced. This is the small heart-shaped cape that is used for the last third of the fight and upon whose manipulation a bullfighter's ultimate success depends. It is essentially a one-handed cape, and I had to learn a whole new set of passes—the natural, the chest pass, the pass of death—with the added complication of always having the sword in the right hand. I seemed to have more aptitude for the *muleta* than the cape. For killing, I would practice with a mechanical bull made out of a bicycle and a pair of horns. One had to run head on to the contraption as a boy made it charge, go through the motion of keeping the bull's attention focused on the *muleta* held low to the right in the left hand across the body while the right arm reached over the horns to get the sword into the five-inch wire mesh which represented the opening between a bull's shoulder blades. It was like rubbing your head and patting your stomach only as Belmonte warned, if you did it wrong the bull would pick up its head as your body went over the right horn and you would get spiked through the chest.

"Well, I think you're ready," said Belmonte casually one day after a long session with the cape and *muleta*. He said it with the deadly calm of a flying instructor climbing out of a plane and telling a student to take it up alone. He had calves brought in from the range to the ring and I had to show how much I had learned. I got dumped several time, but I generally knew why now and would set about to correct it. Belmonte would criticize from the porch but generally he couldn't resist showing how it should be done and in a minute he'd be down in the arena working the animal over himself. It looked so easy when he did it.

The next time the calves were bigger. And then pretty soon they were no longer calves but half-grown animals with blunted horns. And soon they were still bigger. And then, after a year, I was signed by an impresario for a big charity fight on September 23, 1945, to kill my first bull. And on the same program with Belmonte! I wasn't sure I was ready. Killing the bicycle was easy enough, but I didn't know whether I could handle a bull.

For the month before the fight I'd thought of little else. When going over some consular invoices or passport applications, my hands would suddenly begin to tremble as I thought of the onrushing date. Or when I'd go to the movies and relax enough to laugh, right in the middle my brain would remind me, "You're fighting on the twenty-third!"—and the laugh would stick in my throat.

And now, here I was in Castillo and today was the day and there was no getting out of it. I think if there'd been an honorable way to get out of it, I would have. I was scared.

I got up and went down to the patio and practiced with the cape in the sun. Manolo came down and watched me. "You're crazy to practice on the day of the fight," he said. Manolo was a nice young Sevillian who had tried to be a *matador* but who gave up after one disastrously cowardly exhibition in Madrid. He was content to resign himself to the unspectacular and comparatively safe routine of a *banderillero* now.

I did some *verónicas* with an imaginary bull. "Don't do *verónicas* today, Bernabé," said Manolo.

"Why not?" I asked irritably.

"Because it's your weakest pass. They're no good and you get caught when you do them."

"Who the hell is the *matador* around here?" I snapped.

"You," said Manolo, going into the house. "You are, thank God."

I practiced until my arms got a little tired. Then I went back up to bed to rest. I could hear the others down below eating lunch in the patio while I had a coffee with milk. A *matador* doesn't eat the day of the fight so that in case something goes wrong, he can be operated upon immediately. I heard some laughter. It seemed incredible to me that anyone could laugh today. I fell into a fitful sleep about two. I dreamed I was back in America—in San Francisco, riding on the cable car with a girl.

"Come on! To the fight!" Manolo had a rough hand on my shoulder and was shaking me. I had the idea that maybe if I kept my eyes closed and picked up my dream again, Manolo would vanish and there wouldn't be any fight. He shook me again and I got up quickly. It was five o'clock, and the fight was at six-thirty (it stays light in Andalusia until about ten). My costume was laid out neatly on the chair, and after I'd shaved, Manolo helped me into it. I wore the big broad-brimmed hat and sash and white jacket used in fights without *picadors*. Manolo was serious and white and suddenly efficient.

"You look like a third-class funeral," I said, as we went down the stairs. I wanted to see if I was too scared to talk. "You'd think you were going to take the chances."

"I'm not going to take any chances," he answered.

"I know," I said. "Then why are you scared?"

"I'm always scared," he said. "You know that."

"Why do you keep fighting then?"

"I can't help it," he said. "That's why."

We came down to the courtward and the rancher's family clapped and said, *"Olé, matador!"*

They took some photos of us when Chico and Cascabel came down. I looked at my watch. "It's almost six."

They all came up and shook hands seriously, wished me luck, and hoped I'd "get at least one ear." Except the foreman who shook his head and said pleasantly but positively, "He won't kill that animal. I raised that creature and I tell you he won't kill it with anything less than a hand grenade." My heart sank even lower.

"Of course, he'll kill it," said Sona. She was little and dark with black Spanish eyes. "You'll see him come back with the bull's ear." She took a religious medal from around her neck and pinned it on the inside of my jacket. Then she kissed me on the cheek.

"Sure he'll kill it," said Manolo uncertainly.

We stood around awkwardly for a few moments.

"Let's get going," I said. It was six ten. I gave Sona my watch to keep for me and then we swung on the truck and rattled down the road. I could see Sona waving in the courtyard. She wasn't going to the fight because she said she couldn't stand it. We drove very fast and on one of the curves, Manolo said: "This uncle's driving is scaring me to death!" It struck me funny he should be worried about anything but the bull that was waiting for us, and I remember trying to laugh. All the way in as we passed the big posters for the fight, I was constructing a wall of false courage, detaching myself from this person who was trying to be a Hemingway character, who was going to kill a bull with Juan Belmonte, but the sight of the gray and forbidding coliseum rising at the top of the hill brought me back into myself with a rush and there was a sickening knot in my stomach.

It was 6:25 when we arrived at the foot of the plaza hill, and the cathedral bells were starting to ring. We started up the cobbled street and the big crowd that was milling towards the plaza gave us a great ovation, shouting, *"Suerte, suerte"*—Luck, luck—and patting me on the back as we pushed ahead of them. I forgot the knot for a moment and smiled and waved. Then a great shout went up as Belmonte's Fiat pulled up and the Earthquake of Triana stepped out of his car in fighting costume and hurried after us.

"Good afternoon," he said panting, his great jaw stuck out and smiling his great smile.

"Muy buenas," we said.

"Who has seen the bulls?" he asked.

"I haven't," I said, "but I understand they're big."

"What do you mean, big, Bernabé?"

"I've heard that they are about three hundred and sixty."

"Osú, que miedo," he said, with his barracuda jaw jutting out. "Jesus, what fear. What a tragedy."

One could never tell what Don Juan was thinking. Had he expected them to be bigger or smaller? And if Belmonte was upset by their size what was I doing there at all!

We got to the ring and it was already filled to overflowing. Belmonte's *banderillero* was holding his horse for him, a good-looking skittish chestnut.

As we lined up in the entrance to the ring, adjusting the capes over our shoulders, the third *matador* came up. He was a young *novillero* and looked nervous.

"Hello," he said, as he dragged rapidly on a cigaret.

"Hello."

"I'm Chávez," he said.

"Enchanted," I said. "I'm the 'Niño de California!'"

He smiled wanly. "You have a rare name."

"I thought 'el Andaluz' was fighting third today?" That's what the posters had said.

"No," he swallowed dryly, "he's not. I am."

"What happened to the 'Andaluz'?"

Chávez was working his feet in the sand like a boxer in a rosin box. I figured it looked pretty professional, so I did it too.

" 'El Estudiante' got it bad in Logroño yesterday and 'el Andaluz' had to substitute for him in Linares." He ground out the cigaret on the sand under his boots.

"So you're fighting third."

"Yes, I'm fighting third." He yawned, a sure sign that you're scared. I started one but swallowed it before it was out. "What a rare name," he said frowning about its rareness.

"At least there's no wind," I said professionally. I'd heard Belmonte say it.

"No," he said, "At least there's no wind to blow the capes."

I remember thinking throughout this whole day that it seemed as though everyone had read Hemingway and was trying to talk and act like it.

Belmonte got on his chesty horse. We lined up in back of him on foot, Chávez and I in front and our *cuadrillas*—sword handlers and *banderilleros*—in back of us. The crowd was getting impatient and stamping their feet. It was six thirty.

Belmonte swung around in his saddle. I'll never forget the chillingly calm way he said: "I don't know any reason why we shouldn't start this thing."

I knew hundreds of reasons and would have been delighted to suggest them, but his horse moved forward and we all automatically started forward on the left foot. The band struck up with a clash of cymbals as we strode to the center of the ring, then wheeled and walked to the fence, bowing to the president as we did. We got behind the fence, and I looked over the crowd. It seemed that everyone was looking at me because I was American and not at Belmonte who was waiting for his bull in the center of the sunny ring. The look in their faces was a combination of amusement and commiseration and relief that it was I and not them down there. I saw all my friends from Sevilla and they waved and smiled. I nodded back to them and tried to look casual. They seemed so damnably safe up there.

There was a roll of ominous drums and a trumpet split the warm air. Belmonte's bull ran in, black and white and bigger than we had been told. He fought it Portuguese style, on horseback, first, making the trained horse dodge the bull's charges skillfully while he placed *banderillas,* and then he got off to kill it on foot. He was magnificent. The president granted him the ears and tail of the animal, and the crowd gave him a tremendous ovation.

I saw this all through a haze for drumming in my head was, "You're next, you're next, you're next!"

It was a very difficult performance to have to follow, the most difficult in the world, but the crowd seemed in a receptive mood and they weren't expecting much from an American. I made up my mind that I would either leave the ring with an ear or I wouldn't leave the ring. I had to be good! I couldn't let Belmonte down! All these people had heard or read that I could fight, but they hadn't seen me and didn't quite believe that an American could fight at all.

Belmonte sent his horse outside the ring and climbed up into the stands. The trumpet blew for my bull, and the *toril* gate clanged open. Manolo and I stood behind a *burladero,* one of the shields in front of the circular fence, "el Chico" and Cascabel behind another as we waited silently for the bull to come out of the long dark runway from the pens. I felt a little dizzy. It didn't come and it didn't come. Finally, Cascabel went over and cautiously flopped a cape in front of the passageway. Then he beat it for the fence as a black shape skidded out of the *toril* in a wave of dust. The bull hurtled around the ring jabbing and feinting with his horns and snorting, the dust from the corral blowing off its back. After the monster my imagination had conjured up the real bull seemed blessedly small.

"Line him up for me," I said to Manolo. He took his cape and went out to run the bull up and down so that I could see which way he hooked; a bull usually has a right and a left like a boxer. After doubling him two or three times at a safe distance, Manolo got in trouble, the bull was almost on top of him, and he had to throw down the cape and duck inside the *burladero*.

"I can't see which horn he hooks with," I said.

"He hooks badly on both sides!" Manolo panted. "Don't go out there with the cape!"

Then when he saw me getting the red and yellow cape firm and right in my hands, he said: "All right, all right, but don't take him close and don't try *verónicas!* Face-fight him! For God's sake, no *verónicas!*"

Manolo didn't know that Belmonte had never taught me "face-fighting," the only way to fight a bull that won't "pass." I'd always had good bulls and never really had to learn.

Holding the cape for a *verónica,* I stepped out from behind the fence and called the bull:

"Huh-hah-ah-ah-ah, *torito!*" I called, and my voice sounded like someone else's. "Huh-hah!" It wheeled and charged for me, blowing out air as it did. It swooshed by, its horns much closer to my legs than I had intended, as I swung the *capote* just ahead of its nose. It came by again, this time even closer. It had obviously been fought before and I couldn't control it because it went at my body instead of the big cape. It kept crowding me, making me back up. The third time it charged, it hooked to the right and slammed me up against the *barrera* with its shoulder.

I heard Manolo call: "Get the hell out of there!"

I was shaken up, but I changed the grip on the cape and called the bull again, stepping away from the fence. This time it came with its head high. The side of the left horn struck my chest a glancing blow and the right horn caught in the *capote* and yanked it out of my hands. I was disarmed. I wanted out! I fled for a *burladero* and ducked behind it.

The crowd was laughing. They were holding their sides. This is what they expected of *un yanqui* who was trying to invade a strictly Spanish art. They weren't laughing cruelly; they liked the fact that I had tried and they were glad that I hadn't been killed—but then again they were glad that I had been knocked around. It was very funny to see me get knocked around, as long as I didn't get killed.

"*Sabe latín,*" said Manolo, coming over, shaking his head. They say a bull that's been fought before is so smart that he knows Latin. Bulls are supposed to be "*limpio*"—simon-pure amateurs—when they come from the range, but sometimes ambitious kids have sneaked out on moonlight nights to practice on them with capes.

The Day I Fought With Belmonte   313

The trumpet had blown for the *banderillas,* and Cascabel had to go out to try to put in the barbed sticks. He ran at an angle towards the bull, holding the *banderillas* high. The bull knew enough to lead Cascabel by several feet. The *banderillero* ran sideways frantically like a crab and managed to miss the horns, but he also missed putting in the *banderillas* and looked ridiculous.

"For God's sake," I yelled to Manolo, "go out there and show that *tío* how to put in a pair!"

Manolo went out. By sneaking up on the bull from behind, he managed to put in the *banderillas* with great difficulty, getting his pants ripped as he spun away. The crowd was still laughing as the trumpet sounded for the third and last part of the fight. Chico handed me the *muleta* and the wooden sword. A wooden sword is used to spread the small cape until time to kill because of the strain of holding the heavy steel *estoque.*

"Let the burros laugh," Manolo growled. "The animal was impossible with the cape and sticks, but with the *muleta,* I swear you can dominate him."

"I don't know," I said.

I found Belmonte in the crowd; I went through the ceremony of extending my hand with the hat and dedicating the bull. "Thank you, Don Juan, for not having hidden," I started, and the crowd laughed, with me this time. "For you, master of the great masters, who has taught me what little I know, I am going to kill this bull, this difficult cross-eyed bull." I flung my hat up and he leaned forward to catch it. He looked worried.

The bull had taken a spot against the wall for his *querencia,* that arbitrary, unpredictable part of the ring where he decides to stay because there he instinctively feels most secure. Under no circumstances did I want to take him on in there, as a bull fights a defensive and more dangerous battle in his *querencia.* I told Manolo to get him out and into another part of the ring. He went in as close as he dared and cautiously flopped the cape at him several times. "Get in closer!" I shouted.

"You get in closer, he's yours!" he answered without turning his head. But he got in closer and swirled the cape out on the dust in front of the bull again. The animal pawed the ground and shook his horns, but he wouldn't get out of the five-foot circle.

About this time I got mad, mad at the bull for being so rotten, mad at the crowd for not seeing that it was rotten, mad at the *ganadero* for raising such a rotten bull, mad at myself for being so rotten with the cape, and mad at Manolo for not being able to get the bull out.

"Hide yourself!" I shouted.

When Manolo left the ring I stepped out quickly from behind the fence in back of the bull. I took the sword and smacked him hard across the rump with the flat of it. The bull whirled around, his tail went up, and he shot towards me. I waited with my back pressed up against the fence, offering him the heart-shaped rag, spreading it wide with the sword, shaking it, and praying to God that he take it and not my legs, for there was no way out for me if he didn't. Swooooosh, he went by, his head in the *muleta*. The crowd froze. The bull wheeled, came at me again, and setting my teeth, I made myself hold my ground as he hurtled by, the horns about five inches away from my knees.

"*Olé!*" screamed the crowd as I made two more closer passes without moving, and now that I think of it, it was a very sweet sound, but then I was too busy with the bull and too scared to hear. I wanted to get away from the fence, so I worried the animal out across the ring, away from his *querencia,* with choppy, punishing passes.

Once in the middle, I gave him every pass I could think of. I think I even made up one. On the most difficult, the *afarolado,* he tore my sleeve off and raked down my arm. It didn't hurt, but it made me mad and on the next pass I took the wooden sword out of the *muleta* and broke it across his rump as he went by. This left me with just the limp rag and nothing to spread it with, so four times I had to pass him in close against me with the *natural* and *pase de pecho* passes. Finally, I walked away from the bull and Manolo ran out into the ring with the real sword.

"Kill him!" said Manolo.

I lined up the bull with its front legs together so that the shoulder blades would open, as Belmonte had taught me to do. I sighted down the blade, shook the *muleta* to make him charge, and ran at him as he ran at me. But the bull had moved its leg position at the last moment and closed the small opening. The sword hit bone and flew out. I lined him up again. I had to do it this time. As the bull charged, I flung myself over the right horn on top of the animal, and the sword sunk into him up to the hilt as though into a tub of lard. The bull sagged, reeled, headed for the fence drunkenly, and then flopped over dead as though a light had been turned out.

A roar went up from the crowd and Manolo ran out and threw his arms around my shoulders jubilantly. I staggered over to the fence and Belmonte tossed my hat down from the stands.

"*Bastante bien,*" he said quietly. "Not bad, Bernabé."

The president signaled with his handkerchief that I was to be granted both ears. They dragged the bull out of the ring with the mules, and the crowd kept applauding and yelling for me to take a lap around the ring while they threw hats and cigars down to me. It was the happiest moment of my life. I started around shakily, the notched ears in my hands and Manolo in back of me throwing the hats back to the owners and keeping the cigars. But suddenly a trumpet blew, the *toril* opened, and we had to beat it for the fence as Chávez's bull skidded out into the pale sun, blinking its eyes and looking for something to kill.

The Day I Fought With Belmonte   **315**

Lady Love

by *ARMANDO VILCHES CANO*

Armando Vilches Cano, an old friend, is a poet, essayist, fiction writer and world traveler. I have known him in many places, including Spain and Spanish America. He is part Catalonian and part Castilian by heritage but originated in the Valencian area of southern Spain. As an active aficionado, he has seen bullfights in all countries where they are presented. The story, "Lady Love," and the poem, "The Natural," were translated from a forthcoming collection of his writings, *El Romero y Yo*.

The poem on the natural pass shows him at his lyric best, a combination of power and sensitivity. It is fortunate that John Groth, who has these same qualities in art, liked the poem enough to compose an artistic symphony as an interpretation of it.

Don Pío was a congenial gentleman. He could afford to be, with all his quarterings and the length of time they had been in the family. Nothing could happen to him, because he was devout, a good husband, a thoughtful father, and a benevolent owner of a vast estate.

Over those rolling knolls of Andalusia roamed some of the finest fighting bulls bred in Spain. They bore proudly the brand of Don Pío. For several generations bullfighters had encountered these animals with respect and admiration. For Don Pío life was good and he took no part in politics. He cultivated his land, long come by through the might of an ancient warrior in foreign lands for Christ and the King. He kept up the rich blood of his fighting bull herds. And he raised a son and daughter.

The heir to the title and lands, Esteban, was a young man of much promise, and a sort of enlightened independence of thought. He did not worry his father but the old man felt he needed watching. Don Pío saw an inclination toward lack of proper respect for tradition. The young descendant of many grandees did not seem so impressed by his right to wear a hat in the presence of his sovereign and call him cousin. "I do believe that young man is more interested in the ranch than rank," grumbled Don Pío.

He had no such misgivings about his beautiful Inez, who graced eighteen years with dark, somnolent radiance. The tenants named their children for her, and she was a solicitous godmother to them all. But she kept her ladylike distance in this sentimental democracy of the estate. She could ride with the best cowboys. She could test the bravest fighting calves. She could even handle the cape and *muleta* with the cleverest of the young bullfighters who trained at the ranch.

And she was adored by all of them with the respect due the daughter of the rancher.

All except one. That was Ramón Lerena, son of the head cowboy. This Ramón had been raised on the ranch, and he had decided in childhood to become a bullfighter. Before his teens, he had showed extraordinary talent and there was no doubt in anybody's mind that he would be a great *matador*.

Everybody, except Inez. She was just his age, and they had always ridden together, tested calves together, and discussed the fine points of bull-raising and bullfighting together. The difference was that Inez had more talent working with the calves than he did. She knew instinctively what he had to learn, although he was a bright pupil. Old Pepe, the ex-*matador* who had charge of the ranch ring, felt it was a terrible shame that Inez was a girl.

"She has that genius for rhythm and a deep knowledge born in her beautiful head," he said.

Ramón did not think it a shame that she was a girl. He was now eighteen and ready for his first formal fight. He was also ready for manhood. It came to him, all of a sudden, as they were practicing with a heifer in preparation for his debut.

"You must watch your profile," she said, patting his slim stomach.

Her finger tips lit a flame in him. She continued, oblivious of the fire.

"I want to see you the greatest in the great tradition, facing the bull, bringing him around, in rhythm, and control *mandando, templando* . . . not like these bullfighters today, standing sideways to the bull, like a willow leaning over the animal; none of these modern furbelows for you, no swinging of no cape over your head like a sombrero in the hands of a drunken cowboy."

She twirled her lithe body in a dainty burlesque of a fancy pass. Ramón tried to speak. He could not utter a word for a moment, and when his voice finally came out it had changed completely. It was edged with the first halting, hoarse tones of manhood. He trembled, as he spoke.

"That's what I will be! In the great tradition. And I owe it to you, all of it. You know so much, you've been everywhere. I— I——" he faltered in the enormity of his thought.

She noted nothing of this drama, and continued easily.

"You have read in the papers about the changes in fighting styles. First, they faced the bulls like Pedro Romero and Montes. They forced the enemy to encircle them by the power of the *muleta*."

"Yes, I know. I heard that famous writer, Felipe Sassone, talking to the duke the other day. And Julio de Urrutia, too. They explained the oblique stance of Belmonte."

"That's right, and 'Manolete' too, although he was more like the old im-

No parallel natural here

mortals. You have everything, courage, grace, and skill. I don't want you to get into these habits of parallel fighting."

"Like Arruza?"

"Well, no, not Arruza. He's a great fighter but he will not bear imitation. You know what I mean, these fellows who stand sideways. They are actually out of the bull's line of vision, and, although they are fighting closer than anybody ever did they are in less danger."

"The crowds like them," he commented.

"I agree. But you would not like yourself, when you are made another way. You are too sincere, too serious to fool around with those fancy ideas."

They were intent now, heads bent toward each other, making designs with their bodies in illustration of their talk. For a moment he had forgotten she was the youthfully wise and beautiful daughter of a wealthy rancher, and he was the talented son of a cowboy on the estate. A deep sound interrupted them.

"What's going on here?" boomed Don Pío. "Is she telling you how to fight, Ramón?"

"Yes, sir."

"Well," he laughed, "you will do well to listen. I don't know where she got it, but she knows more about the bulls by instinct than I do by long and patient study. I'm sure, if she had been a boy we would have had a noble *torero*."

"Father, get along with you," laughed Inez. "We are too busy for such interruptions. I suppose you do not realize that Ramón fights Sunday, and we are smoothing out some passes with one of the heifers before dinner."

"Very well, but don't be late. I want you to have plenty of time to dress, and clean that very nice but dirty body of yours."

Ramón realized, with smoldering anger, that they were speaking on a high place above him, as if he were not there, about things he blushed to discover even in his mind.

"Come on, little *torero*, let's go out to the ring and I'll show you what I meant before we were so attractively interrupted." She smiled at her departing father and pulled Ramón by the sleeve of his jacket.

"Hold the heifer on the other side for a minute, Paco." She called to the cowboy on horseback. "When it comes in, give it a light pic with the lance, just so Ramón can get the idea of a take out."

"Yes, señorita," replied the man as if orders from her were the most natural things in his life. The door opened, and the animal leaped into the arena. She saw the horse, and charged. The horseman received her deftly with his blunted lance, as Ramón prepared for a *verónica* facing the heifer. She followed the flash of the cape and turned toward him at full speed. He held the cape low and in front, with his feet planted obliquely toward the animal's advance. A slow rhythmic sweep timed just ahead of the horns, leading the charge with control, and the beauty of grace and daring became a living sculpture.

"Bravo!" called the girl. "Pivot on your heels, and bring your back foot up. Keep the line. Hands low. This one follows low."

He passed the animal on its return, with the same ease and naturalness.

"*Olé!*" called the girl.

"*Torero!*" yelled the cowboy.

He continued the series of passes until the animal was tired, momentarily, and baffled by that tantalizing object that eluded the horns.

Inez saw a slight relaxation of line. "Come here, Ramón," she said. "Watch your left arm. It is a little too bent in the elbow. Here take your position. I'll show you."

She came behind him and reached her arms to the cape on each side over his arms. Her body was close to his back; the perfume of her loveliness made him dizzy with a deep anguish. He could hardly hear her voice.

"More like this for true beauty. You must hold the line straight and true, like a *rondeño* that you are."

And she was gone, like a dream he had never dared to dream. There she was walking a few steps away, and he could barely see her for the wetness in his eyes.

"Yes," was all he could say. "Yes, I know."

"All right. Let's see you do it, then," she smiled.

He made the pass, his body quaking with an inexpressible tremor of agony and delight.

A bell rang in the great house.

"Ah, I have to go and dress," she said with a slight annoyance. "But you have to go, too. The help will be already eating." Everything was in that sentence, his position in the household, his hopelessness. The help were already eating. They did not change for dinner. They were part of the family but far, far away. She waved good night to him gaily, unaware.

"I shall be there Sunday, and you will make the family proud of you in your first *corrida*, Ramón."

He stumbled to the cowboys' quarters. "Proud. Proud. Proud." The words came out like epithets.

Sunday. The town was in holiday dress. The *plaza de toros* was wreathed in bunting, for Ramón Lerena, a native of the neighboring Elán ranch, was starting his career among the people who had known him all his life. His family had seats of honor on the *barrera*, the first row. They were dressed in their Sunday best, the women folks in black, and the men in short Andalusian white jackets, and dark cowboy breeches that flared at the bottom over their boots. Their wide, stiff brimmed, high, flat crowned hats were at an angle befitting a *corrida* of importance, and cigars tilted toward the hat brims. The combs of the women spread the decorous black lace of their mantillas.

Don Pío and his family occupied their regular box at the top of the arena. Here there was more color and richness of costume. His dress was in Andalusian style, like the cowboys, but the material was the finest wool, and the buttons were of silver. His Cordovan hat gleamed with its black, rich sheen. The ladies wore *mantones* of many colors and heavy embroidery that had graced beauties of the family for generations. All except Inez. Always unconventional, she wore a grey Andalusian costume, like that of her father and brother, but edged with rose-gold ornaments. Her hat was the faintest dove and rose grey, with a golden chin-strap.

Her brother teased her. "You look like you are ready for the arena yourself, with those soft kid-skin boots restless to step on the sand."

"Don't be silly. I can dress like this for the fights at home here. You know that it is all right."

"Yes, I know. But I have never seen your feet so nervously tapping. Have you any worries about your playmate?"

"No, he's terrific. But he has to watch that line. He is tall and inclined to stoop, and crook his arm."

"Well, relax and let him do his job. Don't try to direct him. I am sure he could not hear you anyway. You tell him all about it later."

The trumpet sounded. A Manta bull came out nobly. The breed was an excellent one, and had been selected for Ramón's debut purposely because he did not want his first fight to be with bulls he had helped to raise. It was a personal superstition which was allowed. The crowd liked the bull. It was full of fire, and followed the cape. The three *matadors* were excellent in the take-outs from the horses. Ramón was solemn and classic in his slow motion. His face was calm and dark. His *verónicas* seemed to last for hours. Somehow, there was a strange absent-mindedness in his movements. He did not appear to be studying the bull.

Inez gasped after a particularly close pass that could have caught him.

"No. No! That bull hooks low and to the left. Lift the cape, cover his head!" She thought she was talking to herself. "You can straighten his head by *muleta* punishment passes. Not this way. You must tire him first!"

The crowd around her paused as her voice was raised above the applause. Her brother cautioned her.

"I asked you to let Ramón fight his fight. He is very brave, and fighting well."

"No, he is my friend and he is not fighting that bull properly."

Her father turned. "Let the boy alone, Inez. He will do all right."

"There's something wrong, Father. He seems to be bothered. I know what he should do."

"He has to find out for himself in the difficult profession he has chosen," replied Don Pío. "You cannot help him now, even if you are right."

"Perhaps not," she sighed. But she spoke quietly to an attendant who hurried toward the walk-way around the ring where the bullfighters awaited their turns.

A few minutes later the phase of the *banderillas* was over. Ramón had not placed any of his own wands, although he was adroit in this maneuver. The time came for the ceremony. Apparently he had been resting for this. Luis Rayo, a fine Valencian fighter, had the honor, by reason of seniority, of sponsoring him as a full *matador*.

While he stood modestly, Luis turned over his *muleta* and sword to the debutante with words of congratulations. Ramón thanked him.

He turned on his heels in a circle surveying the people. At that moment, the attendant had returned to Don Pío's box.

"The *torero* says that he is deeply indebted to the daughter of the Duke of Elán for her noble interest in his humble person. He will not disgrace the home of his birth." The servant added blankly, "That is what he said, very slowly."

"He must be overcome with his debut," she thought. "That does not sound like the gay and dashing Ramón I have known all our lives."

But it was Ramón, who was now at the doorway of his manhood.

The new *matador's* eyes rested briefly at the duke's box. They were dark with the deep and tragic lament of the gypsy south. He bowed slightly and dropped his hat as a dedication to his people.

He placed his feet on each side of his hat, held the *muleta* and sword together straight in front of his body. He did not look toward the bull. A slight breeze rippled the drooping folds of the *muleta*. The animal charged by, inches away. Still he did not move, or recognize its existence. The *muleta* still fluttered as the bull wheeled and charged again, just missing the erect and motionless figure.

The crowd burst out with cries of *"Olé!"* intermingled with a few exclamations of fright, "No, no!"

Like an automaton, he walked to the center of the arena. He turned facing the bull, erect, with the *muleta* in his left hand and the sword in his right hand. He swept the *muleta* slowly forward, and the bull promptly charged toward the movement. He held the *muleta* still until the animal was a few paces before him, then he circled his left hand back around his side. The bull was captured in the drifting folds of cloth. His sword hand stayed on his hip as he turned, keeping an exact distance between the *muleta* and the bull's horns.

The crowd roared an *"Olé!"* of hoarse excitement. He moved again, and again, holding his slim line in similar passes, as the people screamed in cadenced delirium.

All except one small voice. Inez was sobbing, "No, no, no! He hooks to the left. Tire him with punishment! Watch his head!"

Nobody heard her.

The *matador,* intoxicated with the music beating in after-time to his majestic rhythm, swept the bull back across his chest with a *pase de pecho* that darkened his spangles with blood. And then he cited for another series of naturals. Before the bull reached him, a silvery figure streaked down the tiers of the arena.

The bull's left horn caught him in the thigh, as Inez vaulted over barriers into the arena. She seized a cape from a *banderillero* just as the animal wheeled to attack the writhing object toppled on the sand. It did not reach him. A shining new enemy was between them.

Inez took the animal in her cape away from the scene. She halted him and picked up the discarded *muleta.* Before the public had recovered its senses, she was on the right side of the bull, twisting it in a series of right-hand passes.

The attendants carried Ramón to the infirmary under the stands.

The crowd was in an uproar of disbelief. Don Pío and his son rushed to the barrier. Ramón's father and mother scrambled moaning to the exit on their way to the infirmary.

Inez turned the bull in a signature pass, and, as she relaxed, she realized what she had done. With a formal gesture, she walked quietly to the barrier and into the little hospital room, followed by her brother. The people rose in deafening tribute to something they could not understand. She did not see them.

Ramón lay on the white iron bed and the doctor was tightening a torniquet on his thigh. His eyes opened as she came near. They were dark and inscrutable.

"You will be all right, Ramón. It's just that he hooked to the left, and you knew it. Why did you do it? You are the best. You must not make mistakes!"

It was like a mother talking to a recalcitrant child. He said distantly, "You saved my life, and I am sorry. In there is no place for Don Pío's daughter."

"You ought to be ashamed of yourself. You are my friend. I could not help it. What is a friend for?"

"Sometimes for heartbreak," he sighed.

She then knew he was a man and the crisis had come. She turned to his parents and her brother. "He is all right. Let me talk to him a minute." They, strangely, obeyed her because she was suddenly a woman.

"You will not take any more chances, hear? You will be a great bullfighter. You will marry a nice girl and have a family. And I will be godmother for all of them. Is that true?"

He rolled his head weakly, and looked at her a long time. He finally smiled wanly, as a tear traced from the corner of his eye over his bronze cheek.

"I am not sure. All I know now is I would be happier if I could hate you."

Excerpt from To the Bullfight

by JOHN MARKS

John Hugo Edgar Puempin, who uses his mother's maiden name as his surname, and writes as John Marks, is a journalist in Spain. His excellent book on Spanish bullfighting was published in the United States by Alfred A. Knopf, in 1953, under the title *To the Bullfight*. He has witnessed more than 700 bullfights during a total of twenty years in Spain.

The three qualities which a bullfighter must possess are courage, skill, and grace, in that order. If he has them all, and so long as he loses none of them, he is a great bullfighter. If he never loses them throughout his career, and he lasts long enough to prove it, he is a genius. There are very few bullfighters who can combine all three qualities often; they display them together only at certain moments, in favourable circumstances. Every bullfighter has his "on" and his "off" days, just as sooner or later every bullfighter is wounded, more or less seriously. They say it is the brave blood in a man that is shed first. He is liable to lose his nerve before anything else, except pride. Fortunately, if courage is the most important and the most perishable of a bullfighter's assets, it is also the most rudimentary of his qualities and not in the least exceptional among either Spaniards or Mexicans. Cowardly bullfighters are rare because they constitute a contradiction in terms, which must prove unsuccessful, so that unless they happen to have both the other necessary qualifications in an extraordinary degree they are soon lost to view. In the absence of proof to the contrary the Spanish military code takes the valour of cadet-officers for granted. In the bullfighter courage may also be assumed as axiomatic, for two reasons: because he would hardly have adopted such a risky profession, or would not have persevered in it, if he were not naturally brave (despite "el Espartero's" dictum that "hunger can hurt worse than any bull"), and because it is impossible for a man not to fight bravely when he is fighting well. The reverse may seem true only if he is a brilliant actor into the bargain. Cowardice, however momentary, will be detected immediately in the close circle of the arena, where the slightest sign of hesitation is visible, as under a microscope, to the concentrated scrutiny of countless pairs of eyes.

A *torero,* either of the romantic or of the classical school, needs the three qualities in question because he must be able to do three distinct things in one: *parar, mandar, templar.* These are the three indicative moods which conjugate the irregular verb *torear,* and the same threefold rule applies to every single pass in bullfighting. The man must stand his ground; he must dominate the bull; he must temper its wild lunges, suiting his movements to his partner's, as in a dance, yet leading them all the while, moulding them to a pattern of his own design. He is the conductor, the bull is his orchestra; the passes are the score: the tempo is everything. All three functions must be fused in order to fulfil the dual purpose of each pass—control and rhythm. Its whole beauty will be lost if any one of them is neglected, for it may then be effective or balanced, but not both together. The man cannot harmonize the pass unless he masters the bull, whom he cannot command absolutely unless he himself stops still. The great "Lagartijo" once ironically defined the science of his profession in words which, if they were true, would corroborate the judgment of Pepys's friend who said that "the *Juego de Toros* is a simple thing." Nothing indeed could be simpler: "Either you move or the bull removes you." In placing the *banderillas,* more especially *al quiebro,* you entice the bull with your body and evade him, either on the run or by sidestepping. But with the *muleta* or the cape the secret of playing a bull—as opposed to putting him in position—is that you stay where you are, and when the bull charges, you draw him past you with the flag or the cloak, which he attacks by instinct, not because it is red, or any other bright colour, but because it is the nearest thing to him that moves. You ensnare him and subject him to your will—by checking, directing, and attuning his impulse to your actions. There is positively nothing more to it than that. It is not cricket; nor, though magnificent, like the Charge of the Light Brigade, as Bosquet remarked, is it war; it is unsporting, heroic, methodical, and hazardous. Your opponent is a cross between Joe Louis and a light tank.

A *matador,* by definition, should be able to kill—honestly, straightforwardly, without shirking "the moment of truth," which constitutes the climax of the encounter and also its chief peril, since it entails most directly the purely sporting element of give-and-take. The south has produced several good clean dependable killers, including "Manolete" (who was steady and solemn, a genuine Cordovan); but they are the exception rather than the rule. They are so everywhere, it is true; but the southerners—and the Mexicans—are often erratic, temperamental artists in the ring, whereas the *toreros* who hail from other regions belong for the most part to the now somewhat old-fashioned type of brave, honest, reliable performer who is prepared to give regularly his worthy, limited best. Their chief merit, which cannot be gainsaid, is their sense of professional dignity, their willingness and courage: what the Spaniards call *voluntad y valor.* Although his father was Italian, Don Luis Mazzantini, one of the greatest swordsmen in the history of the art, was a Basque; so were "Cocherito de Bilbao," Fortuna (who slew a stray fighting-bull in the main thoroughfare of Madrid), Agüero, Noaín, and other *matadors* worthy of the name. Such men are known as "short" bullfighters, as opposed to "long" bullfighters, because of their restricted range and small repertoire. They reduce *el toreo* to its plain, unembellished essentials; their forte is a fearless ability to kill—which after all was the foundation of the fiesta. A typical example of this breed of fighter was the Aragonese, Villalta, who was awarded thirty-two bulls' ears as trophies due to his excellent killing in Madrid between 1922 and 1931.

Writing of the bullfight at that time (*Death in the Afternoon* was published in 1932), Ernest Hemingway stated: "It is a decadent art in every way and like most decadent things it reaches its fullest flowering at its rottenest point, which is the present." Throughout the 'twenties and 'thirties there were half a dozen Valencians and Castilians, from the ephemeral Granero to the eternal Ortega, none of them "short" bullfighters in the accepted sense, who contributed a plethora of talent to that flowering, already nurtured to an overgrowth by an assortment of *sevillanos,* a pair of entrancing gypsies, and another most notable Mexican, the effortless, academical Armillita. The first of these two decades went on points, as it were, to Marcial Lalanda, a *madrileño* known as "the young master," who defended his title, against stylists far more distinguished than himself, on the strength of an almost dazzling competence. The second period belongs by right to Domingo Ortega, a countryman from Toledo, now in semi-retirement as an elder statesman of the taurine community who has gone in for bull-breeding. The best of the Castilian *matadors* since Sanz or Pastor, and more original than either of them, Ortega was not merely the leading figure for ten years, in succession to Lalanda, but the only big name in bullfighting between Belmonte and "Manolete."

A distinctive artistic personality is a rare possession at the best of times. Ortega sprang, mature, from the land to exert an invigorating influence on the fiesta; but the rot had set in and it was too late for a speedy return to rude health and virility. The yokel's skill was that of the expert craftsman. His accomplishment in dealing with difficult and dangerous bulls was as impressive to watch as the work of a specialist at his job. Ortega's uncannily smooth handling of the cape and *muleta,* without so much as a fold out of place, still reveals the virtuoso when he tests calves on his ranch or performs in mufti for charity. He is unique in this respect. Yet that same overwhelming mastery had become curiously monotonous in the arena; not that it lacked variety or depth, but in the absence of adequate opposition on the part of the undersized average bull, even in his day, it was bereft of aesthetic significance. It was an effortless study in perfection, and it looked casual—because it was so decided and easy. With Ortega, however, the workmanship always was authentic—pure *dominio;* whereas now, ten to twenty years later, the extreme proficiency of his presumptive successor, Luis Miguel Domínguín, is so enormously superior to the raw material in hand that it seems facile to the point of exaggeration and tedium. The tragedy of Luis Miguel is that he is ridiculously good at his task—which is a bitter predicament for an artist, and one that might drive a less haughty Castilian frantic.

Courage and skill make a bullfighter like "Domínguín"; skill and grace make an artist, like Pepe Luis Vázquez; grace and courage make either a corpse or a modern *matador* such as "el Litri"—in some ways there is not much difference; it is largely a question of luck. To tackle the moderately inoffensive bulls of the present day with a modicum of efficiency and immense success, skill is becoming less and less necessary. The typical modern *matador* is a melodramatic dummy, with an unearthly knack of thrilling the audience, because contemporary audiences as a whole are utterly uninterested in the bull and unappreciative of the skill which is needed to play each brutish partner according to its nature. Bulls are extremely varied and extraordinarily variable; four out of five call for different handling; moreover they change their tactics, their very condition alters, in the course of the fight. People still say that they are "going to the bulls," but what they mean is that they are going to see the *toreros,* not the *toros.* It takes a lifetime to begin to learn something about bulls, whereas anyone with eyes in his head can tell at once what he likes about a *torero* and what he thinks of his work. There is a wide margin of opinion about every bull that comes into a ring; but guessing will not help—you have to know your subject, which is profoundly complicated. The bullfighter himself, on the contrary, is an open book; his work may be judged as a matter of taste, for personal tastes are inscribed, as the Spaniards say, in a book of blank pages.

In these days of the standardized bull there is a stereotyped system of defying him. It is the most marvelous, the most refined, the most exciting way to taunt, resist, and overcome a bull. The great public will accept nothing but the best, which is what it has paid good money to see—so the same performance is served up time after time to a set pattern, irrespective of the bull (and disrespectful to the bull), whenever humanly feasible. An occasional failure used to end in storms of abuse and a shower of cushions; now that disturbers of the peace—even in the bull-ring—are fined, the yelling spectators merely feel cheated and the fallen idol sulks—until the next time, when the miracle will come off and they will carry him shoulder-high through the main gates in triumph. If the boy is a courageous artist he finds it easier to defy the bull than to fight it—and more profitable. The crowd has always been more dangerous than the bull, but it calls the tune; its demands increase year by year—and so, of course, do the bullfighters', whose earnings in some cases have soared into six figures. They were doubled and trebled in "Manolete's" day—a rise out of all proportion to mounting costs in general. At a time when a quarter of a million *pesetas* was scarcely less than the official equivalent of $14,000, he was paid that amount on occasion for killing two bulls. Since then multiple rates of exchange have been modified; today [1953], if the calculation is based on the tourist rate, a leading *matador's* average wage may be assessed at approximately $2800 a fight. Belmonte had "Manolete" in mind when, to a pointed question, he gave the oracular reply: "The best is the one they pay the most."

At one time skill and courage sufficed to win the applause and approbation of the mob; the *matador* was expected to pit human intelligence against brute force in a contest governed by rules that were carefully devised to allow the enemy certain fair, if limited, advantages while favouring the man's chances of immunity from harm. To run risks—in fact, to court danger—was always part of his job. But the modern bullfighter is supposed to invent new hazards. His skill was once his only protection; nowadays his popularity depends upon an apparent denial or at least disparagement of the skill which he is hardly given the time to acquire by practice. At all costs he must preserve a supreme hieratic elegance of gesture. His sole attraction is his value as a personal novelty. He has become a conjuror or a circus freak engaged in sensational stunts which he performs with frozen calm for the benefit of an ignorant, excitable audience. At the present pace neither he nor the public interest in him is liable to last long, even if, like Litri, whose brother was killed by a bull, he has the eye of a crack shot, a wizard's gift of concentration, and inspired timing. However brave he may be, the modern bullfighter aims, if he is wise, to make a fortune, invest his millions, and retire from the profession as soon as possible. But he dare not admit it—and we have yet to hear of a successful *matador* who voluntarily gave up the game, in any epoch, until he realized that for him at last the game was up. For sheer intoxication the bullfighter's glory eclipses that of the champion athlete or the filmstar and is comparable only to the triumphs of the greatest national heroes. He is a boy of humble origin, transplanted in adolescence by his own tenacious endeavours, at physical risk to himself, from poverty—most often abject poverty—into a fabulous paradise of wealth, women, praise, and power. At sixteen or twenty he is a conquering caliph, with the world at his feet. And yet, by some strange effect of his vocation and breeding, almost invariably this dignified Spanish urchin will remain unspoilt. Sometimes such a superman succumbs to the vices of vanity and envy, but he will be the exception among his colleagues, who normally betray no trace of arrogance, vulgarity, or affectation in private life, however flamboyant their behaviour in the ring may be.

Spanish moralists have repeatedly argued, in defence of the bullfight, that it inculcates manly virtues both in those who practise the game and in those who watch it. To inflict suffering on a soulless brute is less degrading, in their view, than to deface God's image with boxing-gloves. The theory that the Western Hemisphere was discovered, explored, and colonized in the *plazas de toros* of Spain is no doubt equally pleasing to the patriotic Spaniard and to the Briton who was taught at school that biased version of Spanish history which the descendants of the conquistadors reject as "the Black Legend." Now, as the bullfight evolves to suit the modern taste, the most manly—or the more brutal—aspects of the fiesta are gradually disappearing. Some barbarous details have already become obsolete. In 1951, for the second time since 1928–30, the crude and futile system of punishing cowardly bulls with explosive darts was abolished. Recently a formal and authoritative protest was lodged against the ban; but both the other reforms which General Primo de Rivera introduced, nearly twenty-five years ago, have gone unchallenged. Technically there is little to be said against keeping the horses out of the arena until the bull's first blind fury has abated, instead of bringing them in beforehand, to take the brunt of it. On the other hand the padded cuirass, or *peto,* with which the weak-kneed hacks are harnessed for their protection, has nothing whatsoever to recommend it, except that it was devised with the purest, though most misguided, of "humane" intentions. Deploring the innovation of the *peto,* Hemingway pointed out that the bullfight "has not existed because of the foreigners and tourists, but always in spite of them" and that "any step to modify it to secure their approval, which it will never have, is a step towards its complete suppression." That was twenty years ago; recently the bullfight has attracted foreign visitors by the thousand, from among Mr. Hemingway's compatriots in particular. They seem happily unaware that the protective mattress-covering only serves to protect the management's business interests and the spectators' sensibilities, by prolonging the miserable existence of an aged, frightened, beaten, jolted, blindfold, starving creature, and by sparing the onlooker the ugly sight of major accidents, which constitute the horse's only hope of a speedy and merciful escape from a ghastly ordeal of nervous anguish, physical pain, and internal injury. The *peto,* a hideous contraption in itself, is the subtlest instrument of torture that ever was invented by kind-hearted persons. It thwarts the bull and cheats him of his prey; it adds an extra risk to the *torero's* task by teaching the frustrated bull bad defensive habits; it gives the *picador* a grossly unfair advantage, for he takes fewer falls and can riddle the bull at leisure with his lance; it greatly increases the callousness of the crowd; it has robbed the first act of what gallant, grim, ferocious beauty it once had; and it protracts the moribund horses' lives for an intolerable span of weeks and months, on the hypocritical assumption that, for all concerned, the animal's slow, patient agony is preferable to its violent death in full view of the public.

The refinement and the decadence of the "ungentle sport" are different aspects of the same process. Voltaire might have had the Spanish pastime in mind when he explained that *"la décadence est produite par la facilité de faire et par la paresse de bien faire, par la satiété du beau et par le goût du bizarre."* Some parts of the bullfight have atrophied, while others have gained in importance and length; the first act of the drama has been split into two scenes, of which the second is rapidly declining in popularity as the disproportion between weaker bulls and the excessive mauling they receive at the hands of the *picadors* becomes yearly more evident and more outrageous. There are other, even graver and more insidious abuses, such as the shameful practice of tampering with the bull's horns, that are spoken of in whispers as occurring at dead of night, off-stage. (No longer, since one bull-breeder has stated in public that the "shaving" process is general, and others have denounced it. We even read nowadays of fines imposed officially on bull-breeders who perpetrate or consent to such villainy. Things have come to an ugly pass when the newspapers announce, proudly and unblushingly, that a set of six bulls of the Conde de la Corte will enter the arena on a given date with their horns intact and unimpaired, as God made them. The manager of the Barcelona rings guarantees that no bull is ever "barbered" there.) The mob's hostile attitude toward the *picadors* suggests that the day may not be far off when the last will have been seen of them and their sorry mounts in Spanish bullrings—a good riddance, much to be desired but only practicable when the bull himself has been transformed still further, from a powerful adversary to a rough playmate. The insults hurled regularly and indiscriminately at the horsemen, even when they obey the rules, are not inspired by pity for the horses but by anxiety on behalf of the bull, lest he should get more than his fair share of wounding with the pick, so that he reaches the climax of the fight disabled by the loss of too much blood. The horses and their riders cannot be dismissed until their usefulness is at an end; but to blunt the bull's natural weapons and not, at the same time, to release the horses from commission would be too vile an act of treachery for the *fiesta brava* to survive. Remove the bullfight's basic element of danger and you reduce a manly art to an emasculated form of sport; without that saving grace, its intrinsic cruelty would still rule tauromachy out of any moral comparison to such aesthetic pursuits as, for example, figure-skating, circus riding, or high diving. The bull, by tradition and as a symbol, should be sacrosanct.

At the present time the cult shows signs of spreading. In France, (The Spanish pastime, as distinct from the indigenous Provençal bull-games, was not introduced into France until 1853.) since the Grammont Law was revised February 1, 1951, it is no longer necessary to pay a fine before organizing an illegal show, *avec mise à mort,* in any southern district, from Bordeaux to Marseilles, where an "uninterrupted tradition" of tauromachy exists—as it does, ardently upheld, in a score of *arènes* which range, architecturally, from the Roman circus at Nîmes to the newest bull ring under construction at Toulouse. Following in the footsteps of the Brooklyn bullfighter, Sidney Franklin, and others before him (such as the Chinese, Vicente Hong, the Irishman, O'Hara, the French brothers François and Pierre Pouly, and their mustachioed compatriot, Félix Robert), a confused assortment of aliens, including an Englishman, may be mentioned as having lately let Spain in on a miniature UNO of their own. A bull ring was opened two years ago in Tangier, and the Portuguese West African colony of Angola adopted the practice after the missionary visits of the first top-notch Portuguese *matador,* Manoel dos Santos, whose performances there put him at the head of the general list, in number of fights, for 1950. . . . Vain attempts were made to introduce the games into Argentina, whereas recently *corridas* of sorts have been staged—or simulated—in Guatemala, Costa Rica, Cuba, Honduras, and Puerto Rica. The genuine article flourishes, however, to a greater or lesser extent, but on a serious level, in five of the ten South American republics—Venezuela, Colombia, Ecuador, Peru and Bolivia. Although these countries mostly produce local talent, they enable a number of Spaniards to fight bulls all the year round, by engaging them to fill the bill at Caracas, Lima, and elsewhere, after the close of the season in Spain. On the other hand, for fifteen years the fiesta suffered the effects of an inexplicable mutual boycott on the part of the Mexican and Spanish members of the profession, who fell out on the eve of the troubles in Spain in 1936 and only made up their differences—except for a brief truce in 1944–46—when finally the interchange of *toreros* was renewed by an agreement signed in February, 1951. From the taurine point of view this was even more important than the victory in France that year, for it restored to the audiences of the two chief bullfighting countries the right to judge visiting *matadors* from the other side of the Atlantic, during the alternate hot seasons. Obviously nothing but harm could come of an imbecile quarrel that had begun as a labour dispute and was mysteriously kept alive by vested interests.

It is not the newfangled legions of the Football League or their foreign friends that the old-fashioned patrons of the bull-feast need to fear as the enemies of a cherished tradition. No doubt they represent the modern trend, the ruthless march of time; but the bullfight will last either until the doomsday of diversity among the peoples of the earth, when all separate idiosyncracies are tabu, or until creeping decay destroys it from within, through the unprincipled greed of those who have most to lose if the fiesta is transformed into a farce and abandoned by the *afición* as an anachronism devoid of meaning. Vigilant inner reforms should suffice to save the *plazas de toros* from the fate of Jericho and to keep aloft, in place of motley banners, the single standard of red and gold—or blood and sand—that flies over every bull ring in Spain—or, better yet, hangs limp in a sunny, windless sky—when the ceremony is about to begin. So on "a good afternoon for the bulls" let us hurry along, mingling with the crowd in that selfsame mood of fervent expectation that delighted Ford a century ago, because "nothing, when the tide is full, can exceed the gaiety and sparkle of a Spanish public going, eager and dressed in their best, to the fight."

Lament for Ignacio Sánchez Mejías

by FREDERICO GARCÍA LORCA

Federico García Lorca (1899–1936) was the finest lyrical and popular poet of modern Spain. He was killed in the early days of the Spanish Civil War.

He wrote out of the customs and traditions of the people. He was folk-song singing genius, musician, dramatist and poet. It is with humble respect that this translation is made. Nobody can translate poetry from one language to another. This has been an effort of deep admiration for his poetry and his people.

The Horn Wound and Death

> At five in the afternoon
> Exactly five in the afternoon
> A boy brought a white sheet
>   *at five in the afternoon.*
> And a basket of prepared lime
>   *at five in the afternoon.*
> The rest was death, and only death
> At five in the afternoon.
>
> The wind scattered the fragments of cotton
>   *at five in the afternoon.*

Sánchez Mejías

And the oxide glittered crystal and nickel
at five in the afternoon.
The dove and the leopard are struggling
at five in the afternoon.
And a thigh with a lonely horn
at five in the afternoon.
The songs of bereavement began
at five in the afternoon.
The jars of arsenic and gauze
at five in the afternoon.
Silent groups in the corners
at five in the afternoon.
And the bull alone charging high
at five in the afternoon.
When the cold sweat came
at five in the afternoon.

And the Plaza was covered in iodine
at five in the afternoon.
Death fertilized the wound
at five in the afternoon.
At five in the afternoon.
Exactly five in the afternoon.

A casket on wheels is his bed
at five in the afternoon.
Drums and trumpets sound in his ears
at five in the afternoon.
The bull bellows in his forehead
at five in the afternoon.
Agony trembles in the room
at five in the afternoon.
From far away the gangrene comes
at five in the afternoon.
A lily-white horn in his groin
at five in the afternoon.
The wounds were burning like suns
at five in the afternoon.
And the crowds shattered the windows
at five in the afternoon.
That awful five in the afternoon!
It was five by all the clocks!
It was five at the sombre close of the day!

The Blood Flows

I do not want to see it!

Tell the moon to hurry by,
For I do not want to see the blood
Of Ignacio on the sand.

I do not want to see it.

The full moon,
Steed of the silent clouds,
And the dark plaza of dream
With willows weeping on the barriers.
I do not want to see it.
May my memory consume it!
Tell the jasmines
And their tiny white innocence!

I do not want to see it!

The cow of the old world
Licked her mournful tongue
Over a muzzle of blood
Spilled on the sand,
And the bulls of Guisando,
Half-death and half-stone,
Roared like two centaurs
Weary of walking on the earth.
No.
I do not want to see that!

Ignacio went up the stairs
Carrying death on his back.
He sought the dawn
But the dawn was not there
He sought his faithful shadow
But sleep obscured it.
He sought his fine body,
And found his blood flowing.
Do not ask me to see it!

I do not want to feel the pouring stream
As the pulses weaken;
That stream of splendor
Shining on the worshippers,
Overflowing the plush and leather
Of the thirsty multitude.
Who calls to me that I should see it?
Do not ask me to see it.

He did not close his eyes
When he saw the horns in his face,
But the Fates held his head.
And over the ranches
Went the sound of secret voices
That called to immortal bulls.
They were the herdsman of the far away skies.

No prince of Seville
Compared with him,
No sword with his sword,
Nor any heart so true.

His strength
Was a river of lions;
His cool knowledge
Was a marble masterpiece.

The aura of Andalusian Rome
Adorned his head,
While his smile was a spikenard
Of wit and wisdom.
What a great bullfighter in the ring!
What a fine mountaineer in the highlands!
How gentle with the beards of grain!
How stern with the spurs!
How tender in the dew!
How shining at the fair!
How mighty with the last
Banderillas of darkness!

But now he sleeps forever.
Now the moss and herbs
Open with skillful fingers
The flower of his skull.
And his blood is already singing;
Singing through the marshes and meadows
Sliding off frozen horns,
Flowing blindly through the mist,
Stumbling over a thousand hooves,
Like a long, dark, mournful tongue
That lathers a pool of agony
By the Guadalquivir of the stars.
Oh white wall of Spain!
Oh black bull of despair!
Oh strong blood of Ignacio!
Oh nightingale of his veins!
No.
I do not want to see it!
There is no chalice that would hold it.
And there are no swallows that could drink it,
No cold light to frost it,
No chant and no blanket of lilies,
No crystal to crown it with silver.
No.
I do not want to see it!

Lament for Ignacio Sánchez Mejías   **335**

Body Present

The stone is a forehead where dreams begin,
With no winding stream
And no cold cypresses.
The stone is a shoulder to carry time
With its weeping trees and spheres.

I have seen the grey rains race over the water
Lifting their gentle and wounded arms
That they may not fall on the sloping stone
That shatters off their limbs without spilling
    the blood.

For the stone collects seeds and storm clouds,
Skeletons of leaves and wolves of despair,
But reflects no sounds, nor crystal, nor fire,
Only plazas, and plazas, and more plazas forever.
There on the stone lies the well-born Ignacio
Now it is finished. What happened?
Look at his figure.
Death has covered his head with a sulphur veil
And placed over it the mask of a dark
    minotaur.

Now he is finished. Rain falls in his
    mouth.
The frightened breath has fled from his broken
    breast,
And love, drenched in tears of snow,
Warms the highlands of the ranches.

What do they say?
A sickening silence falls.
We have here a body that crumbles,
A figure once bright with nightingales.
And we see it covered with bottomless
    wounds.

Who rumples the shroud? It is not true
    what they say.
Here nobody sings, nor weeps in the shadows,
No jingle of spurs, and no terrified
    serpent.

Here I only want my wide eyes
To see this body now and forevermore.

I want to see here the hard-voiced men
Who tame horses and conquer rivers,
Whose bones are rhythmic
And who sing through their flint and sun filled
    throats.

I want to see them here. In front of this
    stone.
Before this body with its broken reins
I want them to show me the way of escape
    for this captain paralyzed by death.

I want them to show me a lament like a river
With gentle clouds and dark silences,
That can bear away the body of Ignacio and hide it
Beyond the double thunder of the bulls.

That they lose it in the full plaza
    of the moon
Which seems, when new, a suffering beast.
Lose it in the night when no fish
    play
In the marshes of the cold mist.

I do not want them to cover his
    face with a mantle
That he may become accustomed to death
Look, Ignacio: Do not feel
The fever of sorrow.
Sleep on, fly away, rest. The sea
    will die too!

Soul Absent

The bull does not see you, nor the
    fig tree,
Nor horses, nor the insects on your hearth.
The child does not see you in the afternoon,
For you are dead forevermore

The crest of the rock does not remember,
Nor the black sand where you were destroyed.

Your own mute memory does not know you
Because you have died forevermore.

The autumn will come with its empty shells
Grapevines of fog and huddled mountains,
But nobody will want to see your eyes
Because you are dead forevermore.

Because you are dead forevermore,
Like all the dead of the earth,
Like all the dead who are forgotten,
A pack of spectral dogs.

Nobody knows you. No. But I sing to you.
I sing for tomorrow of your gracious heritage,
The high symbol of your wisdom;
Your appetite for death and its taste
In your mouth;
The sadness of your valiant joy.

A long time will pass before the birth,
If birth there be,
Of an Andalusian so bold
    and rich in venture.
I sing his grace in words that moan
On a sombre wind through the olive trees.

Excerpt from **The Brave Bulls**

by **TOM LEA**

Tom Lea is one of the great creative artists in the United States. He is also an extraordinary novelist of original style. He is a historian in fact and fiction, as the history of the King Ranch and the novel, *The Wonderful Country,* reveal. Lea's murals rank with the finest of symbolic art. His novel, *The Brave Bulls,* is the best novel yet written on the subject. He has high fellowship with El Greco in color and texture and line throughout his wide range of painting. He lives in his ancestral El Paso, as a young master of art and life, beautifully abetted by Sarah, Mrs. Lea. These statements represent my carefully analyzed convictions regarding this man and this friend. It is with pride that I present a selection from *The Brave Bulls,* two original black-and-whites, and the cover of this book from his creations.

He felt dry and brittle when he awoke in the dim pink room and the cold. He dressed quickly, shivering, and took a nip of *tequila* from the bottle in his suitcase before he stepped out into the patio, into a day at Las Astas.

Ruddy light from the early sun warmed the weathered arches and carved stone tops of the columns on the opposite portico, but the rest of the patio was still in chilly blue shadow when he stepped down on the flagstones and looked up between the columns at the pale spotless sky. He took a deep breath then, smelling the air tinged with silage and wood smoke, and looked around.

Under the portico on the other side of the patio he paused to examine the stuffed head of a black bull looking down on him there. It had a Roman nose, and lacked ears. From somewhere in the unknown around him he heard faintly the jangling of spurs as someone walked across a stone floor. Then there was silence again. He scuffed his feet, self-consciously, to make a little noise, and he gave an artificial cough, continuing his circuit slowly, peering at closed doors.

At the far corner he was rewarded. A door opened and a tall old woman with a brown Indian face and gray hair looked out at him. Her two hands were on her stomach, under her black apron. He had found the kitchen of Las Astas, at least.

"Yes, señor?" the woman inquired.

"I arrived in the night. A guest of the dueño," said Eladio Gómez. "Do you know if he is up and if I could see him?"

"Well. He's up with the first light, and gone out," said the woman. She made a sign outward with her hand and followed it with her eye as if her patron had gone to the end of the earth.

"Well," said Gómez. "Well. Could I ask you for a cup of coffee to start the day?"

"How not?"

She came out and opened the door next to the one she had stood in.

"Enter, señor. Be seated."

He stepped into the dim dining room and sat down at the long empty table covered with checkered cloth.

The coffee was black and thick when the woman poured it in the bottom of the big cup and then added the steaming milk to the brim. When he had drunk it, smoking a cigarette, gazing at the ornate crockery on the plate rails, he felt fortified. With his hands in his pockets he sauntered out into the morning where the sun was warming the walls.

Peons stood around outside, waiting for their foreman. They lounged by the tall open door of the saddle-house, by the truck with the bull boxes, by the sunlit walls, warming themselves in the light from the sky, the "stove of the poor" that climbed bright and promising over the hills in the east. They stood in the sunlight gathering unhurriedly the direction and the desire for the work of the day, while the dew dried, and the horses were saddled. In the west the Sierra rose up pale blue and beautiful, like a promise, above them.

"Good morning," said Eladio Gómez, walking out the courtyard gate. Something in his city-dwelling heart expanded there in the open sunlight. His senses reached out beyond the clay they lived in and found the tidings good.

He looked out across the markings in the sunny dust, the tracks of hoofs and paws, the tangled prints of cart wheels and truck tires, of boots and sandals and naked feet, and out beyond the open space he saw the stone pile of the bull corrals with their heavy gates, and walked out to examine them.

As he came around a corner, three horsemen appeared in the lane under the pepper trees. He recognized the rider on the big sorrel. Drawing closer, the horse pitched forward suddenly, answering the spur. Ten paces from where Gómez stood, it reared high, spinning on its hind legs, coming down facing Gómez smartly as the rider grunted "Ho!" and dismounted, throwing down the reins.

"Señor Gómez!"

Don Tiburcio Balbuena came forward, extending his hand. He was tall, spare, with white mustaches, and he was dressed in tight leather charro clothes, well worn, under a magnificent sombrero with a hat string biting into his monumental chin.

"You arrived, Señor Gómez. Now you know where your house is." His voice was deep and strong as a bull's.

"Eladio Gómez at your orders, Don Tiburcio."

"At yours, Señor Gómez. I feel deeply I did not meet you last night. . . . The lateness of the hour——"

He walked over and caught up his reins.

"This morning we have been cutting out horses for the *charro* Iturbide here, to take to Michoacán." He turned to the two riders who had come up.

"Iturbide! My friend Gómez, impresario of the plaza at Cuenca. Señor Gómez, I might mention that Iturbide is the proud and happy father of twenty-six children, at last tally."

"Only twenty-five," said the *charro* smiling, shaking hands.

"This is my foreman," said Balbuena, pointing to the other horseman in the crimped straw sombrero and the old rawhide leggings with the iron buckles. "If he will permit me, I will mention that my foreman is a boar hog in the swill when he's drunk, Señor Gómez! The Whore of Babylon on Saturday nights. But he knows the bulls, Gómez, he knows them. He has faculties. Tuerto, shake hands with the *dueño* of the plaza at Cuenca."

The foreman took off his hat, grinning at Gómez with his mouth like a bear trap, and his one eye.

"Doroteo Paz," he said. "Your orders."

"You had some breakfasts?" boomed Balbuena, looking at Gómez.

"Not yet."

"Neither have we," said the old man. "Tuerto, take these horses. We are going to eat. And saddle one more while we're gone. Señor Gómez wants to see brave animals."

My God, thought Gómez.

"We'll get Serafina, that old cow, to put something on the table," said Balbuena. His spurs were like bells, on the flagstones. "Serafina!"

They had a tumbler of claret first. Then canned asparagus laid out on a platter, soaked in vinegar, to whet their tongues; then Spanish sardines and claret and fried beef and *frijoles* with plenty of chili and more claret.

"You need a foundation to look at bulls in their pastures," said Balbuena picking his teeth. "More claret, señores?"

At the courtyard gate Gómez eyed the bay horse the one-eyed foreman had saddled for him. "I didn't bring any boots," he said.

"Don't think of it," said Balbuena. "El Tuerto has mounted you on velvet, on baby hair. Here."

El Tuerto had also sent the peons to work. "You want me with you?" he asked his patron.

"Come along," said Balbuena. "We might need you."

They mounted and rode down the lane.

"Too bad you weren't here yesterday, Señor Gómez," said Balbuena. "Tonio Algara was here. He drove out from Mexico to look at some bulls for his El Toreo. But you'll see the ones he picked. We'll load them for shipping tomorrow."

The sun climbed high and strong in the sky. The horsemen jogged across the grassy hills.

"The *charro* here, he probably doesn't know our Brave Bulls, our *Toros de Lidia,* are greater of family and purer of blood than thoroughbred horses. Do you think he knows that, Gómez?"

Gómez and the *charro* smiled.

"Of course I knew that," said Iturbide.

"We like the stuff with the horns, don't we?" said the *dueño* of Las Astas.

"Well armed with points," added el Tuerto, half to himself.

"Which points are you talking about?" asked his patron. "Anyway we like them. Let's go in this pasture and see the cows."

Tuerto took down the cedar poles across the narrow opening in the mortarless rock walling that divided the pastures of Las Astas, and the horsemen rode through.

They found a herd on the slope beyond the spring in the thicket of cottonwoods. Gaunt and baleful-eyed, the black cows lifted their sharp-

The bulls are born ferocious

horned slender heads and snorted at the riders. Their calves jumped from their nursing or from their rest in the shade, nimble as goats, and stood braced on their wiry legs, snuffing.

"The old cow at the right, the one with the twisty horns," said Don Tiburcio, trying to whisper, "she's the only one left that was dropped in Spain."

At the sound of the voice the cows and calves started away on their spring-steel legs, more like deer than cattle.

"You see the heifer turning to watch us? Can you see her shoulders? Twenty-seven times she took the iron at the *tientas* three weeks ago! Twenty-seven times before she had enough iron in her shoulders. Oh, she will make formidable sons! Tuerto, the shoulders are healing nicely."

"Don Tiburcio," Eladio Gómez said, "it would be a privilege to hear from your own lips how you do things here at Las Astas."

"Thank you, Señor Gómez. Of course you know everything here is purebred fighting stock which I originally, myself, brought from Spain—the *casta* of Saltillo, later refreshed with Murube and Pablo Romero.

"All the breeding is based on selection for bravery alone. Nothing else. As a real fighting bull can issue only from a brave sire and dam, it follows that everything depends on creating a breed herd distinguished by fighting spirit. To build it, each animal must be tested before it can be placed in such a herd.

"That is the function of the *tienta*, the test for fighting spirit.

"It is performed by allowing each individual heifer and young bull, at about the age of two years, to charge a mounted *picador* armed with a lance bearing a steel point that is sharp but which cannot penetrate to any damaging extent. The animal is then classified according to the fierceness with which it charges the horseman and receives the pain of the lance point in its shoulders.

"Bull calves are never allowed to charge more than three times, and they are never worked with the cape. This is to keep them unspoiled and innocent when they enter a bull ring two years later.

"The heifers, on the other hand, are allowed to charge as much as they will; and they are worked hard with the cape to further test their desire to fight.

"I find, for my purposes, about one heifer in five brave enough to join my breed herd, where she will pass her exceptional bravery on to her sons.

"Even so, of those sons I find only about one bull in three meeting my standards at the *tienta* and worthy to go to a plaza wearing my ribbons.

"Certain rare, completely exceptional bulls I choose to retain at Las Astas as herd sires, to mount my cows. These seed bulls must be of the best blood lines and display the most extraordinary bravery at their *tientas*. After choosing them, I retest them, to make sure.

"The culls? I sell them to butchers. Or to less particular men who breed them, or sell them to plazas, calling them 'brave'!"

The remark made Eladio Gómez slightly uncomfortable. "How do you put the seed bulls to the cows?" he asked.

"I allow them to mount from June to January only, so the calves will come when the grass is good. There is a bull with the cows in this pasture now. Old Cantarillo.

"A *vaquero* is assigned to watch each bull, to note down upon paper the branded number of each cow his bull mounts, together with the date. Nine months later when the calf is born, I have not trusted to fences and guesswork. I have an accurate record for the registry."

"How far does the Las Astas book go back?" asked Iturbide.

"Fourteen generations now. Of course we lack data for the time of the Revolution. In our book we record not only the heredity but the history of each animal, in this order: branded number, name, description, sire, dam, date of birth, *tienta* date and rating, and if the animal has gone to the ring we note behavior in plaza. With this information we can breed selectively."

Around the slope they sighted Cantarillo, in the shade of a tall *nopal*. His man Teclo sat on a horse, keeping his distance. Cantarillo pawed the dust. He tossed it high over his shoulders, grumbling, as the horsemen went through a gate.

"Here the sucking calves stay with their mothers while their brands and earcrops heal, getting strong and learning to eat grass before they are weaned," said the *dueño* of Las Astas.

"The branding of brave calves is a work of talent. Tuerto here, he's a genius, wrestling the fighting devils to the mat. You ought to see it. We throw them on a pad, you know, handling them like angels. Their horn buds must not be injured, nor dirt get in their eyes, to cause defects later.

"Now we go into the big bull pasture."

He swept his arm out in a great curve.

"See it? Grass, water, and shade. See the bluffs and the breaks down that draw? Protection. See those hills? Strength of leg. See those stony ridges? Hardness of hoof. You see what gives Las Astas bulls their form?"

The sun was past the zenith, hot and bright. Eladio Gómez could feel it burning the back of his neck. His pants legs had worked up so the wrinkles chafed his legs against the stirrup leathers. He could feel the saddle soreness coming in his groins and backside. He had not been so happy in a long time.

"Here my bulls live from the time of their *tientas*," said Balbuena as the horses paced through the high grass, "until I put them in feed lots to fatten for the ring. Two years they live their lives here, untouched. Born of a fierce breed, living the most of their days like ranging wild animals, their power and savagery develops. They learn to use their horns among themselves.

"The festival has symbolisms that sometimes strike me, gentlemen. I love the brave bulls. For them there is no coming of old age and weakness and dying fire. No servitude, no toil. Yet we deny them the benignity of reproducing their kind. Certain of their male relations will stay home to take care of the cows and carry on the breed with those formidable sacs that swing between their legs. But not our fighters to the death. They are virgins. It is a curious thing, our festival.

"Ah," he said, trying to whisper again. "Look at them! We will not talk. Ride slowly, with care."

In the tawny grass beyond a *huisache* thicket a score of black bulls had tossed their heads up, gazing at the intruders squarely with their horns held high, their legs ready. The horsemen reined, stopping. From the distance of forty yards they heard the snorts, the breath plunged from the massive lungs. One bull lowered the horns, backing two steps, head down, and pawed, throwing dust. The horsemen stood rooted, facing the bulls. A breeze rippled the grass and carried the dust away in silence. Then a bull blew, whistling the air through his black nostrils, and turned slowly away, stepping with majesty through the grass. The others turned, following.

"Precioso!" whispered Eladio Gómez when they were gone.

"Some of the three-year-olds," boomed Don Tiburcio again. "They will be going next year. There should be two oxen with that bunch, Tuerto."

"The oxen are somewhere close," said the foreman. "I saw their tracks."

The horsemen rode on.

"It is strange," said Eladio Gómez, "how the herd instinct makes it possible to husband such beasts. The herd makes the tranquillity, the feeling of well-being. Take a bull suddenly from that divided responsibility of herd thinking, make him an individual, and he tries to kill you."

"Exactly!" said Balbuena. The old man winked. "The symbolism there may be why I prefer the country life!"

"The most symbolical part," said Gómez, "is the ox. Our castrated friend. Our servant with the empty sac, who is traitor to his kind. We use him to trap the savage bull from freedom, to manipulate him by deceit to where he would not go."

"Clearly symbolical!" said Balbuena.

Eladio Gómez was surprised with himself, talking like that. Symbolically. Riding a pacing bay horse in a bull pasture.

The sun was down so that their hat brims no longer shaded their faces when they stopped at the old well La Noria under the trees, and drank the cold water, and rode on toward the walled lane that led to the bull corral.

"Along this lane," said the *dueño* pointing to the gates along the side, "are the feed lots for the bulls being readied for the plazas, the four-year-olds. I give them several weeks of heavy feed to build their weight and strength before they leave."

"You have any trouble getting them to take grain, after bringing them in from grass?" asked the horse buyer, Iturbide.

"Sometimes. They have to be taught. This is done right after their *tientas* when they are not so hard to handle. They are penned in a lot where there is nothing to eat but cracked corn in individual stone troughs. Most of the young bulls take to it and learn right away. A few refuse. They learn to eat corn from a trough, or they starve. When they are four and come in to the feed lots, they remember.

"There is a little bull in a pen back of the house where I have him now, taking his lesson. He has refused to eat for nineteen days. He is a black bag of bones. If he does not eat his cracked corn he will die, and I will let him. Starving or not, at this moment he is as full of fight as any animal at Las Astas. In a brave bull, spirit withers last of all."

"When do you bring the four-year-olds in from the grass?"

"I try to time it so they will be finish-fed, rounded out but not too fat, at my delivery dates during the bullfight season which in Mexico, of course, is from November into March. Late in September I divide the four-year-olds into *encierros,* groups of six which will go to the same ring together for the same *corrida.* Each *encierro* goes to a separate feed lot, along with a couple of extras, so I'll have six for sure at shipping time. Bulls kill and injure each other, and they can get sick.

"Let me tell you the kind of heavy feed they get in the lots. Two feedings a day, one in the early morning, another soon now. The total daily ration for each bull is forty-odd pounds. About thirteen of corn, twenty-two of silage, and five or six of boiled *frijoles!* All this in addition to what a bull will munch of dry corn stover between feeds. Daily each bull gets a little more than an ounce of saltpeter mixed with his corn, to quiet the natural urges of bullhood. Bulls will masturbate, you know.

"Here come the feeders, the only men at Las Astas that work afoot among the bulls. They are rarely attacked, for the beasts identify them agreeably with the bringing of aliments."

A *vaquero* on a tired old nag preceded the squeaking, tall, two-wheeled cart that came up the lane, drawn by a team of shaggy burros. A driver sat on the cart beside the sacks of cracked corn and the *frijole* cans, with the sour-smelling silage stalks piled up high at his back. Another peon walked alongside. They stopped by the gate at the side of the lane where the four horsemen had dismounted.

When the feed was down from the cart, the gate was opened quietly and the *vaquero* on the old horse rode in. Behind him silently walked the peons carrying feed. They made four slow trips with their burdens, while the mounted man stood motionless between the feeders and the bulls that watched from among the thorn trees fifty yards away. Silently the peons portioned the feed into the troughs, then filed back to the gate, the horseman following them out as the shielding rear guard. The eight bulls came up to their troughs like milk cows and began eating.

A flock of blackbirds from the sunlit tops of the thorn trees flew in by the bulls and hopped around for crumbs.

"Pretty?" asked Balbuena in his rumbling whisper, after the long silence. The bulls looked up toward the gate, their ears cocked forward. "You want to go inside where you can see better? They are gentle while eating."

"This is fine," said the *charro,* Iturbide. "From here."

Eladio Gómez stood with his eyes fastened to the bulls, saying nothing. Oh, they were beautiful! A peon closed the gate, and the cart creaked down the lane.

The sun stood on the edge of the Sierra and the shadows were long and violet when the horsemen rode up to the courtyard.

"I'm dry, dry in the throat," said Balbuena. "Serafina! Serafina, brandy and some glasses—in my room."

At a rickety card table in his bedroom, the *dueño* of Las Astas tallied his account book for the day. He wore little steel-rimmed spectacles, penciling in the figures slowly from a paper his foreman had brought him. El Tuerto stood by, with his hat in his hand. Then they discussed tomorrow's work, while the *dueño* had a brandy and ate *tortillas* from a saucer on the spotted table.

Gómez and Iturbide sat happy and relaxed in straight chairs tilted against the wall, with brandy glasses in their hands. Gómez gazed at the framed enlargement of a bull photograph over Balbuena's iron bed. He had read the lines of white lettering at the bottom, "The Noble Bull

Finito of Las Astas. Died by the Sword of Lorenzo Garza at the Plaza El Toreo on Christmas Day of 1935."

There were tumblers of claret for dinner, and marinated fish in fiery sauce. There was a hard mountain ham from Spain, and fried beef again and more *frijoles* and stacks of hot *tortillas*. When Serafina brought in the coffee and *Fundador,* there were dried sweet pastries in a round tin box from Madrid.

"Of course I have been gored," Don Tiburcio was saying, "but never gravely." He knocked on wood. "I carry only a scar here on my leg and these three stiff fingers. I have had horses ripped to shreds while I lay on the ground beside them, but nothing serious. El Tuerto lost his eye here at Las Astas, falling with his face in a cactus when a bull knocked over his horse. Most of us carry the marks of the bulls. But they are usually too eager with their horns; their first thrusts are not often accurate. They butt and bump and seldom cut meat. In forty years we have had but two fatalities from bulls at Las Astas. Victims are saved by diverting actions, most often by the horses. If a man is mounted and careful, as he should be, accidents are foolish.

"Some wonderfully foolish things happen," the old man laughed, "when a bull gets hot and goes on the prod. About a month ago two agrarians from San Ysidro came over here riding one burro about the size of a dog. A handsome trio, 'on a visit to relatives.' I was standing in front of the house when they came ambling across the road. I heard Policarpo yell from down the lane, and he yelled loud, 'Here comes a hot bull!'

"It had climbed a wall of the feed lot, I found out later. It was really hot, coming around the corner of the corral. When something like that happens, all my people take cover. Fast. They know what it means.

"I yelled to the idiots on the burro, 'Get off! Run for the wall!'

"The fool in front didn't even turn around. I heard him say, 'He will do nothing. His anger is not for us.'

"But the man by the tail took a look. He flailed the burro in the flanks and yelled, 'Oh yes his anger is——'

"I crossed myself, seeing the vision of a lawsuit before my very eyes. The donkey and the two passengers all sailed into the air. As the bull ripped the burro's belly, the front man lying down very flat said to the rear man praying flat on his back, 'Juan, this bull has anger for us.' That's what he said!"

"Yai!" said Iturbide, slapping his breeches. "What happened?"

"Nothing. They had to walk home to San Ysidro. Tuerto made a fine *quite,* taking the bull away with his horse. Policarpo had oxen with the bull in no time. They led him back to the feed lot.

"But handling bulls is no dull way to earn bread, gentlemen. Have more brandy. We eat early and go to bed with the chickens at Las Astas. Tomorrow we ship Tonio Algara's *encierro* to Mexico."

"Tomorrow I go with the horses to Michoacán," said Iturbide.

"Tomorrow I take the train," said Gómez.

"Tomorrow we find you some bulls for Cuenca," said his host.

"Don Tiburcio," said Gómez with the supper and the brandy warm and fine in him, "permit me to say I feel the privilege tonight of being the guest of a happy man."

"Gómez, you are kind." Tiburcio Balbuena fingered his brandy glass. His voice was not so loud. "I am getting old. In a long life I have lost much. I lost my wife, my two boys. I have lost a great part of my patrimony. Revolutions, agrarians, misfortunes, they have taken five sixths of the Balbuena property and I have wasted and rioted much else besides. But I have had luck, Gómez. In all of it I have found more than I could lose. I was born, as the Marqués de Bradomín said of himself, 'ugly, Catholic and sentimental.' I was also born ready. I'm still ready." The old man grinned. "My family furnished the formalities. The common sense is my own."

"And the bulls of Las Astas," said Gómez.

"The festival is brave, friend Gómez, and the bulls are the finest part. Listen. I will tell you and the *charro* the story of a spectacle I saw with my own eyes in Sevilla when I was young.

"The old Conde de la Plata had a daughter. She rode hot-blooded horses and she loved the bulls. One of de la Plata's herd cows died and left a bull calf starving and the daughter of de la Plata saw the calf and said, 'I will tend it.' By the bottle she fed that calf for five months. The animal grew big and strong with her care, and was weaned and turned out to grass.

"At the *tientas* everyone wanted to see how this pet calf that showed affection for a girl would charge and bear against the iron. The little bull was very brave; de la Plata classed him superior and pastured him with his best. The bull was savage to all but the girl; to her he came when she called the name she had given him—Caribello. And he ate from her hand.

"When the bull had four years the girl pleaded with her father to spare Caribello. But the father refused and this bull went in his box to Sevilla.

"And, womanlike, the daughter went to save her bull. In Sevilla she told friends of her family why she had come. The *afición* and the bull critics heard of it. The papers printed it. On Sunday the ring was jammed.

"I was there. Caribello was the fifth bull. He killed four horses and was very brave. When the time came for the *faena*, and the *matador* Antonio Montes brought out his sword and *muleta*, Caribello was still strong, ready. People began to understand they were seeing something. Not the pet of a daughter of a Count, but a noble bull. He gave pass and pass again to Montes: it was enormous. Montes and Caribello. Dancing the strange dance with the scarlet cloth, with Death looking down upon them.

"The time for the sword arrived. Caribello stood fixed, tired at last.

"The rare thing began. Someone shouted for the *indulto*, the indulgence, the pardon of this bull's life. Then the sand of the ring shook, with a shout from twelve thousand throats, for the *indulto*.

"Montes walked to the center of the ring, head up, and looked to the box of the Authority. He received the sign. With the crowd roaring, slowly he put down upon the sand first the *muleta,* then the sword, and last of all his hat upon them. Thus was granted, according to the old and yet very rare custom, the *indulto.*

"But that was not the spectacle.

"When the oxen came out to lead the bull away, the daughter of the Conde de la Plata walked down into the ring and held up her hand for silence. A breathless quiet came over the plaza. 'Caribello,' the girl called. He raised his head. Slowly she walked up to that hot and bloody bull, and then stroked him between the eyes. The oxen were not necessary. With her hand upon one of his horns she walked Caribello from the ring."

He poured their glasses full and they drank.

"The strange thing about breeding bulls is that you never know how successful you have been until a few minutes before your bull dies. The man who has breed a brave bull had bred a quality without measure, a spirit, that may be tested only in the destruction of it.

"To get a fighting bull you study blood lines and you balance your breed herd and hire cowboys to see that the right bull mounts the right cow. You watch the little bull nurse his mammy, and you brand him with your mark, and you study him closely when he takes the iron at his *tienta.* Carefully you tend him, building his size commensurate with the spirit you hope he has. You speak very confidently to impresarios like Señor Gómez here, and you sell your bull and you ship him. And it is very possible that after four years of your work and hope and expense, people in the plaza will whistle and throw bottles at your bull that is not brave.

"The bulls are a gamble. You hope they will be fine some Sunday afternoon when they are four, but you never know until that Sunday comes.

"Meanwhile, you are grateful. You know the light of morning on the grass where your cattle are feeding. You know the smell of horse sweat and cow pens at noon, and the dry squeak of your stirrup leathers coming down the lane from the feed lots, and the dust, and the taste of brandy clearing your gullet after a ride.

"You know the long slanting afternoon light that makes the thicket of *nopal* seem so high above the old spring where the calves are bawling, and the water ripples going down to the corn patch. You know the smell of wood smoke at dusk when your cowboys sing going home to supper, and always you are hearing the talking of your bulls.

"You know the fun at the *tientas;* and the strong feeling that comes up in you, there with the crowd, when your bull comes out of the *toril* and charges the men resplendent with crimson and gold in the sunlight. You belong to an ancient art. It is an art that speaks to the hearts of men who understand violence. It is," said Don Tiburcio Balbuena, "a thing for glory, and to stir the multitude."

That night, asleep on the bed where "Manolete" once slept, Eladio

Gómez in his dreams saw the most majestic bull in the history of the world. It was huge and black. He saw the immense muscles sliding under the fine-haired glossy hide. The short head was narrow at the nose and wide at the forehead where sharp and smoothly tapered horns sprang outward, then forward with upward tilting curves. The weaponed head was drawn up proudly on a massive neck where a crest of muscle, swollen into a hump, joined with a curve of brutish power into the deep shoulders. The line of the back was concave in connecting those shoulders with the high rounded rump, and the flanks were slick. The hindquarters were all rippling muscle; the lower legs were light-boned right down to the small sharp hoofs. There were glossy curls between the angry eyes and the silky tassel of the tail touched the ground. Upon the left hip was burned the brand of Las Astas, the mark of Tiburcio Balbuena:

The driver got in, started the engine, and moved the truck forward slowly, inch by inch.

"Hold it!" yelled Policarpo from on top of the bull box at the end of the truck. "Back a little!" The truck backed, barely moving.

"Stop!" Policarpo signaled the driver to cut the engine.

"One more now," said Balbuena, standing by Eladio Gómez.

The truck had moved into position so that the last box stood squarely at the mouth of the loading chute. Policarpo reached down and pulled up the sliding gate on the near end of the box. When it was raised, squeaking up its grooves, the inside of the box formed a fitted terminal to the chute.

Policarpo kept his station behind the raised end gate, ready to lower it at the proper time. The box he stood on was exactly like the other three on the truck. Built of almost a thousand pounds of wooden planking reinforced with iron straps and lined at the forward end with iron plates to keep bulls from shattering the planking with their horns, each box was a standard eight feet long, six feet high, and thirty-two inches wide. Trap doors were cut in the end gates for handling feed and water, and there were ventilation slots along the sides near the top. The three loaded boxes on the truck were queerly alive. They shook, creaked, and thumped with the blows delivered against them invisibly from the inside where in each one a bull pounded with raging hoofs and horns.

"Ready!" Balbuena shouted. He and Gómez took up their stations on the masonry ledge built along the outside of the chute where they could duck down out of sight, or raise their heads to see over the wall.

The gate to the trap at the far end of the chute opened silently, manipulated with ropes handled by two peons lying flat on their bellies atop the wall at each side of the gate, the three belled oxen trotted into the trap leading and flanking a black bull. When they had led the bull in far enough,

En route to the arena

the oxen circled away and headed back out of the half-closed gate where the foreman el Tuerto, mounted on horseback, whistled softly to the oxen, cleverly speeding them out, leaving the bull alone, shut in the trap, in the silence, facing the chute with the box at the end.

The bull's great neck muscle swelled and he bellowed, pawing the dust and scouring, furious with the sudden solitude and stillness. Shut within the high stone walls the bull searched for some hint of movement, some target for his horns.

The target appeared suddenly. Up the chute near the box Tiburcio Balbuena lifted his head above the wall and swung his arm over the top, shaking his hat at the bull.

"Huh! *Toro!*"

The bull charged through the chute after the lure, snorting and hooking at the hateful movement of the hat—and ropes pulled a gate shut at his tail, trapping him further, his head almost inside the dark box.

Without allowing the bull a pause, Tiburcio Balbuena reached over the top of the chute with an electric prod pole in his hand. He jammed it under the bull's tail, pressed the button, and with the shock the bull gave a wild snort and lunged involuntarily forward into the box.

Excerpt from "The Brave Bulls"   **351**

"Now!" thundered Balbuena, and Policarpo slammed the end gate down its grooves, scraping the top of the bull's tail, hitting the hocks as they plunged while the gate came down all the way and latched into place.

"Ho!" said the *dueño* of Las Astas. He was smiling. "Another *encierro*. All safe. We had good luck this morning." He turned towards the corrals where heads had appeared from behind most of the walls. "Well done!" he boomed out. "A good *faena!*"

Policarpo climbed down. The bulls were jarring the boxes, plunging and bawling; he walked around peering up at the ropes and wire that fastened the load on the truck bed.

"When are you leaving?" Balbuena asked, coming down from the side of the loading chute.

"As soon as we eat," Policarpo answered.

"I will mention your responsibility again," Balbuena said. "As mayoral you have complete charge. Keep the trucks in sight of each other all the time. You ride in the lead; go slow, and take no chances. You know how many *pesos* are in those boxes. Take care of them. You ought to be in Mexico before sundown tomorrow. When you get to El Toreo you tell Morenito to unload you immediately. Send the trucks back Tuesday morning; you stay, and see that the bulls are cared for exactly the way we would do it here. Be there when the vets make their examinations and watch the scales when the bulls are weighed. Remember you are responsible for the animals until they come out of the *toril* Sunday. Don't get drunk in Mexico. You'll hear from me later in the week."

"Yes, *patrón.*" Policarpo got in the cab.

Balbuena and Gómez waved as the truck lumbered down the road. One of the bulls was bellowing.

Balbuena sat down on the ledge by the chute in the bright sun and wiped the sweat from his face. Gómez lit a black tobacco cigarette. They were alone. Gómez knew what was coming next, and tried to plan what he would say.

"Now tell me what you have in mind for your *corrida*, friend Gómez."

"Well," said Eladio, drawing a breath. "Don Tiburcio, as you know, my plaza is modest. The *corridas* there are the best I can afford, but the box office is limited. I am forced to practice economy to keep my enterprise sound. I seldom pay the high fees currently received by ranking *toreros,* nor can I afford the kind of bulls great plazas buy."

"I understand clearly."

"The season at Cuenca usually opens on the fourth of December, as the main feature of the festival of our town's patron, Santa Bárbara. This year I thought I might make that first *corrida* something special, if I could manage. I am about to sign Luis Bello as First Sword."

"Luis Bello," Don Tiburcio said. "A real *torero,* and my good friend. He's in the Plaza Mexico this afternoon; we'll listen to the *corrida* on the radio. Luis says his career was born at Las Astas: he came here as a boy herding horses. The bay you rode yesterday, Gómez, is out of a Pedrazo mare Luis Bello drove to Las Astas. To be honest, I don't remember him then. There were so many kids wanting to wave their shirts at the bulls. But I do remember the Bello uncle, an old man with spurs on his sandals. He delivered the horses. Luis is in the grand tradition all right: his people were hungry enough! He has fought many bulls from these pastures——"

"He wants Las Astas bulls at Cuenca, Don Tiburcio. I want them too ——" Gómez added. "That's why I came——"

"You ought to have them. Who's alternating with Luis?"

"He wants his kid brother Pepe on the card."

"The kid, eh? Who else?"

"Nobody yet. And if I get Las Astas bulls, I can't afford six of them, nor three *toreros*. I can't."

"Raise the price of seats for a gala festival on the Saint's Day."

"I'm afraid of that, Don Tiburcio. Circumstances—the people of Cuenca, they——"

"Then what you are thinking is this: a *mano a mano*, a hand to hand, between the two brothers. And only four bulls."

"What do you think of it?"

"Well—why not? A short one. But quality not quantity. Something special. The Great Swordsman of Guerreras with bulls of the first class from Las Astas. What's wrong with that?"

"The only thing is the kid. Pepe. That part don't seem so strong. It's no *mano a mano* because it's no heated competition."

"Luis insists on the kid of course?"

"That's it."

"Go on, Gómez. You know Luis will put on a show. You know that. And the kid will be trying. Trying hard. Suppose he did take his *alternativa* a little early, that the public remains, shall we say, somewhat cynical regarding Pepe Bello. He will be trying, with good bulls. And the two brothers together in the ring will give a color, a certain interest."

"The Cuenca public is hard, Don Tiburcio."

"The public anywhere is hard, my friend. It's a gamble. From my standpoint, from yours, from the *toreros'*, from the public's, it's a gamble. Everybody risks something. Whether it's the price of a back row seat on the sunny side, or death on the horns, everybody has to risk something."

"It's the only thing to do, I guess," said Eladio Gómez.

"I'm going to take you out now and show you some bulls for the Bello boys at Cuenca," said Balbuena. "I have something in mind."

Out at the feed lot they leaned with their chins on their hands, looking over the high wall. The peon that went with them threw rocks at the bulls in the enclosure, so that they stood up, alert, in the shade of the *huisache*.

"I will take the two reserves from this *encierro*, Gómez, and two from another. You understand that these are absolutely Number Ones. I will show you the book when we go to the house. Write down those numbers, seventy-four and one hundred seven, and we will check their ratings in the registry."

"They are wonderful bulls, Don Tiburcio. But I can't pay the price you get for them at the big plazas. Have you got——"

"I have something in mind," said the *dueño*. "Now let's look at the other pair I want to show you in the lot down the lane."

The peon got the other *encierro* up, throwing more rocks.

"Ho! *Toros!* Ho!"

One of the bulls in the enclosure stood out from all the rest. His horns were good, turning slightly toward each other, like parentheses. His barrel and legs were well shaped and powerful, matched in size and line with the other bulls. But he was ugly. He had a marked Roman nose. Coarse hair grew under his jaws like a beard, along the brisket, under the belly to the pizzle. And the tassel of his tail was missing. He was a whiskered, bob-tailed bull.

"What's that one doing in there?" asked Gómez. He sensed the impending offer. He understood now what Balbuena might have in mind.

"Listen," said Balbuena. "That nose and that hair are just one of those rare matters that crop up in breeding. There is nothing wrong with that bull, Gómez. Unfortunately a coyote nipped the end of his tail off when he was a calf, and left him *rabón*. But I gave him four stars at his *tienta*. I'll show you in the book. Number twenty-three. Write that down. You can see he's the *amo*, the master of that *encierro*, now. I've had my eye on him since he lost his tail. He deserves a *torero*. I say he is a Señor Toro!"

"People expect something different from that, wearing the green and gold ribbons. No, Señor Balbuena! That buffalo would make people laugh and then get mad and throw things!"

"Señor Gómez. That bull is out of the best cow at Las Astas. He will give a *torero* worth the name a real time. The horns are nice to work. Look at them. Turned in just right."

"With the whiskers and that *rabón?* No, señor! Begging your pardon, it is a cartoon of a bull. Like the funny papers."

"All right, Gómez. Look. Granted I can't sell Rabón to the big boys. They say he's ugly. All right. I say I like the bull. I say he will wear my ribbons very well. You are looking for four Number One Las Astas and— if we must be brutal a moment—you cannot pay what I ask for them. I can only make you this offer. You take the bobtailed bull along with three other Number Ones, and we will do business. I'll give you that number thirty-seven, the pretty one by the wall, to go with Rabón."

"How much?" Gómez asked. He was sweating.

"What do you offer? You know the worth of the bulls."

"Well——"

"For four selected Number Ones I can get above twenty thousand pesos in the Capital this season. What can you afford?"

"Nothing like that, Don Tiburcio."

"All right. You take the bobtail. What can you afford?"

"Fifteen thousand?" Gómez asked.

Tiburcio Balbuena broke into a laugh. "Gómez, the devil sits on the shoulders of hagglers. Take the bulls for sixteen thousand."

"I'll take them."

Gómez had to laugh then himself. "That bug without a tail!"

"That's a bull. You wait and see. Of course the Bellos will be mad. But they won't stay mad. They'll see. The crowd won't laugh long. They'll forget the whiskers."

"You've settled it, Don Tiburcio."

"Good. Now. I want to find Tuerto and have him put your four together so they'll get used to each other and not cause injuries in the pens at Cuenca."

Sitting alone on a bench in the courtyard sunlight, waiting for his host to return, Gómez probed at the work and the worry he saw ahead, promoting the half-born *corrida*. It was hard to wait until he could notify Raúl Fuentes, to get that signature on the dotted line. He wished it were train time. If the Bellos refused *a mano a mano* with the four bulls . . . well . . . that would be the fat pearl in the crown! That would chill him. He was glad when Don Tiburcio walked into the courtyard.

Gómez had not seen the parlor in the big house. He was surprised it was there, when his host opened a door from the patio and asked him in.

"The radio's here; I can't move it because of the antenna attachment into this window," said the *dueño*. "It's about time for the *corrida*. Serafina is going to bring refreshments. Except for the broadcasts, I seldom use this room." He extended his arm as if in explanation, indicating the oil portrait over the mantel and the two large elaborately framed tinted photographs on either side. Gómez understood by the gesture these were portraits of the wife and the sons Balbuena had lost. He nodded, and said nothing.

The rest of the room was a dusty museum of tauromachia. Gómez noticed first the dim crimson and silver wallpaper with its design of garlanded *plazas de toros* and its beribboned bright instruments of the *lidia*. Up toward the ceiling, extending around all four walls, was a papered frieze of matched hand-colored lithographs by Daniel Perea, a hundred scenes of all the pageantry of a nineteenth-century *corrida de toros*. Hanging on the walls were stuffed heads of bulls with engraved plaques under them. The bulls' necks were encircled by braided silken cords of green and gold. There were elaborate *banderillas* with sharp barbs and dusty satin flowers held by ribbons to the wall. Two *picador's* lances and a *picador's* wide beaver hat were fastened above a *torero's* rose silk cape draped on the wall by the scarlet wool of a *muleta* formally folded over the blade of a *matador's* red-handled sword. In the corner by the door was a great silk rosette lettered LAS ASTAS in gold, with wide satin streamers of green and gold hanging from it almost to the floor. A long double line of photographs stretched along one wall, action scenes in bull rings, pictures of bulls, autographed portraits of *toreros*. The radio sat on a scratched old library table by tall stacks of bullfight magazines, and chairs upholstered in worn, torn leather, and a tall brass spittoon.

"Enormously interesting," said Gómez.

"No," said Balbuena. "It's a warehouse. There's no one to tend it. Before the Revolution this room was different. The draperies were all embroidered *toreros'* capes held in place by the polished horn tips of Las Astas bulls. There were Moorish rugs and the furniture was carved with bulls and gilded in Sevilla. On a night in 1915 bandits threw everything into the patio. They had a bonfire. No, Gómez. You see only remains. Some souvenirs accumulated since those days. But all the great figures have been in this room—'Bombita' to 'Manolete'—all of them."

Serafina brought in the *manzanilla* rack, loaded with food on the compartmented wooden plate that formed the base around the tall bottles in the center and the circle of thin cylindrical wineglasses.

"Help yourself, Gómez," said the host, pouring two glasses of *manzanilla* and starting to eat. "It's good."

With the cool wine they ate creamed goat cheese and *tortillas,* spiced mountain ham, cold fried anchovies and little green olives soaked in lime juice, and they poured more wine.

"You know how I saved the *casta* of my brave bulls when the *revolucionarios* took this place, Gómez? Have you heard the story? I loaded my great seed bull, Flamenco, and eight of my best cows in boxes. I armed my people and we hauled those boxes on wagons, fighting, in the night, all the way to my father's old house in the city of Zacalisco. We tended those animals in four bedrooms of that house in town with mattresses hung in the windows to keep out bullets, for fifteen weeks, and by God we kept the *casta!* Your bulls, Señor Gómez, come from animals we fed in my family's bedrooms long ago."

Gómez had another glass of *manzanilla*.

"Ai! What time is it?" Balbuena asked. "We're forgetting the *corrida!*" He turned on the radio. "What station do you get it best in Cuenca?"

"XEW," said Gómez.

"The same out here," said Balbuena, twisting the dial so that the red needle pointed straight up on the kilocycle band. "Don Verdades is not a bad narrator."

When the tubes warmed, a blare of sound blasted out at them.

"Ho!" Don Tiburcio shouted, as if the radio were a horse. He turned the volume down, tuning.

"——and, there go the third pair! Served by Monkey García fast and badly placed," the radio said, intelligibly.

"That's it!" Balbuena said. "We're late. They're nailing *banderillas.*"

The two listeners lit cigarettes and settled back in the leather chairs.

"Luis Bello has the sword and the rag in his hand now, he's coming out. He walks over and looks up to the Judge, and salutes the Authority. He will now make the dedication of his bull, the third bull of the afternoon here at Plaza México."

"We are really late, Don Tiburcio," said Gómez.

"——the dedication is to an individual. Ah! It is to Bello's manager and friend, Señor Raúl Fuentes, sitting in the first row. I beg your pardon, ladies and gentlemen, it is not to Señor Fuentes. The dedication is to a beautiful young lady sitting next to Fuentes. A very beautiful girl. She is smiling. She catches the *matador's* hat when he tosses it up to her. Bello is now walking around the *barrera* to face the bull, which has taken up a position near the *toril*.

"Bello is citing the bull with *muleta* in right hand. There! No, no. The bull did not follow! Bello chopped with the rag from horn to horn. He is having difficulty adjusting. Now he tries again, approaching, for a two-handed pass with the cloth held high. There! But a very mediocre high pass. The bull does not turn for a repeat. Luis Bello is trotting after the bull. There is some whistling from the crowd.

"This is very dull, friends of the radio audience. Bello is angry. The Swordsman of Guerreras has not shown us anything yet this afternoon. He has not shown his usual feeling of domination.

"He is chopping at the horns again, without undue risk. There is more whistling. Loud remarks from the sunny side——"

"Bad!" Eladio Gómez said.

"The bull won't charge past him," Balbuena said. "He's sweating a bull made of lead."

"Friendly listeners," said the voice on the radio, "Luis Bello has just made two inconclusive passes with the right hand, and has continued chopping at the horns. Bello is being intelligent and discreet with a difficult bull, but his work is without spirit. The crowd demands more. Bello has given up the idea of developing a *faena*. He is trying to square the bull for a sword thrust. There is whistling and booing.

"The sword hit bone! It's still in Bello's hand! He's squaring again, mounting the sword. Oh! Bello is having a bad time! He hit solid bone again and the sword bent and whistled into the air. He's disarmed, the *muleta* is hanging on the horns. Somebody has just thrown a cushion. More cushions! Bello is at the *barrera* taking another sword and rag. He's sweating ink."

"Fiasco," Gómez said.

"There!" said the radio voice. "Bello has delivered half the blade. It is on the bias. It is not sufficient to bring the bull down! There is a strong demonstration arming against Bello from the sunny side. There is a scandal of cushions and whistling. Bello is attempting to sever the spinal cord at the base of the skull with a *descabello*. One jab. No good. Another. O ladies and gentleman! The Plaza México is the scene of a near riot."

The roar blurred the broadcaster's voice.

"At last." Balbuena and Gómez heard it with difficulty. "The ninth intent to *descabellar* is successful. The ninth! The bull is dead, the mules are coming out. The demonstration continues. Bello is walking very slowly now, across the ring. His head is down. I see tears on the face of Luis Bello, ladies and gentlemen. Police are making arrests of demonstrators in the stands. The *monos* are clearing the cushions from the ring."

"Holy Mother," Balbuena said. He filled his glass. "But they all have afternoons like that. They all have them. It starts with something very small, and once it's started, the devil builds a monument. Imagine that funnel of fifty thousand screamers pouring their venom down on you, flooding your brain."

A gloom descended upon the impresario of the plaza of Cuenca. Luis Bello would be a savage this week. He would be a son of filth to deal with, signing a contract with a fiasco still in his teeth. He might not come to Cuenca at all. He might go into a slump and be terrible even if he came to Cuenca. Gómez looked up at the bull heads, and bull pictures, the bull business, that surrounded him, and he thought of sixteen thousand *pesos*, and he hated the bulls. He wished he owned a grocery store.

"This is Don Verdades bringing to you a regular Sunday afternoon chronicle of bulls from the Capital of the Republic, sent to you for your listening pleasure over radio station XEW."

It happened suddenly during the fourth bull. Skinny Salazar had been the soul of caution, the competent old craftsman on tired legs, working his last animal of the afternoon, for money. The glory for Juan Salazar was past and no longer necessary to him; Don Verdades droned the period of the cavalry, the period of the sticks, and now, the period of the blade. Salazar was making a pass with the sword and *muleta* in his right hand, a pass he had made ten thousand times, when the bull got him.

The tone of Don Verdades's voice jerked Gómez and Balbuena up in their chairs.

"Sacred Name, the bull has Salazar! Ahh! Ai ai ai! Oh, friends! Ai!" The voice was silent. The static popped and crackled. Balbuena jumped up and turned the volume knob, waiting, with a wrinkle like a gash between his brows, with the static crashing.

"Ladies and gentlemen," the voice resumed, trying to control itself. "Friends. This is Don Verdades at the Plaza México. I will try to recount the tragedy just witnessed by the plaza. Juan Salazar has been gored, horribly gored, by the fourth bull of the afternoon. They are carrying Juan to the infirmary. His blood stains the sand, stains his clothes. He appears unconscious.

"Ladies and gentlemen. Salazar was intending a low pass with the right. It is impossible for me to say at this moment the reason for what occurred: the bull cut in from his charge and the right horn caught Salazar in the right thigh, tossing him. Before intervention was possible, the horn found Salazar again on the ground, and again. At least ten capes were at the rescue. It was very confused. I believe Salazar's swordhandler pulled him from under the bull while a cape was over the beast's face. Someone had the bull by the tail, twisting. It is impossible to give details at this time, ladies and gentlemen. Salazar is now in the infirmary. This announcer will give you full word from the operating room at the earliest possible moment. Stay tuned to Don Verdades, XEW."

Balbuena and Gómez were standing, looking at each other.

"Luis Bello," continued the radio, "whose cape was prominent in the rescue, Luis Bello has *muleta* and sword, is walking out to kill the Salazar bull. The bull has a wet horn, ladies and gentlemen. The horn is red. Bello is squaring, mounting the blade. There it is! Now we have the great Swordsman of Guerreras! A tremendous lunge in over the horns, ladies and gentlemen. An enormous *volapié* by Luis Bello! A revenge by Luis Bello. The bull is dead! A terrible drama. Bello stands over the beast. Bello has thrown the *muleta* on the ground; he is walking to the *barrera*, wiping the blood of the bull from his sword hand."

The voice of Don Verdades was hoarse and tired as it came with the static to the two waiting listeners at Las Astas. It recounted without excitement the regular progress of the fifth bull toward death at the hand of Luis Bello before an unresponsive, almost silent plaza.

"The crowd is not seeing the ring. The crowd is imagining a white room under the plaza. It is waiting for word from under the bright lights in the white room," said Don Verdades.

Young Chato Palacios was placing a pair of *banderillas* on the last bull of the afternoon, his bull, when the word came.

"Attention! Attention, all Mexico. Juan Salazar, beloved veteran matador of Teotihuacan, is dead. He died in the infirmary of the Plaza México in the Capital of the Republic approximately three minutes ago, as a result of wounds suffered at the horns of a bull in this afternoon's *corrida*, reported to you by Don Verdades, radio station XEW. The name of another glorious martyr is now inscribed on the golden catafalque of the brave festival! Juan Salazar is dead. The nation's heart mourns. Rest in Peace, Juan Salazar, *torero*."

The loud-speakers at the Plaza México boomed and rattled above the voice of Don Verdades on the radio.

The crowd was not interested in watching Chato Palacios finally kill his last bull on the day of his doctorate, in the center of the world.

"I've got to get the train tonight," Eladio Gómez said to his host. "The train to Mexico, not Cuenca!"

"We'll get you to Cienleguas in time. I think I'll go with you, Gómez. To pay my respects to the remains. Salazar sat in this room many times. I didn't think the bulls would ever get him. He wasn't the type. The public will make him a hero now for a couple of days while they bury him, after making him a cynic while he lived, past his day. Dying on the way down."

"I'm wondering about Luis Bello," Gómez said. "My *corrida*."

The National Fiesta

by MANUEL MACHADO

Manuel Machado, born 1875, Sevillian poet who found in the deep song of Andalusia inspiration and musical feeling. Although he studied in Paris and began his career under French influence, the call of his native land was too strong and he achieved a true Spanish folk style. The *fiesta brava* figured in several works but "La Fiesta Nacional, Red and Black," 1906, is one of the popular poems in tauromachian literature. Former director of the Madrid Museum and Library, a member of the Spanish Academy, his position is high in the lyric writings of modern Spain.

A trumpet call
Sounds clear
   and piercing,
Rends the air
Like a quivering
   blade.
Hoarse beat of drums.
The bull charges
Into the arena,
Heaves, and rumbles . . .
Where unfolds and crackles
A *capote* of percale.

He lunges
And, bellowing,
Crashes down
The horse and horseman.
Thus begins
The unique
   spectacle of Spain.

The glittering festival of courage,
Terror, and delight,
Of this proud and ancient people . . .
Gold and silk and blood and sun!

II

In the folds of the mantle,
And the bull in circling menace.
He moves with southern grace
And classical disdain,
A tapestry of death
Beneath the shining sky.

Elegant,
Valiant,
And a casual
Air of skill,
He ignores
The avalanche
And risks
His life
At will.

III

A mass
Of leather and splinters,
Of trembling forms
Forlorn . . .
A crash
Of broken shoulders,
Costumes torn
And slashed to pieces . . .
Blood on the earth . . .
A cloud of dust, a cry . . .
Olé!

On the red sand
Of blood and sun
In the welter
Of confusion,
Silk and fringes,
Steel and leather,
Stir the horse and picador,
And to the quaking mountain
Drives the bull;

In fire and frenzy
Aims his horn
Against the reddened form.

And encounters,
In his plunging,
Nothing . . . but the border of a cape,
A figure who evades him
Scoffing at his rage,
Who weaves and turns serenely,
Draping from his arm
The shining silk. Step by step
The bull seeks blindly,
Mesmerized,
Until he stops, exhausted.
Horn against the reddened form.

Peace is a pond
Of black and evil blood,
And those cold and yellow teeth.
A hoe, a basket of earth,
And that mound
Of spangled costume,
Lying quiet by the silent horse
In the arena.

IV

Lithe and gay, a willow,
Without losing the line—
Nothing but grace
Against fury—
Walking,
Posing,
Rhythmically,
A special way,
Of delicate daring . . .
He comes,
He faces,
And pauses—
Arms lifted—
And, then,
Above the horns,
And over the heart,
Banderillas

Miraculously hanging . . .
The man spins,
Lithe and gay, a willow,
Without losing the line.

V

Twenty thousand hearts
Throb in the hot and shining
Silence. Bravo!
A soft sound,
The mournful clack
   of *banderillas*
On his back,
Around his neck
The warm blood
Makes a bright cravat.
On one side, under
The red flag, the bull
Hooks vainly
Into eddies of sand . . .
On the other side
A brown face smiles.

And then,
In the three times
Of natural passes,
He moves his arms,
Enveloped in gold,
With tranquil poise
And stateliness.
Twenty thousand throats,
As one, scream out—
An unexpected horn thrust
Makes the elegance
A nightmare.
And there
Against the barrier
Is something
That moves . . . Above
Are faces of terror.
In flashes of scarlet
And tinsel, the bull tosses
High on his horns
A tragical doll.

VI

Yonder the music divine,
The Giralda, which is all of Seville,
The bulls, the grace and gaiety.
Talk is of a lovely lady
Who is waiting . . . thought
Of lemon and orange blooms,
And fragrant cane,
With pleasant rhythm
Of a folk song's magic . . .
To a vague and lusting
Gloom.
The whips crack,
Arousing the mules
For their race, to tinkling bells,
Across the sand.
While the people
Dry their foreheads
Wet with sweat,
And in their breasts
The heavy heart-beats;
Pound in time to Sevillian music;
Across the sand a furrow
Black and scarlet trails the body of the bull.
And on his horn still hangs
A golden spangle . . .
Then the music, light, and tumult
Disappear,
And at the stroke
Of a phantom baton,
All movement ceases.

VII

An endless sigh, the haunting afternoon,
Swells in the breast of the multitude.
The sun dims down.
The spectacle of red and gold is over.
There is left
Only a shadow
On the yellow, blood-stained sand.

Excerpt from The Spanish Temper

by V. S. PRITCHETT

V. S. Pritchett is a noted British novelist, journalist and critic. His singularly evocative and thoughtful book, *The Spanish Temper,* was published in 1954. He has known Spain since the 1920's. The following excerpts are from a chapter in this recent book. It is more than an analysis of bullfighting by a distinguished writer. His observations are interesting as he places in focus the form of British institutions and conventions as contrasted with the Spanish way of life.

The high moment of Seville is at Easter, when, after a week of the most ornate and pagan processions in Europe, in an atmosphere of theatrical piety and picturesque remorse, the Fair begins and the Andalusian riders in their high hats and leather trouser-facings go by. This is the moment of street parties, pride and ceremony, the supreme moment of display for the women of the city. There is a heavy, torpid beauty. And it is the time of the great bullfights.

Not all the bull rings of Spain are fine. Many of them rise like great red gasworks outside the cities, but the bull ring in Seville by the wide slow river is one of the prettiest in Spain. Seville is the city of the bull. The very day when when Fernando VII closed the university in Seville, he opened a school for bullfighters there!—a characteristic gesture of Spanish reaction. Outside the city are the estates where the fighting bulls are bred. In any Spanish town it is common to see boys playing at bullfighting. One sees them waving their shirts at dogs, pretending they are bulls, and the thing to notice is that they are neither playing nor fighting in any violent sense, but going through the stances, the passes, the exhibitions of the national ritual. Outside Seville it is common, at some noisy fair, for someone to shout out: "The bulls!" and for the boys to race down the hill, clamber over the stone walls, and jump down among the bulls to drive them away or to bait them. There is a respect for the bulls. There is admiration of them, but there is no fear, and indeed, in their herds, the bulls are not dangerous. All the same, the Spaniards never lack the courage to make the heroic gesture. The bull is admired, almost worshipped, as the horse is in Ireland. He is admired because he is great and capable of fury, and the Spaniard requires that furious force against which to display his singularity—the most precious of his possessions—and his courage. Always an extremist, he likes to test his courage and his whole personality to the utmost, and he has so contrived the phases of the bullfight that each one has the crisis of decorative perfection that he loves.

Bullfighting is not a sport, and it is therefore not a cruel sport. It is a ritual and a ceremony. It is primitive, barbarous, possibly religious in its remote origin, a descendant of the gladiatorial contest and the mediaeval tournament. There are ugly moments in the bullfight, for there are good and bad fights; but since it is conducted in hot blood and in an atmosphere where the swell of great emotion is natural, the killing of the bull is not a sadistic performance; nor does it awaken, I think, cold sadistic emotions in the audience. Their senses are stirred by danger, for the wounding or killing of the bullfighter himself has often occurred. About this one can only say that the Spaniards retain something primitive in their character which was possibly fostered by the autos-da-fe of the Inquisition. Here indeed a terrible and gloating sadism was displayed by the public, sanctified by the Church and approved by the rulers. The Spaniards have strong stomachs. They do not flinch when the blood gushes out of the bull's mouth as he goes down heavily to his death, but in their eyes one sees that proud, frightening brillance of the conqueror who has emerged from great emotion, who is elated by victory and satisfied by performance. Spanish religious art and the work of Goya reveal a people who do not shy from strong feeling or from the tragedies that fall upon the human body. Above all, they are caught by the drama and the supreme dramatic moment. Undoubtedly there is something savage in it. All historians and the soldiers who have fought against them in the great ages have mentioned the lack of all fear of death in the Spaniards, their stoical indifference to it; all have mentioned the *"furia española."* We know that the Civil War was fought without remorse or quarter, and that indeed the bull rings and vacant lots of the Spanish towns were the scenes of atrocious mass executions. The barbarian is strong in the Spanish people.

The most damaging criticism of the Spanish taste for bullfighting is rather different: the bullfight suffers from the monotony of sacrifices, and it is one more example of the peculiar addiction to the repetitive and monotonous in the Spanish nature. Many foreigners who have known Spain well have noted this taste for monotony. The drama of the bullfight lies within the frame of a foregone conclusion: whatever danger the bullfighter may be in, whatever may be his fate, the fate of the bull is certain. This fact alone removes the bullfight from the complete uncertainty of a sport. It is never certain that the fox will be killed or the boxer knocked out. Inevitably, an English writer is swayed a little by the passionate feeling for animals in England, and will forget the extreme danger to the man. He will forget his bearbaiting and cockfighting past; but even if he does not, and argues that his civilization has come out of that brutal phase, he will fail to notice that although Spain often looks like a modern country, it is not. The life of Spanish cities runs much closer to what life was like in England in the seventeenth century; indeed, if one wants to imagine the habits of London life in the time of Defoe, one cannot do better than study Madrid or Seville.

Logically the Englishman ought to protest against the annual casualties in horse-racing and the hunting field, in a monstrous race like the Grand National, where fine horses are killed every year. We ought to see that in the bullfighter the danger is to the man. A number of excellent bullfighters have died in the ring, for the risk is supreme. In the seventeenth century, when the bullfight was conducted by the aristocracy—under more danger-ous conditions than are seen today—the Pope tried to stop the fights be-cause of the great number of deaths. In northern countries, in the course of the refinement of our civilization, we have developed a peculiar perver-sion: better that a man should be killed than a poor helpless bull! Not all the hypocrisies are one-sided in this foolish controversy: the Spaniards grimly reply that they need no Society for the Prevention of Cruelty to Children in Spain. In fact, they have such societies in the religious orders. The fatalistic neglect of poor children in the great cities is hardly touched by charity.

Our final emotion in the bullfight is not with the bull, which was bred to fight and would, in any case, have gone to the slaughterhouse, but rests upon the triumphant fighter who has not only pitted his wits against a sav-age animal and outdone him, but who has done this with the skill, the dec-orative grace and panache of the artist. It is a male triumph, achieved by courage, art and obedience to traditional rules.

But the horses? This is a question which has been explained and argued many times since Hemingway became the first Anglo-Saxon apologist of the bullfight. To most people who are sensitive to spectacle and are capable of pleasure in strong feeling, the sight of these wretched nags blindfolded and weighed down by absurd cushions is grotesque. Before this protection six thousand horses were killed every year. They creak stiffly in like old people, ghastly in their bandaged eyes, repellent in their suggestion of a public hypocrisy. If the bull is killed in hot blood and at the supreme moment of his raging life, the horse is generally injured, and though he might have gone to the knackers the day before, his last moments are ones of terror. For Hemingway, the horse introduced the grotesque note, the necessary element of parody in the spectacle, the counterpoise of low comedy and calamity of the tragic intention of the ritual, for the *picador* is traditionally an absurd and clumsy fellow, the poor man of the ring. This is an ingeni-ous literary argument; when we consult our reactions at the time we do not find that they confirm Hemingway's definition. Is it really low comedy such as Shakespeare pushed into his tragedies to catch the attention of the low audience? The elegance of the ritual is broken up by these ghastly buffoons, who are lifted up bodily by the enormous shoulders of the charging bull. Even when we are told by sound authorities that horses are indispensable, for only a rider has the reach, the strength, and the position for paralyzing the formidable neck muscles of the bull, and that, until he does that, the man on foot has no chance of handling the beast—even when we know this, we squirm at the sight of the pitiful and absurd cavalcade, which now looks like the man-horse of the comic circus. And for myself, Hemingway makes the great error of thinking this comic even in the macabre sense. It is merely ghastly, a mess; and now that the horses are cushioned, a cruel and hypocritical mess. Yet Hemingway has this on his side; the Spanish devotees of the bullfight—the aficionados—have never objected to the horses, cushioned or uncushioned: the mass of Spaniards have a rage for tradition; and the bullfighting public is "the people" par excellence.

In the last thirty years a puritan opposition to the bullfight has grown up in Spain. It began with the intellectuals who refused to have anything to do with the fights, and spread especially among the Left-wing groups. The typical Left-wing, anticlerical professor of the Spanish revival in the 1920's and early '30's would say: "The Jesuits told us to go to as many bullfights as we liked, but to avoid the theatre where one picks up dangerous ideas." The liberals and socialists, those engaged in educational, social, and religious reform, thought of the bullfight as the opium of the people.

But when Hemingway wrote *Death in the Afternoon* in 1932 and recorded so intimately both the facts and the gossip of the bullfighters' bars, he noted that the point of decadence had been reached. In "Manolete"—who was killed and has become a kind of saint to the very emotional following of the bullfight—and in the strange, twisted, intellectual revolutionary, Belmonte, the art (Hemingway thought) had reached a refinement too great for the spectacle. And as the art changed, so—or people complain—the bulls are smaller, faster, but not so furious as they used to be. In Madrid today one hears that the days of the great bullfighters are gone.

In the last twenty years very much has been written about the decadence of the art. The public complains that the bulls are fought too young, before their terrible horns have spread wide. There are too many small fast bulls, not enough ferocious monsters. I have seen many dull and monotonous bullfights. A foreigner who is not a fan cannot judge these public criticisms. He can only record that many people regard this period as a poor one and, like so many enthusiasts, think the great bullfights took place in their youth.

368   **Excerpt from "The Spanish Temper"**

"Papa" Goes to the Fights

by ROBERT RUARK

Robert Ruark is one of the versatile writing men of our time. He is a newspaper columnist with a following of millions. He is a satirist in fiction, with books to prove it. He is a novelist of great power, demonstrated in *Something of Value,* a realistic sensation on the Mau Mau in Africa. He is a famous hunter of all kinds of game. He is an artist, and illustrated his book on hunting in Africa, *Horn of the Hunter.* A short essay by Ruark, who now lives in Spain, and his first bullfight drawing are in this book.

PAMPLONA, SPAIN—You will pardon a small boy's enthusiasm for a current event, but the other day I sat with Ernest Hemingway to watch a bull-fight in the same town he immortalized in the best book he ever wrote, called *The Sun Also Rises,* a quarter-century ago.

This was at the fiesta of San Fermín, where they let the bulls run loose in the streets, clobbering the citizens at an alarming rate, and where, for a week, all the outriding Basques come in to get fearfully drunk and dance in the streets. When Papa did his book about it, all those years ago, there was a hell of a bullfighter named "Niño de la Palma" around, a slim brave boy who got made into the hero of Papa's book.

The slim, brave boy is no longer slim, and no longer brave, but he is around today as the manager of the best and bravest *torero* in Spain, a kid called Antonio Ordóñez. I sat with the *gran maestro* while we watched Ordóñez, who, as ungainly in build as Yogi Berra, is such a miracle of grace that Hemingway says he is as good or better than his father when his father had youth and grace and courage.

I wouldn't know, really. All I know is that this kid was so good the judges let him cut two ears on his first bull, and one on the second. He killed the second by holding a sword in a hand that had been ripped wide open by an accident on his first attempt to kill his second bull, which he had handled marvelously up to the killing. Then his hand slipped on the sword, wounding him badly. But he still took the *estoque* in the bleeding hand and laid the blade into the bull, literally pinning him to the sand. Then he went and had his arm put into a sling.

Racing the bulls through the streets of Pamplona at dawn

This at a time in Spain when they have let the horns grow back onto the bulls, and when most of the *toreros* are either awkward or cowardly or a bad combination of both, was a fresh and lovely sight—a man who knows his business from cape to *muleta* to sword, and who is not afraid of any of the media. There has been very little good bullfighting in Spain since they quit sawing the horns off the bulls. The *picadors* do most of the killing and early cape work is almost unknown.

Please do not blame me too much for the technicality. I am writing this piece for Rex Smith, who was supposed to come over with us this year, and who couldn't. He went to Mexico instead, so I got to tell him what I and Papa saw in Pamplona. End of personal message to R. Smith.

What I started out to say was that this was a thrill, for me, to sit at this festival I had memorized as a kid, with the guy that made it worth memorizing. The old gentleman is as white as an alp, but he's still got his zing, and he is still the gran maestro of the bull business in Spain. The autograph hunters, after all this time, and after his strong stand on the wrong side —the losing side—in the revolution, still pulled at his shirttails. And I got to listen to some talk about what it was like then and what it's like now. Everybody ought to have one hero, whether it's DiMaggio or Hemingway.

A bull killer named Córdoba dedicated a bull to Mr. Hemingway. He sent up the cape and we spread it on the *barrera* in front of us. Then he flipped up his hat, and we held that in our laps as well. Then Córdoba, whose first name is Jesús, went out and performed very badly with the bull. We had a wineskin along and took a slug out of it, and hoped for something better on the second bull.

Señor Jesús Córdoba was no better with the second bull, because this was a very bad bull indeed, unwilling to fight and anxious to leave. There was a small scattering of cushions and a conglomeration of hisses to greet Señor Córdoba's second effort at distinction in the *corrida*. Mr. Hemingway looked sadly at his dedicating friend, and even more sadly at me. He took a large bite out of the wineskin, and spoke.

"There is nothing we can do for our friend, now," he said. "Except not to spill any wine on his cape."

It seemed a fitting accolade.

Convert

by TOMASITO BORRÁS

Tomasito Borrás, young writing wonder of *España Nueva,* anti-toros, went to a *corrida* May 12, 1912, and wrote about his conversion in the publication.

Defense of a bullfighter named "el Gallo" (older brother of Joselito, who was also called "Gallito"). Rafael Gómez is elegance in the service of instinct. Fine art embellishing the attitude. "Gallo" is neither beautiful nor arrogant like "Machaquito," nor like Fuentes in harmonic movement. "Gallo" is plastic. This *torero* is a gypsy, and, therefore, has that aloof grace that is a part of the gypsy figure's natural purity and line. The plasticity of "Gallo" consists of his graceful walk and posture of a svelt body.

The head of Rafael is worthy of a painting by Lucas, who painted the great Montes. Perhaps Rafael has appeared in the pages of Frank Harris?

He has oblique, haughty eyes of penetrating expression and are similar to the ingenuousness and melancholy on the faces of Pharaohs.

This *torero* possesses the undulating rhythm of the cape. His passes create living visions enfolded and caressed in the silk. . . . Rafael is a true example of the fiesta. To accomplish this performance, one must blend the serene lines of statuary with a momentary movement. That is, when the danger is imminent, the *torero,* moving the cape in defense, avoids peril, but maintains a posture in graceful repose that is living sculpture.

"Gallo," also, is a perfect *torero* because he fights very well and very badly. The fiesta of the bulls is essentially passion. Rafael creates great enthusiasm or rage. The *torero* who can create passionate response is the ideal *torero.*

The Diamond in the Horn

by JOSÉ MARÍA CRUZ

José María Cruz is a traveled and gifted Spanish writer whom I have known for many years as a friend of the spectacle. This selection, "The Diamond in the Horn," is from his novel, *The Duke of Death,* which exposes the condition that existed for a while when the blunting of the horns of fighting bulls was current in Spain, before the practice was outlawed.

His face, silhouetted against a battlement of the castle had the lines of a falcon. Hooded eyes moved possessively over the valley toward Toledo, but his gaze was too soft to be predatory. It was an expression of old and emphatic faith in a hard land under a high sky. The duke moved into the great hall with the measured steps that were a mark of ancestors who long had walked in armor. Twilight over Castile lit the tapestries designed by that irreverent Aragonés, Goya. But the then duke had his reasons for disliking the Royal Household of Charles IV, and especially the Queen's favorite Godoy, who had succeeded in putting through a brief abolition of bullfighting in 1805. He even had the castle's hall modernized as a background for the tapestries. He felt that Goya was right in crucifying the royal family on canvas, because the King could not master his own household nor outwit that French upstart, Napoleon.

But none of these Kings were on the mind of the Duke of Eda, as he opened a high western window that overlooked a winding silver road up the green valley to the castle, now covered with the grey and crimson shadows of a setting sun on ancient stone. He saw the car moving in expensive majesty around the curves, and watched the smooth progress of the Twentieth Century beauty with admiration. He prided himself on his adjustment to his age, over fifty, and his time. He granted the world the right to material improvements, but he was a stern champion of inherited standards of human behavior. He knew he would have to test his faith very shortly as he reached for the bell-rope that caused a very efficient electric light to flash on a switchboard in the servant's quarters. This meant that the visitor was to be sent directly to his study. The duke went in to wait.

The study was a combined office and small library. The available space on the walls was covered with mounted bulls' heads, art of bullfight scenes by Goya, Lucas, Doré, and Domingo. The upside down crescent, the Eda brand, was visible in some of the pictures. It had been devised from an incident in the family history, when an ancestor had toppled a Moorish prince in combat.

The duke stretched his slim legs in an easy chair for a brief rest before the arrival of his guest. His glance rested on the coat-of-arms over the door. Its motto, "honor is the best companion," traced through his mind as he dozed fitfully. A decision must be made tonight.

The door opened and Gregorio Gómez entered. He was large and heavy but dressed in the most meticulous Spanish imitation of English tailoring and haberdashery. As the two men shook hands it would have been possible for an observer to have thought of a bull and a *matador*. The mighty Gómez, impresario of ten bull rings, and the slender duke, owner of one of the greatest ranches for fighting bulls in Spain. They were old friends.

"Ah, Jaime," said Gómez, "it's been weeks that I have tried to reach you."

"How are you, Gregorio?" The duke chuckled, "But why should I ask, you look as healthy as a fighting bull, to coin an expression."

"I'm all right, Jaime, but I'm in trouble, and I've been trying to talk with you."

"I have been away, Gregorio. Away up in the recesses of my soul, and not available for mundane matters."

"Always with a joke, Jaime. But I'm glad you are back. I really have problems."

"Well, before the problems . . . Ah, here is old Pablo with the ingredients." The butler placed the decanter of *manzanilla* with two *chatos*, slim wine glasses, on the table.

The duke poured the pale gold, cool wine. "*Salud, pesetas, y amor,* Gregorio."

"I'll take the *salud* and *pesetas*, Jaime, but *amor*, I must confess is mostly memory."

"You really are in a sad state of mind, Gregorio, for a man in his frolicsome fifties, too!"

"My friend, the reason I am here makes me older just to think of it."

"Yes, I know, Gregorio. Let's get on with it then."

"All right, Jaime. You see, it is now about two months before the bullfight season begins. And you have not sold a *corrida* of your bulls."

"Yes, I know."

"And you know why, too."

"Yes, I know why."

"And you sold very few *corridas* last year."

"Very few. Six."

"Both you and I know that you are one of the few ranchers who depend to a large extent on that income."

"Yes, Gregorio."

"Then why don't you set up a little barber-shop on the ranch?"

"Don't use that word, Gregorio."

"Why not? Let me use just a few words from one old friend to another. I know that it is a delicate subject. I know that you go to very few fights recently. . . ."

"How can I go to that emasculated fiesta . . . to see those boys prancing around like ballet dancers . . . with not a care in the world . . . no danger . . . no heroic beauty . . . and the disgrace of the supreme moment of truth, killing those dehorned cattle . . . it's worse than slaughterhouse killing." The duke paused for breath. "The fiesta of the bulls is dead, Gregorio."

"The fiesta is not dead, Jaime," protested Gómez. "Times have changed. The people want these fancy young fighters. They do not want to see them killed. The bulls are still dangerous, even if they are slightly smaller, and the tips of their horns are altered a little."

"A little! Listen to the man! The impresario! This is not my old friend, Gregorio Gómez. This is that monopolist of arenas! This is that destroyer of Spain's own spectacle! This is a stranger in my house!"

"No, no stranger in your house. This is your friend, Jaime. Do you know that the people are saying you are no friend of the fiesta? Do you know what they call you?"

"What who calls me?"

"The people call you the Duke of Death."

"What people?"

"The people who want to see the Eda bulls fought, whose ancestors for generations have seen Eda bulls fought by the greatest *matadors* to the glory of the Eda brand. There may be no Belmontes and Joselitos today, but they want to see the Dominguíns, the Dos Santos, the Manolo González, and some of the others. You do not have to shave all your bulls, merely some *corridas,* the biggest ones. A lot of fine ranch owners recognize the practice. Even those not dependent on their ranches."

"Again you bring up an unworthy subject. I know I have some financial problems. But it is not polite of you to threaten me."

"I am not trying to threaten you. I am trying to help you. As you well know, the bulls are still dangerous."

"They are not the same animals at all, Gregorio. I should not have to repeat this to you. But when you take that 'diamond' off the end of the horn you have removed the point nature placed there for its weapon. The tiny core of flint-like hardness in the tip has its purpose to catch on any surface and lead the horn to its deadly penetration. That is why the diamond in the horn is vital to the completeness of the mighty beast, the fighting bull."

"I know. But think of the bullfighters we have."

"That's only another way of saying it is people like you who have created the ones we have. And why? Tell me that, Gregorio."

"Well, I suppose we should blame Belmonte. . . ."

"What are you saying. Are you out of your mind? Blame Juan, for what?" The duke almost lost his temper.

"It's maybe a round-about story."

"It's perhaps a figment of your disordered imagination. First, they call me the Duke of Death because I will not dehorn my bulls for a lot of ballet dancing *matadors*. Now you blame it all on Belmonte. That's like charging Palestrina with being the ancestor of that popular jazz almost fresh out of the jungle, where improvisation spreads its clatter around musical ignorance, and rhythmic license replaces liberty. Look at the gesticulations of these dancing savages. Where is majesty of the solemn ritual, fear disciplined by beauty, courage blending the fugues of emotion into a slow processional hymn of man's dignity in the face of death? I do not hear the stupid vituperations of the rabble. Duke of Death? Indeed? Duke of Tradition! Yes! We must keep inviolate the ancient destiny of the Spanish heart and the Spanish heritage. Though our days of empire are over, and we are not trying to impose our way of life on others, let us live true to ourselves." The duke sank back in his chair, exhausted by his deep feelings. He glared at Gómez.

"I really believe you do not know you are to blame, Gregorio," he muttered. "You think the public wants a circus not a serious spectacle. You are wrong. If you go on, one day you will find that the spectacle has left the arena to a rigadoon of acrobatic dolls . . . for tourists."

"I still think Belmonte is to blame," Gómez muttered stubbornly. "He brought the *matador* into positions nobody had ever known before, created a rhythm that had never existed before, and inspired a fanatic loyalty in his partisans. Thereafter everybody tried to improve on the impossible, either by bravery or by guile. This finally ended in the situation today. Incredible tricks of geometry; analyzing the range of the bull's eyesight and working in his frontal blind spots; profiling with the thinness of the body no target compared to that fluttering *muleta* no matter how little exposed; scientific curves and angles of careful but exciting design. Nowadays the *muleta faenas* could be plotted by algebraic signs and symbols. The public is aware of all this complicated pattern and they pay for it."

"But you are taking the easy way, Gregorio, and it will end in destruction. The fiesta of our history will disappear. You will be rich, but you will have destroyed the national spectacle. It seems strange that a bullfighter should be the first to rise against the crime—not the press—not the ranchers—not the public—but Antonio Bienvenida, who deserves a place in history, beyond the fact that he is a fine *matador* and probably the best of the Bienvenida dynasty. Others will follow. They will hate him for awhile, but they will follow and he will be a savior."

"I don't know," Gómez murmured.

"You mean you are concerned about your investment, Gregorio?"

"No, I'm not interested in money that much, Jaime. You understand that. I am a true believer in the fiesta. I want to give the public fine bulls

La Punta bulls have Eda blood

and fine *matadors*. We cannot have one without the other. I realize that. But I just don't know." Gómez was morose. He saw no possibility of getting Eda bulls that were not complete.

"I'll tell you how we can find out, Gregorio."

"How?" asked Gómez disconsolately.

"Well, my friends Pepe Madrazo and Toño Algara from Mexico are here now. Pepe is looking for some fresh blood for his La Punta ranch. We are going to see what can be done about government permissions on a seed bull. You know, it is prohibited to export now. Since Pepe has a trace of our blood in his fine strain, I would like to help him. I shall give out a press interview tomorrow that I have talked with Pepe, and during the interview I shall talk about my plans for this season. I shall say that no Eda bull will have its horns mutilated in any way. Somebody has to maintain the vigor of the blood lines. The *matadors* have an obligation to the characteristics of the brave bulls, not dehorned cattle. There are the wise and slow Castilian bulls that twist and turn; the nervous, fast and strong bulls of Narvarre; the heavy Aragon animals that need to be fought close and sure; the noble and smooth beasts of Andalusia with the slow and solemn attack of great power. Despite the blending into many types from the original strains, it is the duty of the ranchers to keep their brands above reproach. I am asking other ranchers to join me in a national protest. And I have signed with you for ten *corridas* of the finest full-grown animals."

"But I haven't . . ."

"No, I know you haven't. But I believe we shall have volunteers from the brave *matadors* and the others will be afraid not to come along, or they will retire." He laughed coldly. "And you do not have to risk anything. If you fail to sell to the public any or all of the *corridas,* you are under no obligation to me."

"I can't help myself. I don't know whether I can help you. But I'll go along."

Gómez slouched his heavy shoulders. "You are a wonderful, arrogant, impossible, narrow-minded man. But you are also a high-minded man. I don't know what is going to happen to you. But whatever happens will also happen to Spain." He rose to go.

"Adios, my friend," he bowed slightly.

"Go with God," the duke replied, as he placed an arm on his friend's shoulder.

Gómez straightened with pride as he walked out the door.

The duke pulled aside the brocade hanging of the window and watched the long automobile move noiselessly into the night. Moonlight gleamed on its sleek metallic form.

"The only thing that shines like that is armor," mused the duke to himself. His right hand strayed to the horn of a mounted bull's head. He clasped it tightly, unconsciously, until he felt a sharp prick of pain. It was as if a needle had broken the skin on his thumb.

"Go with God, you modern *caballero.*" He smiled as he turned off the light. Toledo outlined on its height beyond the low hills. The city lights silhouetted the Alcázar from which an emperor once ruled a realm that penetrated the regions of the known world.

"There are stones in these foundations laid by the Romans. I think I shall stay here awhile this night and not think of them as battlements." The duke sat on the rough and time-worn rocks, carefully shielding his injured hand with a handkerchief of manila silk. On the slope below were the malevolent shadows of the bulls of Eda, complete with lethal horns.

Finale

by *FEDERICO M. ALCAZAR,*

a famous writer on bullfighting, in *Madrid,* June 18, 1947

To fight bulls—anybody fights bulls. The cowboys fight in handling the animals on the ranch, and they are not toreros. *To stand close—anybody gets close to the bulls. Either the man gets close or the bull gets close, and each has equal effect on the nerves of the public. The difficult thing is to fight with art, because art is a position of privilege. And more difficult than fighting is to fight with grace, and grace is reserved for the select few. Technic is very estimable, so is knowledge of the bulls, and so is valor. But bullfighting interpreted technically, bravely, is only a quality that needs nothing more than artisan expertness, and a small effort of will power to stand in front of the bulls. And this strength . . . (1) employed in remaining still, cold and inarticulate as a stick, (2) or in running, trotting, jumping or climbing over the bulls . . . seems to me violent, mannered, anti-natural, and inartistic. The bullfighting of "eat 'em alive" or "bring on the bull" is an ugly formula. Anything that is a part of bullfighting must be done with art first and elegance second. As Belmonte performed. Or Pepe Luis Vázquez: as if the bulls were made of crystal and they should not be broken.*

Pepe Luis Vázquez

Glossary

The bullfight terms in this book, as a rule, are generally known or explained in the text. However, this brief glossary is presented for clarification of certain words.

Afición	The informed bullfighting public.
Aficionado	Enthusiastic and understanding fan.
Al Alimón	Social and safe pass when two persons hold opposite ends of cape and bull is guided between them.
Alguacil	Ceremonial horseman who heads bullfighters' entry parade.
Alternativa	Ceremony where the killer of young or imperfect bulls becomes officially a killer of the full-fledged fighting bull.
Asta	Another word for horn of the bull.
Ayudado	Any pass where the *muleta* is spread or aided by the sword.
Banderilla	Barbed wand.
Banderillero	A bullfighter who helps with cape work and places *banderillas* for the matador.
Barrera	Red wooden fence that encloses the bull ring, also first rows of seats in the amphitheatre.
Brindis	Dedication.
Burladero	Planked shield in front of the openings in bull-ring fences.
Capote de brega	Fighting or working cape.
Capote de paseo	Dress cape for ceremonial entry.
Cogida	The wounding of the man by the bull.

Cola	Tail.
Coleta	Short artificial pigtail, formerly of growing hair to which was attached the *moña,* a round decoration that came from the original decorative knot gathering long hair in the old-time net, or *redecilla.*
Cornada	Horn wound that penetrates the skin.
Corrida de novillos toros	Bullfight with young or defective animals.
Corrida de toros	General meaning is a Spanish bullfight.
Cuadrilla	The staff or team of bullfighters working with a matador.
Cuarteo	Manner of placing *banderillas,* quarter-circling across the bull's charge.
Diestro	Term for matador.
Divisa	Colors of the bull's breeding ranch.
Dueño	Owner, the boss.
Duro	Silver five-peseta piece about the size of a silver dollar.
Empresa	Organization that promotes bullfights in any ring.
Espada	Sword, and also a term used for the matador.
Estocada	Sword thrust.
Estribo	Sort of ledge of wood around the inside of the ring which aids the bullfighter in vaulting the fence if in immediate danger.
Faena	The manipulations of the *muleta* in the final phase of the fight.
Farol	A cape pass in which the fighter circles the cape over his head. It is called an *afarolado* when done with the *muleta.*
Fiesta	Celebration or festival.
Fiesta brava	The exciting spectacle of the bulls.
Fiesta de los toros	Bullfight.
Ganadería	Fighting bull ranch.
Ganadero	Fighting bull rancher.
Hora de Verdad	The moment of truth, death.

Izquierda	Left.
Lidia	The bullfight, *toro de lidia* fighting bull.
Lidiar	To fight.
Manola	A Madrid girl-about-town.
Matador de novillos toros	A killer of young or imperfect bulls.
Matador de toros	An officially recognized killer of full-grown selected bulls.
Mona	Metal leg protection of the picador.
Moña	Simulated knot, or flat button which holds bullfighter's pigtail.
Molinete	*Muleta* pass where man turns completely around.
Mozo de estoques	Personal assistant and sword handler for the matador.
Muleta	Red woolen serge cloth folded over a short stick used in the last phase of the bullfight, at the same time as the sword.
Novillada	Bullfight with *novillos toros.*
Novillero	Matador of *novillos toros.*
Novillos	Young, light, or imperfect bulls.
Pase	Pass made with either cape or *muleta.*
Pequeño	Small.
Pica	Picador's blunt-tipped lance.
Picador	Man who used the *pica* under orders of the matador.
Plaza de toros	Bull ring.
Querencia	Place in the ring that the bull favors as a refuge or a place for attacking the enemy.
Quite	Maneuver of taking the bull away from any place in the ring, mostly refers to the movement taking the bull away from a collision with the picador's horse and lance.
Rabo	Bull's tail.
Rebolera	Long circling cape pass holding only one end.
Recorte	Any cape pass that turns the bull sharply.

Rejón	Javelin used by *rejoneadors*.
Suerte	Word means luck, and also has the different definition as a term for any of the regulated maneuvers in the arena.
Tauromaquia	The art of fighting bulls.
Temporada	Bullfight season.
Torero	Professional bullfighter of any rank or specialty, general term such as baseball player.
Toril	Place from which the bull enters the ring.
Traje de luces	Bullfighter's costume.
Vaquero	Bull herdsmen, cowboy.

Special appreciation is recorded for the first publication, in these pages, of illustrations by the notable American artists Tom Lea and John Groth; to Mr. Lea for the painting on the jacket and the front of the binding and for those pictures on pages 342 and 351; to Mr. Groth for the end papers, the frontispiece, the drawing on the back of the binding, and those pictures on pages 5, 318 and 380; to the American Museum of Natural History for "The Urus," or "Auroch," on page 8; to the Metropolitan Museum of Art for the Goya drawings on pages 9, 21 and 114; to José C. Madrazo for the Salvador Carreño picture on page 377; and to *Sports Illustrated* for the John Groth illustration on page 370.

The following illustrations are from the Author's Collection: those on pages 11, 15, 17, 18, 19 and 25 from HISTORIA DEL TORO, by Bedoya; those on pages 40 through 50 from the album, A LOS TOROS, by Daniel Perea; the series on pages 280 through 289 and those drawings on pages 31 and 332 by Roberto Domingo; those on pages 35, 52, 71, 73, 76 and 99 from IMPRESIONES, by C. Ruano Llopis, published in Valencia, Spain; the Fernandez Noseret illustration on page 22; the William Lake Price illustration on page 159; "The Noble Fighters on Horseback" which appears on page 13; the Robert Ruark picture on page 53; the illustration by Barnaby Conrad which appears on pages 54 and 55.